Advertising Sales:
advertisementsales@theAA.com

Editorial:
lifestyleguides@theAA.com

Typeset by AA Lifestyle Guides

Printed and bound by Graficas Estella, Spain

Editorial contributors: Ali Moore and Penny Phenix

Cover credit:
Front cover: Clanville Manor, Somerset

A CIP catalogue record for this book is available from the British Library

ISBN-13: 978-0-7495-5625-9

Published by AA Publishing, which is a trading name of Automobile Association Developments Limited, whose registered office is:
Fanum House, Basing View
Basingstoke
Hampshire RG21 4EA

www.theAA.com

Registered number 1878835

A03523

Britain's
Best**B&B**

Contents

Welcome	**4**	**Useful Information**	**11**
Using the guide	**5**	**International Information**	**13**
Best Quality	**8**		

Welcome

Britain's Best B&B is a collection of the finest Guest Houses, Farmhouses, Inns and Restaurants with Rooms offering bed and breakfast accommodation in England, Scotland, Wales, the Isle of Man and the Channel Islands.

A Place to Stay

This fully revised and updated guide makes it easy to find that special place to stay for a weekend or a longer break. There are more than 540 establishments to choose from, including smart town guest houses, contemporary city B&Bs, accessible country farmhouses and undiscovered gems in hidden-away locations.

Best Quality

Establishments in this book have received either a top star or a highly commended star rating following a visit by an AA inspector. This helps to ensure that you have a friendly welcome, comfortable surroundings, excellent food and great value for money. Further details about the AA scheme, inspections, awards and rating system can be found on pages 8–10.

Before You Travel

Some places may offer special breaks and facilities not available at the time of going to press. If in doubt, it's always worth calling the establishment before you book.

Using the Guide

Britain's Best B&B has been created to enable you to find an establishment quickly and efficiently. Each entry provides clear information about the type of accommodation, the facilities available and the local area.

Use the contents (page 3) to browse the main gazeteer section by county and the index to find either a location (page 472) or a specific B&B (page 477) by name.

Finding your way

The main section of the guide is divided into five main parts covering England, Channel Islands, Isle of Man, Scotland and Wales. The counties within each of these sections are ordered alphabetically as are the town or village locations (shown in capital letters as part of the address) within each county. The establishments are then listed alphabetically under each location name. Towns names featured in the guide can also be located in the map section (page 457 onwards).

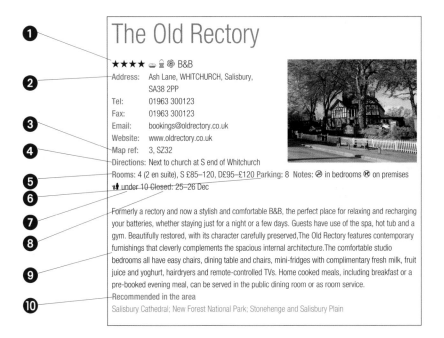

The Old Rectory

★★★★ ⬗ ♨ ◉ B&B

Address:	Ash Lane, WHITCHURCH, Salisbury, SA38 2PP
Tel:	01963 300123
Fax:	01963 300123
Email:	bookings@oldrectory.co.uk
Website:	www.oldrectory.co.uk
Map ref:	3, SZ32
Directions:	Next to church at S end of Whitchurch

Rooms: 4 (2 en suite), S £85–120, D£95–£120 Parking: 8 Notes: ⊘ in bedrooms ⊗ on premises ⛔ under 10 Closed: 25–26 Dec

Formerly a rectory and now a stylish and comfortable B&B, the perfect place for relaxing and recharging your batteries, whether staying just for a night or a few days. Guests have use of the spa, hot tub and a gym. Beautifully restored, with its character carefully preserved,The Old Rectory features contemporary furnishings that cleverly complements the spacious internal architecture.The comfortable studio bedrooms all have easy chairs, dining table and chairs, mini-fridges with complimentary fresh milk, fruit juice and yoghurt, hairdryers and remote-controlled TVs. Home cooked meals, including breakfast or a pre-booked evening meal, can be served in the public dining room or as room service.

Recommended in the area

Salisbury Cathedral; New Forest National Park; Stonehenge and Salisbury Plain

❶ **Stars and Symbols**

All entries in the guide have been inspected by the AA and, at the time of going to press, belong to the AA Guest Accommodation Scheme. Each establishment in the scheme is classified for quality with a grading of one to five stars ★. Each establishment in the Best B&B guide has three, four or five stars and many have a yellow star (highly commended) rating (see page 8 for further details). Establishments with a star rating are given a descriptive category : B&B (BB), GUEST HOUSE (GH), FARMHOUSE (FH), INN (INN), RESTAURANT WITH ROOMS (RR) and GUEST ACCOMMODATION (GA). See pages 8–10 for more information on designators and the AA ratings and awards scheme.

Egg cups 🥚 and Pies 🥧 : These symbols denote where the breakfast or dinner has exceeded the quality level for the rating achieved by the establishment.

Rosette Awards ◉ : This is the AA's food award. See page 9 for further details.

❷ Contact Details

The establishment address includes a locator or place name in capitals (e.g. NORWICH). Within each county, entries are ordered alphabetically first by this place name and then by the name of the establishment.

Telephone and fax numbers, and e-mail and website addresses are given where available. See page 13 for international dialling codes. The telephone and fax numbers are believed correct at the time of going to press but changes may occur. The latest establishment details are on the B&B pages at www.theAA.com.

Website addresses have been supplied by the establishments and lead you to websites that are not under the control of Automobile Association Developments Ltd. AADL has no control over and accepts no responsibility or liability in respect of the material on any such websites. By including the addresses of third-party websites AADL does not intend to solicit business.

❸ Map reference

The map reference is composed of two parts. The first number shows the atlas map number (from 1–13) at the back of the guide (see pages 457 onwards). The second part is a National Grid reference. To find the town or village location on one of the maps, locate the lettered square and read the first figure across and the second figure vertically using the main gridlines to help guide you. For example, a map reference of '3, TQ28' refers to map 3 in the atlas section, grid square TQ on the map and a location of two across the grid square, running east-west, and eight in a north-south direction. The map section of this guide also provides road and county information.

Maps locating each establishment and a route planner are available at www.theAA.com.

❹ Directions

Where possible, directions have been given from the nearest motorway or A road. Distances are provided in miles (m) and yards (yds).

❺ Room Information

The number of letting bedrooms with a bath or shower en suite are shown. Bedrooms that have a private bathroom adjacent may be included as en suite. Further details on private bathroom and en suite provision may also be included in the description text (see ❾).

Always telephone in advance and check to ensure that the accommodation has the facilities you require.

Prices: Charges shown are per night except where specified. S denotes bed and breakfast per person (single). D denotes bed and breakfast for two people sharing a room (double).

In some cases prices are also given for twin (T), triple and family rooms, also on a per night basis. Prices are indications only, so do check before booking.

❻ Parking

The number of parking spaces available. Other types of parking (on road or Park and Ride) may also be possible; check the descriptions for further information. Phone the establishment in advance of your arrival if unsure.

❼ Notes

This section provides details specific details relating to:

Smoking policy: In 2007 smoking was banned in public areas in England, Wales and Northern Ireland, following a similar ban in Scotland in 2006.

The proprietor can designate one or more bedrooms with ventilation systems where the occupants can smoke, but communal areas must be smoke-free. Communal areas include the interior bars and restaurants in pubs and inns.

Dogs: Establishments that state no dogs may accept assist/guide dogs. Some places that accept dogs may restrict the size and breed and the rooms into which they can be taken. Always check the conditions when booking.

Children: No children (⫯) means children cannot be accommodated, or a minimum age may be specified, e.g. ⫯ under 4 means no children under four years old. The main description may also provide details about facilities available for children.

Establishments with special facilities for children may include additional equipment such as a babysitting service or baby-intercom system and facilities such as a playroom or playground, laundry facilities, drying and ironing facilities, cots, high chairs and special meals. If you have very young children or no advice is given under notes, it is always wise to check before booking.

Other notes: Additional facilities, such as access for disabled people, or notes about other services (e.g. if credit card details are not accepted), may be listed here.

❽ Closed
Details of when the establishment is closed for business. Establishments are open all year unless Closed dates/months are shown. Please note that some places are open all year but offer a restricted service in low season. If the text does not detail the restricted services, always check before booking.

❾ Description
This is a general overview of the establishment and may include specific information about the various facilities offered in the rooms, a brief history of the establishment, notes about special features and descriptions of the food where an award has been given (see ❶ above).

❿ Recommended in the area
This indicates places of interest, local sights to visit and potential day trips and activities.

Key to symbols

★	Black stars (see page 8)
☆	Yellow stars (Highly commended) (see page 8)
⌂	Breakfast award
⌒	Dinner Award
◉	AA Rosette (see page 9)
3, TQ28	Map reference (see pages 457–471)
S	Single room
D	Double room
T	Twin room
Triple	Triple room
⊘	No smoking in area indicated
⊗	No dogs allowed in area indicated
⊣	Dogs allowed in area indicated
⫯	No children under age specified
Wi-fi	Wireless network connection

Best Quality

To achieve one of the highest ratings, an establishment in the AA Guest Accommodation Scheme must provide increased quality standards throughout, with particular emphasis in five key areas: cleanliness, hospitality, food quality, bedrooms and bathrooms.

The AA inspects and classifies more than 4,000 guest houses, farmhouses and inns for its Guest Accommodation Scheme. Establishments recognised by the AA pay an annual fee according to the rating and the number of bedrooms. This rating is not transferable if an establishment changes hands.

Common Standards

The AA has introduced new quality standards for inspected accommodation. This follows extensive consultation by the inspection organisations (the AA, VisitBritain, VisitScotland and Visit Wales) with consumers and the hospitality industry in order to make the rating systems for hotels and guest accommodation easier to understand.

Guests can now be confident that a star-rated guest house or a B&B anywhere in the UK and Ireland will offer consistent quality and facilities. The development of these new quality standards has received government support.

Stars

The AA Stars classify guest accommodation at five levels of quality, from one at the simplest, to five at the highest level of quality in the scheme. Each rating is also accompanied by a descriptive designator (further explained below).

★ Highly Commended

Yellow Stars indicate that an accommodation is in the top ten percent of its star rating. Yellow Stars only apply to 3, 4 or 5 star establishments.

The Inspection Process

Establishments applying for AA recognition are visited by a qualified AA accommodation inspector as a mystery guest. Inspectors stay overnight to make a thorough test of the accommodation, food, and hospitality. After paying the bill the following morning they identify themselves and ask to be shown around the premises. The inspector completes a full report, resulting in a recommendation for the appropriate Star rating. After this first visit, the establishment will receive an annual visit to check that standards are maintained. If it changes hands, the new owners must re-apply for rating, as standards can change.

Guests can expect to find the following minimum standards at all levels:
- Pleasant and helpful welcome and service, and sound standards of housekeeping and maintenance
- Comfortable accommodation equipped to modern standards
- Bedding and towels changed for each new guest, and at least weekly if the room is taken for a long stay
- Adequate storage, heating, lighting and comfortable seating

- A sufficient hot water supply at reasonable times
- A full cooked breakfast. (If this is not provided, the fact must be advertised and a substantial continental breakfast must be offered.)

There are additional requirements for an establishment to achieve three, four or five Stars:
- Three Stars and above - access to both sides of all beds for double occupancy.
- Three Stars and above – bathrooms/shower rooms cannot be shared by the proprietor.
- Three Stars and above (from January 1 2008) – a washbasin in every guest bedroom (either in the bedroom or the en suite/private facility)
- Four Stars (from January 1 2008) – half of the bedrooms must be en suite or have private facilities.
- Five Stars (from January 1 2008) – all bedrooms must be en suite or have private facilities.

Designators

All guest accommodation inspected under the new quality standards are given one of six descriptive designators to help potential guests understand the different types of accommodation available in Britain and the facilities they can expect to find (see also ❶ on page 5). These descriptive designators are described in detail as follows:

B&B (BB): B&B accommodation is provided in a private house run by the owner and with no more than six guests. There may be restricted access to the establishment, particularly in the late morning and the afternoon, so do check this when booking.

GUEST HOUSE (GH): A Star-rated Guest House provides for more than six paying guests and usually offers more services than a B&B, for example dinner, served by staff as well as the owner. London prices tend to be higher than outside the capital, and normally only bed and breakfast is provided, although some

AA Rosette Awards

Out of the many thousands of restaurants in the UK, the AA identifies some 1,800 as the best. The following is an outline of what to expect from restaurants with AA Rosette Awards. For a more detailed explanation of Rosette criteria please see www.theAA.com

◉ Excellent local restaurants serving food prepared with care, understanding and skill, using good quality ingredients.

◉◉ The best local restaurants, which aim for and achieve higher standards, better consistency and where a greater precision is apparent in the cooking. There will be obvious attention to the selection of quality ingredients.

◉◉◉ Outstanding restaurants that demand recognition well beyond their local area.

◉◉◉◉ Amongst the very best restaurants in the British Isles, where the cooking demands national recognition.

◉◉◉◉◉ The finest restaurants in the British Isles, where the cooking stands comparison with the best in the world.

establishments do provide a full meal service. Check on the service offered before booking as details may change during the currency of this guide.

FARMHOUSE (FH): A farmhouse usually provides good value B&B or guest house accommodation and excellent home cooking on a working farm or smallholding. Sometimes the land has been sold and only the house remains, but many are working farms and some farmers are happy to allow visitors to look around, or even to help feed the animals. However, you should always take great care and never leave children unsupervised. The farmhouses are listed under towns or villages, but do ask for precise directions when booking.

INN (INN): Traditional inns often have a cosy bar, convivial atmosphere, and good beer and pub food. Those listed in the guide will provide breakfast in a suitable room, and should also serve light meals during licensing hours. The character of the properties vary according to whether they are country inns or town establishments. Check your arrival times as these may be restricted to opening hours.

RESTAURANT WITH ROOMS (RR): These restaurants offer overnight accommodation with the restaurant being the main business and open to non-residents. The restaurant usually offers a high standard of food and service.

GUEST ACCOMMODATION (GA): Within this edition of the Best B&B Guide this includes any establishment that meets the minimum entry requirements with a rating of three stars or more and outstanding results from an inspection visit.

Useful Information

There are so many things to remember when embarking on a short trip or weekend break. If you are unsure, always check before you book. Up-to-date information on contacting all B&Bs can be found at the travel section of www.theAA.com

Codes of practice

The AA encourages the use of The Hotel Industry Voluntary Code of Booking Practice in appropriate establishments. The prime objective of the code is to ensure that the customer is clear about the price and the exact services and facilities being purchased, before entering into a contractually binding agreement. If the price has not been previously confirmed in writing, the guest should be handed a card at the time of registration at the establishment, stipulating the total obligatory charge.

The Tourism (Sleeping Accommodation Price Display) Order 1977 compels hotels, motels, guest houses, farmhouses, inns and self-catering accommodation with four or more letting bedrooms to display in entrance halls the minimum and maximum prices charged for each category of room. This order complements the Voluntary Code of Booking Practice.

Fire precautions and safety

Many of the establishments listed in the guide are subject to the requirements of the Fire

www.theAA.com

Go to www.theAA.com to find more AA listed guest houses, hotels, pubs and restaurants – some 12,000 establishments.

The AA home page has a link to a route planner. Simply enter your postcode and the establishment postcode given in this guide and click Confirm. Check your details and then click GET MY ROUTE and you will have a detailed route plan to take you door-to-door.

Use the Travel section to search for Hotels & B&Bs or Restaurants & Pubs by location or establishment name. Scroll down the list of finds for the interactive map and local routes.

Postcode searches can also be made on www.ordnancesurvey.co.uk and www.multimap.com which will also provide useful aerial views of your destination.

Precautions Act 1971. This Act does not apply to the Channel Islands or the Isle of Man, where their own rules are exercised. All establishments should display details of how to summon assistance in the event of an emergency at night.

Licensed premises
Whereas inns hold a licence to sell alcohol, not all guest houses are licensed. Some may have a full liquor licence, or others may have a table licence and wine list. Licensed premises are not obliged to remain open throughout the permitted hours, and they may do so only when they expect reasonable trade.

Children
Restrictions for children may be mentioned in the description. Some establishments may offer free accommodation to children when they share their parents' room. Such conditions are subject to change without notice, therefore always check when booking.

Complaints
Readers who have cause to complain are urged to do so on the spot. This should provide an opportunity for the proprietor to correct matters. If this approach fails, please inform AA Hotel Services by writing to:
Fanum House, Basingstoke, Hampshire, RG21 4EA. The AA does not, however, undertake to obtain compensation for complaints.

Booking
Advance booking is always recommended to avoid disappointment. The peak holiday periods in the UK are Easter, and from June to September; public holidays are also busy times. In some parts of Scotland the winter skiing season is a peak holiday period. Some establishments may only accept weekly bookings from Saturday, and others require a deposit on booking. Please quote this guide in any enquiry. Guest houses may not accept credit or debit cards – ask when booking. VAT (Value Added Tax at 17.5%) is payable in the UK and in the Isle of Man, on basic prices and additional services. VAT does not apply in the Channel Islands. Always confirm the current

price before booking; the prices in this guide are indications rather than firm quotations. It is a good idea also to confirm exactly what is included in the price when booking. Remember that all details, especially prices, may change without notice during the currency of the guide.

Cancellation
Advise the proprietor immediately if you must cancel a booking. If the room cannot be re-let you may be held legally responsible for partial payment. This could include losing your deposit or being liable for compensation. You should consider taking out cancellation insurance.

Bank and Public Holidays 2008

New Year's Day	1st January
New Year's Holiday	2nd January (Scotland)
Good Friday	21st March
Easter Monday	24th March
May Day Bank Holiday	5th May
Spring Bank Holiday	26th May
August Holiday	4th August (Scotland)
Late Summer Holiday	25th August
St Andrew's Day	1st December (Scotland)
Christmas Day	25th December
Boxing Day	26th December

International Information

If you're travelling from overseas, the following information will provide some useful guidance to help you enjoy your stay in Britain. The individual entries in this book will also give you information regarding travel and the best routes to take.

Money

Some establishments may not accept traveller's cheques, or credit or debit cards, so ask about payment methods when you book. Most European and American credit and debit cards allow you to withdraw cash from British ATMs.

Driving

In the UK you drive on the left and overtake on the right. Seat belts are worn by every occupant of the car, whether they sit in the front or the rear. Speed limits are displayed in miles per hour.

Car rental

You will be required to present your driving licence and credit or debit card. You can also provide an International Driving Permit along with your driving licence. Further identification, such as a passport, may also be required. A minimum age limit will apply.

Trains

The UK has an extensive rail network. To find out about routes, special offers or passes, contact National Rail (www.nationalrail.co.uk, tel: 08457 484950; from overseas +44 20 7278 5240, and international rates apply) or a travel agent.

Medical treatment & health insurance

Travellers who normally take medicines or carry an appliance, such as a hypodermic syringe, should ensure that they have sufficient supply for their stay and a doctor's letter describing the condition and treatment required.

Before travelling ensure you have insurance for emergency medical and dental treatment. Many European countries have reciprocal agreements for medical treatment and require EU citizens to obtain a European Health Insurance Card (EHIC) before travel.

Telephones

Many guest houses have direct dial telephones in the rooms. Always check the call rate before dialling. Payphones usually take cash, credit or debit cards, or phonecards. Phonecards can be purchased from newsagents and post offices.

The telephone and fax numbers in this guide show the area code followed by the subscriber number. When dialling from abroad first dial the international network access code, then the country code (44 for the UK). Omit the first digit of the area code then dial the subscriber number. For example:

From Europe	00 44 111 121212
From the US	011 44 111 121212

When dialling from the UK, dial the international network access code, then the country code.

Electrical appliances

The British electrical current is 220–240 volts and appliances have square three-pin plugs. Foreign appliances may require an adaptor for the plug, as well as an electrical voltage converter that will allow, for example, a 110-volt appliance to be powered.

ENGLAND

North Cornish coast

BERKSHIRE

Windsor Castle

The Crown & Garter

★★★★ ⇔ INN

Address: Great Common, Inkpen,
HUNGERFORD RG17 9QR
Tel: 01488 668325
Email: gill.hern@btopenworld.com
Website: www.crownandgarter.com
Map ref: 3, SU36
Directions: 4m SE of Hungerford. Off A4 into Kintbury,
opp corner stores onto Inkpen Rd, straight for 2m
Rooms: 8 en suite **Parking:** 40 **Notes:** ⊗ in
bedrooms ⊗ on premises ⚫ babies/young children Free Wi-fi access

Family owned and run, this 16th-century inn set in the beautiful Kennet valley. The bar and restaurant are in keeping with the character of the building, and real ales, spiced wine and a selection of malt whiskies are available. The restaurant offers an interesting range of country dishes freshly prepared from local produce.The spacious bedrooms are in a courtyard around a tranquil garden. Each room has a bath and power shower, a hairdryer, television and video, and tea and coffee facilities.
Recommended in the area
Historic Marlborough; Lambourn Downs; Salisbury Plain and Stonehenge

The Swan Inn

★★★★ ⚍ ⇔ INN

Address: Craven Road, Inkpen, HUNGERFORD
RG17 9DX
Tel: 01488 668326
Fax: 01488 668306
Email: enquiries@theswaninn-organics.co.uk
Website: www.theswaninn-organics.co.uk
Map ref: 3, SU36
Directions: 3.5m SE of Hungerford. From Hungerford
Common, right signed Inkpen
Rooms: 10 en suite, S £60–£70 D £80–£95 **Parking:** 50 **Notes:** ⊗ in bedrooms ⊗ on premises ⚫
Closed: 25–26 Dec

The peaceful north Wessex downs provide an idyllic setting for this 17th-century inn. Inside there are oak beams, open fires and a warm welcome from the Harris family. The owners are organic farmers, and the restaurant and an adjoining farm shop feature superb produce. The spacious en suite bedrooms are firmly rooted in the 21st century, with direct-dial and Internet connections.
Recommended in the area
Combe Gibbet; Kennet and Avon Canal; Avebury stone circle

Black Boys Inn

★★★★ ◉◉ RR

Address: Henley Road, HURLEY
         SL6 5NQ
Tel: 01628 824212
Email: info@blackboysinn.co.uk
Website: www.blackboysinn.co.uk
Map ref: 3, SU88
Directions: 1m W of Hurley on A4130
Rooms: 8 en suite, D £85–£95 Parking: 40
Notes: ⊘ on premises ⊗ on premises ⚲ under 12yrs
Closed: 24 Dec–9 Jan

This 16th-century inn, just a five-minute walk from the River
Thames and a short drive from Henley, provides stylish accommodation in a lovely rural setting. The traditional exterior of this restaurant with rooms is in contrast to the smart modernity that lies within. With views across the Chiltern Hills, the characterful bedrooms are situated in converted barns close by – all are en suite and beautifully appointed, and the furnishings complement the original features of the building very well; some rooms boast oak beams. Guests will find themselves well supplied, with tea and coffee-making facilities, hairdryer, TV with DVD player and Internet connection all standard. The water in the bathrooms – all with power shower or bath – comes from the inn's very own well. Food is taken seriously here, with excellent and imaginative modern British cooking featuring quality local produce is a real draw, and the lively restaurant is popular with locals and guests alike. Fresh fish is sourced from Devon and Cornwall and a weekly trip is made to Paris's Rungis market to stock up on delicacies such as foie gras, while fine cheeses come from La Fromagerie. In addition, an impressive 41 wines are available by the glass.

Recommended in the area

Henley-on-Thames; Cliveden (NT); The Herb Farm, Sonning Common

Weir View House

★★★★ GA

Address: 9 Shooters Hill, PANGBOURNE RG8 7DZ
Tel: 0118 984 2120
Fax: 0118 984 3777
Email: info@weirview.co.uk
Website: www.weirview.co.uk
Map ref: 3, SU67
Directions: A329 N from Pangbourne, after minirdbt under rail bridge, opp Swan pub
Rooms: 9 en suite, D £80–£95 **Parking:** 10
Notes: ⊘ on premises ⊗ in bedrooms ▮ **Closed:** 23 Dec–1 Jan

In an enchanting setting beside the River Thames, this inviting guesthouse offers spacious en suite bedrooms (many with four-poster beds and river views) equipped with TV with Freeview and DVD, Wi-fi, tea and coffee facilities, telephone, fridge, hairdryer and trouser press. Continental breakfast is served in the bright breakfast room, and cooked meals can be delivered to your room from the pub across the road. During the day coffee and tea are available in the breakfast room.

Recommended in the area
Basildon Park (NT); Child Beale Wildlife Park; The Living Rainforest in Hampstead Norreys

Bull Inn

★★★★ INN

Address: High Street, SONNING RG4 6UP
Tel: 0118 969 3901
Fax: 0118 969 7188
Email: bullinn@accommodating-inns.co.uk
Website: www.accommodating-inns.co.uk/bullinn.html
Map ref: 3, SU77
Directions: Opp St Andrew's Church
Rooms: 6 (5 en suite), S £65–£125 D £65–£125
Parking: 14 **Notes:** ⊘ in bedrooms ⊗ in bedrooms

The 16th-century Bull Inn stands opposite the village church. Refurbished in keeping with the original character, its lovely bedrooms are individually furnished with high-quality fabrics and carpets, and their facilities include flat-screen televisions and DVDs. Jerome K Jerome mentions the Bull Inn in his comedy novel *Three Men in a Boat* and rooms are named from this book. Manager Dennis Mason is a real card and the epitome of a great barman. The bar blackboards display an extensive range of good pub grub and award-winning ales are sold.

Recommended in the area
River Thames; Windsor; Reading

BRISTOL

Clifton Suspension Bridge, Clifton

Bitton station, Bristol

Downlands House

★★★★ GA

Address: 33 Henleaze Gardens, BRISTOL BS9 4HH
Tel: 0117 962 1639
Fax: 0117 973 8081
Email: info@downlandshouse.co.uk
Website: www.downlandshouse.com
Map ref: 2, ST57
Directions: 2m NW of city centre off A4018. M5
junct 17, signs Westbury-on-Trym/City Centre, pass
girls schools, Henleaze Gdns on left
Rooms: 10 (7 en suite), S £38–£50 D £60–£75 **Notes:** ⊘ on premises 🐾 allowed in bedrooms ♦♦

Combining Victorian elegance and the charm, atmosphere and comforts of a large family home,
Downlands has pretty, well-equipped rooms – single, twin and double – including a large double room
on the ground floor. There are smart facilities en suite, and each room is thoughtfully supplied with
hairdryer, hospitality tray, colour TV and free wireless broadband access. There is a comfortable lounge
and the tasty cooked breakfast can be served in the delightful conservatory or the stylish dining room.
Recommended in the area
Durdham Downs; SS Great Britain; Clifton Suspension Bridge

Westfield House

★★★★ ➘ GA

Address: 37 Stoke Hill, Stoke Bishop, BRISTOL
BS9 1LQ
Tel: 0117 962 6119
Fax: 0117 962 6119
Email: admin@westfieldhouse.net
Website: www.westfieldhouse.net
Map ref: 2, ST57
Directions: 1.8m NW of city centre in Stoke Bishop
Rooms: 3 en suite, S £59–£89 D £85–£120
Parking: 5 Notes: ⊘ on premises ⊗ on premises ⚼ under 11yrs

Set in 2.5 acres of private grounds, this large white-painted Georgian-style, family-run guesthouse makes an ideal retreat from Bristol's city lights. Westfield House is close to Durdham Downs – a vast expanse of open space which stretches from Bristol's suburbs to the cliffs of the Avon Gorge – and the Bristol University Halls of Residence. The very comfortable bedrooms (there is a choice of single and doubles) are well equipped with TV, tea and coffee-making facilities, and are decorated in pastel shades. The living room centres round a cosy fireplace while large bay windows lead onto a spacious terrace. Owner Ann cooks more or less to order using quality local ingredients, and a typical meal may include dishes such as salmon en croute with puréed spinach and hollandaise sauce accompanied by potatoes dauphinoise, followed by a delicious home-made apple pie – all the better in the summer months when served on the patio overlooking the lovely rear garden. The grounds are also a haven for a variety of wildlife including owls, badgers, falcons and hedgehogs. If you still hanker for the the bright lights, Westfield House is just a short walk from Bristol city centre. There is ample off-street parking for guests.

Recommended in the area

Clifton Suspension Bridge; SS Great Britain; Bristol Zoo

CAMBRIDGESHIRE

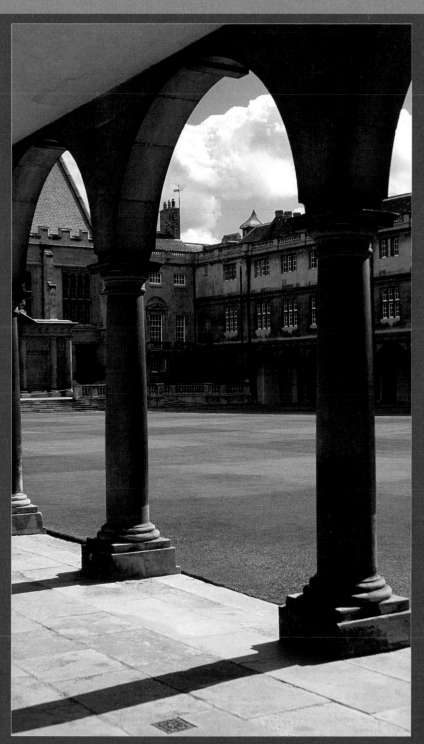

Trinity College, Cambridge

Rose garden, Elton Hall

Rose Bungalow

★★★★ BB

Address: 68 High Street, Great Wilbraham,
CAMBRIDGE CB21 5JD
Tel: 01223 882385
Email: rose.bungalow@btinternet.com
Website: www.rosebungalow.co.uk
Map ref: 3, TL45
Directions: 6m E of Cambridge in Great Wilbraham
Rooms: 2 en suite, S £30–£40 D £50–£60
Parking: 3 Notes: ⊗ ⊗ ⊮ under 12yrs

A hidden gem, this attractive bungalow has the advantage of a quiet village location, yet is close to the park and ride for Cambridge with its many attractions. There are two well-equipped rooms, (a twin and a single) each with TV, DVD and video and hospitality tray including fruit and chocolates. There is also free wireless internet. The full English breakfast is a speciality with Suffolk bacon and sausages, local eggs, home-made bread, fresh fruit and organic apple juice. A continental breakfast can be requested. Other meals can be taken at one of the two local pubs. Please note that credit cards are not accepted.

Recommended in the area

Anglesey Abbey (NT); Wimpole Hall (NT); Cambridge; Duxford Imperial War Museum; Newmarket

CHESHIRE

Cholmondley Castle

Cheshire Cheese Cottage

★★★★ BB

Address: Burwardsley Rd, BURWARDSLEY CH3 9NS
Tel: 01829 770887
Fax: 01829 770887
Email: r.rosney@yahoo.co.uk
Website: www.cheshirecheesecottage-bb.com
Map ref: 6, SJ55
Directions: Travelling N on A41 to Chester, follow
signs to Tattenhall and Burwardsley. Situated
between the two villages
Rooms: 2 en suite D £75 Parking: 4
Notes: ⊘ on premises ⊗ in bedrooms 🐾

This delightful little cottage is set in its own extensive grounds and colourful gardens on the outskirts
of the village of Burwardsley, right in the heart of the Cheshire countryside and ideally located for
visiting the ancient Roman city of Chester. It offers superb views of Beeston Castle, which is 1.5 miles
away. Set within a working farm with its own grazing sheep, this friendly, family-run establishment
provides two en suite bedrooms, each on the ground floor. Each room also enjoys a private lounge area
that doubles as a breakfast room (there is also a separate dining room at Cheshire Cheese Cottage).
Rooms here are tastefully decorated and well equipped and come with free wireless internet access,
central heating, flatscreen TV with Freeview, CD and DVD players, tea and coffee-making facilities and
hairdryer. Breakfasts, full English or lighter options, are freshly cooked and hearty, and vegetarians can
be catered for. The B&B has recently won an award for its food and hygiene. Owner Rose Rosney is a
qualified masseur and reiki practitioner, and guests can book treatments with her if they wish. On-site
parking is available, and guests are welcome to make use of the patio and half acre of gardens.

Recommended in the area

Sandstone trail; Chester; Beeston Castle

Sandhollow Farm B&B

★★★★ BB

Address: Harthill Road, BURWARDSLEY, Tattenhall,
Chester CH3 9NU
Tel: 01829 770894
Email: paul.kickdrum@tiscali.co.uk
Website: www.sandhollow.co.uk
Map ref: 6,SJ55
Directions: From A41, turn off to Tattenhall, follow
signs to Burwardsley
Rooms: 3 en suite, S £55–£65 D £75 Parking: 4
Notes: ⊘ on premises ⊗ in bedrooms ⅓ under 12yrs Closed: Xmas & annual holiday

Nestling in the sandstone ridge of the Peckforton Hills this lovely farmhouse, with spectacular views over the Cheshire Plain and Welsh hills, is very handy for Chester, Liverpool and Manchester. There are lovely views from the bedrooms, which also benefit from en suite bathrooms, and the public areas are comfortable and inviting. The dining room is the setting for hearty breakfasts that feature local, organic produce and home made preserves. Two acres of well-kept grounds complete the peaceful idyll.

Recommended in the area

Beeston Castle; Oulton Park; Chester

Lavender Lodge

★★★★ GA

Address: 46 Hoole Road, CHESTER CH2 3NL
Tel: 01244 323204
Fax: 01244 329821
Email: bookings@lavenderlodgechester.co.uk
Website: www.lavenderlodgechester.co.uk
Map ref: 5, SJ46
Directions: 1m NE of city centre on A56, opp All Saints' Church
Rooms: 5 en suite, S £32.50–£50 D £60–£80 Parking: 7
Notes: ⊘ ⊗ ⅓ Closed: 24 Dec–2 Jan

Lavender Lodge, a friendly, family-run establishment in a smart house, is located off the A56. Inside, all of the comfortable, centrally heated bedrooms, including two family rooms, are pleasantly decorated and come equipped with thoughtful extras such as hairdryer, colour TV and tea and coffee-making facilities; all have modern en suite bathrooms. Guests can enjoy high-quality full English breakfasts, served at individual tables in the attractive dining room. Free on-site parking is available.

Recommended in the area

Blue Planet Aquarium; Chester Zoo; Chester's Roman walls

Bridge Street, Chester

Rowton Poplars

★★★★ GH

Address: Whitchurch Road, Rowton,
CHESTER CH3 6AF
Tel: 01244 333010
Fax: 01244 333020
Email: val@rowtonpoplars.co.uk
Website: www.rowtonpoplars.co.uk
Map ref: 5, SJ46
Directions: 2m SE of Chester. A55 onto A41 for
Whitchurch, premises before fuel station
Rooms: 8 en suite, S £55–£65 D £65–£75 **Parking:** 30 **Notes:** 🛏 allowed on premises ♦♦

Close to Chester and the M56, this stylish Victorian house is a friendly, family-run establishment.
The en suite luxury bedrooms are furnished to a high standard and come with TV and tea and coffee
facilities. The attractive lounge is the perfect place to unwind with a drink after a busy day sightseeing
or shopping. Breakfast, and dinner by arrangement, is served in the pleasant dining room with
individual tables. The property has secure parking and is close to Chester's park and ride.
Recommended in the area
Chester Zoo; Blue Planet Aquarium; Cheshire Oaks

CORNWALL

St Germans Viaduct, Tamar Valley.

Bude Haven

★★★★ GA

Address: Flexbury Avenue, BUDE EX23 8NS
Tel: 01288 352305
Fax: 01288 352662
Email: enquiries@budehavenhotel.com
Website: www.budehavenhotel.com
Map ref: 1, SS20
Directions: 0.5m N of Bude in Flexbury village centre
Rooms: 10 en suite, S £30–£42.50 D £60–£85
Parking: 4 Notes: ⊗ on premises ⊗ in bedrooms ⚥

Bude Haven is a charming building in a quiet residential area, with the town centre and two lovely beaches just a short walk away. Natural hosts Alison and Richard Long foster a friendly, homely atmosphere. They offer comfortable en suite bedrooms, each with a clock radio, hairdryer and a beverage tray. An inviting lounge features a television, video and DVD, music centre, books and games. There is a well-stocked bar and interesting meals are served in the evening. For complete pampering retreat to the hot tub in the secluded garden, or the services of the qualified masseuse.

Recommended in the area

South West Coast Path; Tintagel; The Eden Project

Cotswold House

★★★★ GH

Address: 49 Melvill Road, FALMOUTH TR11 4DF
Tel: 01326 312077
Email: info@cotswoldhousehotel.com
Website: www.cotswoldhousehotel.com
Map ref: 1, SW82
Directions: On A39 near town centre & docks
Rooms: 10 en suite Parking: 10 Notes: ⊗ on premises ⊗ on premises ⚥ Closed: Xmas

With Falmouth's superb sandy Gyllyngvase beach and the busy estuary, harbour and yachting marina just a short walk away, this small family-run hotel is ideal for both a holiday or a short break. The smart Victorian property is also close to the picturesque, cobbled town centre with its historic buildings and range of specialist shops. All the bedrooms have a bath or shower room en suite and hospitality trays; and many have lovely views of the sea and the River Fal. Well-cooked traditional cuisine is a feature of a stay here, and the friendly owners offer attentive service. The convivial bar is another plus at this relaxed house, and a popular place for socializing in the evening.

Recommended in the area

Falmouth National Maritime Museum; The Eden Project; Trebah and Glendurgan gardens

Dolvean House

★★★★★ GA

Address: 50 Melvill Road, FALMOUTH TR11 4DQ
Tel: 01326 313658
Fax: 01326 313995
Email: reservations@dolvean.co.uk
Website: www.dolvean.co.uk
Map ref: 1, SW82
Directions: On A39 near town centre &
Maritime Museum
Rooms: 10 en suite **Parking:** 10 **Notes:** ⊗ on
premises ⊗ on premises ✚ under 12yrs **Closed:** Xmas

The Dolvean is a traditional Victorian residence situated between Falmouth's main golden sandy beach and its internationally renowned harbour which shelters all types of seagoing craft including tall ships and visiting cruise liners. In the main streets and narrow alleyways of the historic town you'll find restaurants, cafés and pubs situated alongside specialist antiques and arts shops – many exhibiting local works. Paul and Carol Crocker, resident proprietors of Dolvean House since 1994, are passionate collectors of antiques, curios, old books (on travel, cookery, remedies, household hints and woodwork), advertising memorabilia, sewing machines and sewing ephemera. These fascinating collections have spilled out of their home into every corner of Dolvean, and the Crockers enjoy sharing their interests with guests, some of whom have contributed to the collections. Pretty pictures and an abundance of lace and ribbon bring a special touch to the bedrooms, each of which has its own character. All the rooms have full facilities en suite with fluffy towels, luxury toiletries and wireless broadband access. Thoughtful extras include hospitality trays, Cornish mineral water and chocolates by your bed. The traditional English breakfast menu uses only the finest Cornish produce.

Recommended in the area

Pendennis Castle; Falmouth National Maritime Museum; Trebah Garden

Lugo Rock

★★★★ GA

Address:	59 Melvill Road, FALMOUTH TR11 4DF
Tel:	01326 311344
Fax:	01326 311567
Email:	info@lugorockhotel.co.uk
Website:	www.lugorockhotel.co.uk
Map ref:	1, SW82

Directions: On A39 near town centre & docks
Rooms: 12 en suite, S D £60–£76 Parking: 12
Notes: ⊘ ☂ ⚐ under 12yrs

Lugo Rock promises friendly, relaxed and high-quality bed and breakfast accommodation in spacious surroundings. Well-located for touring South-West Cornwall, it offers a range of attractively decorated en suite bedrooms, all with shower, digital TV, hairdryer and beverage tray, as well as a complimentary tourist information pack. Guests can relax in the smart licensed guest lounge, or take time out on the sun deck or in the well-tended garden. Breakfast is served in the stylish breakfast room, and there is good off-road parking for guests; wireless free internet access is also available.

Recommended in the area

Falmouth town; Gyllyngvase beach; Pendennis Castle

Rosemullion

★★★★ GA

Address:	Gyllyngvase Hill,
	FALMOUTH TR11 4DF
Tel:	01326 314690
Fax:	01326 210098
Email:	gail@rosemullionhotel.demon.co.uk
Map ref:	1, SW82

Directions: A39 to Portdennis. Turn right after bridge.
Rooms: 13 (11 en suite), S £35–£40 D £58–£68
Parking: 18 Notes: ⊘ on premises ⊗ on premises ⚐
Closed: 23–29 Dec

This striking mock-Tudor property caters for the discerning guest and its peaceful atmosphere draws people back again and again. Bedrooms are beautifully decorated and furnished, and some have glorious views over the bay. Breakfast is served in a smart wood-panelled dining room, and the drawing room is delightful for relaxing. Rosemullion is a stroll from Falmouth's main beach, and handy for the town and harbour.

Recommended in the area

Gyllyngvase Beach and Pendennis Castle; Helford River and Trebah Garden; The Eden Project

Tregerrick Farm B&B

★★★★ FH

Address: GORRAN, St Austell PL26 6NF
Tel: 01726 843418
Fax: 01726 843418
Email: fandc.thomas@btconnect.com
Website: www.tregerrickfarm.co.uk
Map ref: 1, SW94
Directions: 1m NW of Gorran. B3273 S from St
Austell, right after Pentewan Sands campsite to The
Lost Gardens of Heligan, continue 3m, farm on left
Rooms: 4 (2 en suite) S £25-£45 D £50–£90 **Parking:** 4 **Notes:** ⊘ on premises ⊗ on premises
🚼 under 4yrs

This is an interesting place to stay for anyone who is enthusiastic about ecological issues, as it is
a working farm where sustainability and biodiversity are paramount. The varied and imaginative
breakfasts, based on locally produced food, are served in the dining room or conservatory. The
bedrooms, are tastefully furnished in keeping with the age of the property and there's wireless internet
in the main house. A delightful garden annexe can sleep up to five.

Recommended in the area

Lost Gardens of Heligan; South West Coast Path; The Eden Project

Calize Country House

★★★★ GA

Address: Prosper Hill, Gwithian, HAYLE TR27 5BW
Tel/Fax: 01736 753268
Email: jilly@calize.co.uk
Website: www.calize.co.uk
Map ref: 1, SW54
Directions: 2m NE of Hayle. B3301 in Gwithian at
Red River Inn, house 350yds up hill on left
Rooms: 4 en suite, S £40–£60 D £70–£90
Parking: 6 **Notes:** ⊘ ⊗ in bedrooms 🚼 under 12

Calize has superb views of the sea and countryside, and is close to the beaches and coves of West
Penwith. Jilly and Nigel Whitaker are naturally friendly and their hospitality is outstanding (home-made
cake and tea are offered on arrival). Guests are invited to share their comfortable lounge, which has
a log-burning fire during colder months. Memorable breakfasts are served around a communal table
with sea views – treats include home-made walnut bread and blackberry jelly, seeded toast, fresh fruit,
creamy scrambled eggs and fresh smoked salmon. The local seals are also an attraction.

Recommended in the area

South West Coast Path; St Ives Bay; St Michael's Mount (NT); National Seal Sanctuary

Hurdon Farm

★★★★ ⊜ FH

Address: LAUNCESTON PL15 9LS
Tel: 01566 772955
Map ref: 1, SX38
Directions: A30 onto A388 to Launceston, at rdbt take the exit for hospital. Take the 2nd right signed to Trebullett. Hurdon Farm is first on right.
Rooms: 6 en suite, S £28–£32 D £50–£60
Parking: 10 Notes: ⊗ on premises ⊗ in bedrooms
♦♦ Closed: Nov–Apr

Situated just south of the historic Cornish capital of Launceston, Hurdon Farm is a 400-acre working farm with cows, sheep and pigs, where guests are welcome to wander around and enjoy the countryside. Quietly located at the end of a tree-lined drive, the elegant eighteenth-century stone and granite farmhouse has retained many original features, especially in the kitchen, with its open granite fireplace, original Dutch oven and collection of old jacks and trivets. Bedrooms, including one ground-floor family room with adjoining children's room, are all en suite and individually furnished. They come with many thoughtful extras such as electric blankets and hot-water bottles, bathrobes, colour TV, hairdryer, playing cards, magazines and tea and coffee-making facilities. Breakfasts, and delicious dinners by prior arrangement, make use of produce from the farm whenever possible, and the home-made clotted cream is a special treat. Meals are served in the dining room, with its sash windows, original panelled shutters, built-in dressers and tables overlooking the garden, while the lounge features a log stove and has large, comfortable chairs, colour TV and a selection of books, magazines and games. Hurdon Farm makes an ideal base for exploring Cornwall and its coastlines.

Recommended in the area

The Eden Project; South West Coast Path; Dartmoor and Bodmin Moor

Primrose Cottage

★★★★★ GA

Address: Lawhitton, LAUNCESTON
          PL15 9PE
Tel: 01566 773645
Email: enquiry@primrosecottagesuites.co.uk
Website: www.primrosecottagesuites.co.uk
Map ref: 1, SX38
Directions: Exit A30 Tavistock, follow A388 through Launceston for Plymouth then B3362 Tavistock 2.5m
Rooms: 3 en suite, S £60–£80 D £100–£120
Parking: 5 Notes: ⊗ on premises ⊗ on premises ⚲ under 12yrs

Set in four acres of gardens and ancient woodland on the banks of the River Tamar, Primrose Cottage is located between Dartmoor and Bodmin Moor, and within easy reach of both the north and south coasts. The three luxury suites – The Stable, The Tamar and The Garden Room all enjoy beautiful views across the Tamar valley, and all have their own private entrance, sitting room and en suite facilities. Furnished with designer fabrics, antiques and thoughtful extra touches, every luxury is provided. A bottle of chilled white wine will be waiting to welcome you on your arrival. Sip your wine admiring the stunning views from your sitting room or choose one of the secluded corners of the garden. Once settled you can stroll down through the woods to the river to watch the salmon jump or wait quietly for a kingfisher to dive. Each season brings its own delights; the woodland is an untouched natural haven where wildlife lives undisturbed. After a day out exploring this beautiful undiscovered part of the south west return to Primrose Cottage and enjoy afternoon tea in the garden or by the log fire on a colder day.

Recommended in the area

Dartmoor; Tavistock; North Coast

Waterfront, Looe

Redgate Smithy

★★★★ BB

Address: Redgate, St Cleer, LISKEARD PL14 6RU
Tel: 01579 321578
Email: enquiries@redgatesmithy.co.uk
Website: www.redgatesmithy.co.uk
Map ref: 1, SW26
Directions: 3m NW of Liskeard. Off A30 at Bolventor/
Jamaica Inn onto St Cleer Rd for 7m, B&B just past x-rds
Rooms: 3 (2 en suite), S £40 D £60 Parking: 3
Notes: ⊘ ⌖ ⌖ under 12yrs Closed: Xmas & New Yr

Redgate Smithy, situated just above the beautiful Golitha Falls on the southern edge of rugged Bodmin Moor, was built around 200 years ago and is a good option for walkers and less energetic holidaymakers alike. Guests can relax in the comfortable cottage-style bedrooms, which come with TV, hairdryer, local information and tea and coffee-making facilities. A full breakfast made from local produce offers a range of options, including Full Cornish and continental. Guests are welcome to use the garden and patio, and the owners are happy to recommend local dining options.

Recommended in the area

Golitha Falls; The Eden Project; Bodmin Moor and Cheesewring

Barclay House

★★★★ 🏠 🍽 GA

Address: St Martin's Road, LOOE PL13 1LP
Tel: 01503 262929
Fax: 01503 262632
Email: reception@barclayhouse.co.uk
Website: www.barclayhouse.co.uk
Map ref: 1, SX25
Directions: 0.5m N of Looe bridge on junct A387 & B3253
Rooms: 11 en suite, S £50–£105 D £100–£140
Parking: 25 Notes: ⊘ on premises ⊗ in bedrooms ♦♦

Perched on the hillside overlooking the harbour of historic Looe, but within walking distance of the town, Barclay House has captivating views over the water and countryside beyond. Originally a Victorian family home set in 6 acres of grounds, the house is now a family-run B&B with a spacious elegance and relaxed air about it. On the ground floor are a large lounge bar and a sitting room offering light meals, snacks and cream teas, and there is a panoramic terrace where you can enjoy an aperitif in summer. Enjoyable, freshly made dinners prepared by head chef Ben Palmer, including fish caught locally that day, are also served most evenings in the light and airy restaurant, which is popular with tourists and locals alike and has French doors opening out onto views of the East Looe river valley. The bedrooms, including one on the ground floor and a family room, have modern facilities and are decorated in pastel shades. All have been thoughtfully provided with extras such as Cornish bottled water, Sky TV, backlit bathrooms with make-up mirrors and hairdryers. Guests who wish to take a break from the abundant sightseeing the area has to offer can choose instead to relax beside the heated pool, or wander round the peaceful gardens and woodland.

Recommended in the area

Lost Gardens of Heligan; The Eden Project; Lanhydrock (NT)

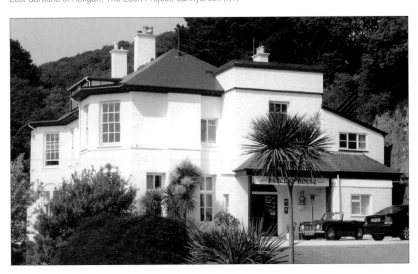

Bay View Farm

★★★★ 🛏 FH
Address: St Martins, LOOE PL13 1NZ
Tel/Fax: 01503 265922
Website: www.looedirectory.co.uk/bay-view-farm
Map ref: 1, SX25
Directions: 2m NE of Looe. Off B3253 for Monkey
Sanctuary, farm signed
Rooms: 3 en suite, S £28–£32 D £52–£56
Parking: 3 Notes: ⊘ on premises ⊗ on premises
🧒 under 5yrs

A genuine warm Cornish welcome, an air of tranquillity and great food are the hallmarks of Bay View Farm, which is home to a team of prize-winning shire horses. Mrs Elford is a delightful host and it's easy to see why her guests are drawn back to this special place again and again. The renovated and extended bungalow is situated in a truly spectacular spot with ever-changing views across Looe Bay, and is beautifully decorated and furnished throughout to give a light, spacious feel. The three en suite bedrooms each have their own very individual character – one is huge with comfy sofas and a spectacular view, the others smaller but still very inviting. Two of the rooms also have spacious private conservatories. Guests can relax at the end of the day either in the lounge or on the lovely patio and watch the sun set over Looe. Breakfasts at Bay View Farm are substantial and the evening meals feature home-made desserts accompanied by clotted cream. If you do choose to eat out there are numerous restaurants and pubs nearby. The coastal path outside the entrance takes you to Millendreath beach and on to Looe and Polperro. The old town of East Looe is a delight of tall buildings, narrow streets and passageways and the fishing industry brings a maritime bustle to the harbour and quayside. West Looe, the smaller settlement, has a lovely outlook across the harbour to East Looe.
Recommended in the area
Lost Gardens of Heligan; The Eden Project; Looe

The Beach House

★★★★★ 🛏 GA

Address: Marine Drive, Hannafore, LOOE PL13 2DH
Tel: 01503 262598
Fax: 01503 262298
Email: enquiries@thebeachhouselooe.com
Website: www.thebeachhouselooe.com
Map ref: 1, SX25
Directions: From Looe W over bridge, left to Hannafore & Marine Dr, on right after Tom Sawyer Tavern
Rooms: 5 en suite, D £80–£120 Parking: 6 Notes: ⊘ ⊗ on premises ⊀ under 16yrs

This big, white-painted house is on the seafront at Hannafore, with the South West Coast Path running past the front gate. Huge windows make the most of the stunning views and create a lovely brightness in the interior. The bedrooms are equally light and many enjoy the sea views; the ground floor rooms have the use of the garden room. All rooms have quality linens, luxury towels and bathrobes, toiletries and TV. Breakfast is served in the balcony dining room. A particularly relaxing place to stay.

Recommended in the area

The Eden Project; Lost Gardens of Heligan; walking the South West Coastal Path to Polperro.

Bucklawren Farm

★★★★ GA

Address: St Martin-by-Looe, LOOE PL13 1NZ
Tel: 01503 240738
Fax: 01503 240481
Email: bucklawren@btopenworld.com
Website: www.bucklawren.com
Map ref: 1, SX25
Directions: 2m NE of Looe. Off B3253 to Monkey Sanctuary, 0.5m right to Bucklawren, 0.5m on left
Rooms: 6 en suite, S £30–£50 D £58–£66
Parking: 6 Notes: ⊘ on premises ⊗ on premises ⊀ under 5yrs Closed: Nov–Feb

With a lovely beach just a mile away, this spacious 19th-century farmhouse, set in 500 acres, is the perfect place for a holiday. Front-facing rooms have sea views, and all bedrooms are attractively furnished; one room is on the ground floor. The Granary restaurant in an adjacent converted barn is the setting for evening meals prepared from fresh local produce. Jean Henly is a charming hostess.

Recommended in the area

The Eden Project; fishing villages of Looe and Polperro; Lanhydrock (NT)

Coombe Farm

★★★★ GA

Address: Widegates, LOOE PL13 1QN
Tel: 01503 240223
Email: coombe_farm@hotmail.com
Website: www.coombefarmhotel.co.uk
Map ref: 1, SX25
Directions: 3.5m E of Looe on B3253, S of Widegates
Rooms: 3 en suite, S £50–£60 D £70–£82
Parking: 20 Notes: ⊗ on premises 🐾 allowed on premises ♦♦ Closed: 15 Dec–5 Jan

Coombe Farm offers distinctive accommodation and perfect solitude in 11 acres of lawns and woods with views down a valley to the sea. An additional bonus is the outdoor heated swimming pool. The spacious garden rooms have beamed ceilings and a warm friendly atmosphere, and the farm is convenient for sandy beaches and glorious walks. Each has its own door into the gardens and a dining area with breakfast delivered to your room. Decorated in a fresh and cheerful fashion, they have shower rooms en suite, modern facilities, and one room is ideal for families.

Recommended in the area
The Eden Project; Bodmin Moor; West & East Looe

Trehaven Manor

★★★★ 🛏 🍽 GA

Address: Station Road, LOOE PL13 1HN
Tel: 01503 262028
Fax: 01503 265613
Email: enquiries@trehavenhotel.co.uk
Website: www.trehavenhotel.co.uk
Map ref: 1, SX25
Directions: In East Looe between railway station & bridge. Trehaven drive adjacent to The Globe PH
Rooms: 7 en suite Parking: 8 Notes: ⊗ on premises ⊗ on premises ♦♦

Neil and Ella Hipkiss, the enthusiastic owners of Trehaven Manor, are committed to providing the best service. Bedrooms provide a high level of comfort and style, with quality furnishings and thoughtful extras such as clocks and hairdryers; most overlook the estuary. Guests are welcomed on arrival with home-made scones and local clotted cream in the lounge. Fresh local produce again features at breakfast. Evening meals are available on request or Neil and Ella can recommend local restaurants.

Recommended in the area
Polperro; Looe town and beach; St Mellion Golf Course

Padstow harbour

Tremaine Farm

★★★★ FH

Address: Pelynt, LOOE PL13 2LT
Tel/ Fax: 01503 220417
Email: rosemary@tremainefarm.co.uk
Website: www.tremainefarm.co.uk
Map ref: 1, SX25
Directions: 5m NW of Looe. B3359 N from Pelynt, left at x-rds
Rooms: 2 (1 en suite) D £56–£62 **Parking:** 6
Notes: ⊘ on premises ⊗ in bedrooms 👶 under 4yrs

This working farm is set within an area of outstanding natural beauty. The farmhouse retains many original features and the mature gardens provide a haven of tranquillity. Accommodation consists of a luxury family suite with a king-sized double room, an adjoining twin room and a bathroom with power shower; and a luxury double suite with pretty furnishings and a splendid bathroom. Each has a hospitality tray and TV. A hearty breakfast is served in the dining room and there is a pleasant lounge.

Recommended in the area

South West Coast Path; The Eden Project; The Monkey Sanctuary Trust

Woodlands

★★★★ GH

Address: St Martins Road,
LOOE PL13 1LP
Tel: 01503 264405
Website: www.looedirectory.co.uk
Map ref: 1, SX25
Directions: 0.5m N of Looe bridge on B3253
Rooms: 5 en suite, S D £60–£80 Parking: 6
Notes: ⊗ on premises ⊗ on premises 🧒 under 7yrs
Closed: Dec–Jan

Woodlands is a lovely Victorian country house with stunning views over the peaceful Looe estuary and valley. An attractive wood borders one side of the property, and the shops, harbour and beaches of Looe are within walking distance. The well-appointed and comfortable bedrooms include double, twin and single rooms, all with en suite facilities; two rooms are easily adapted into accommodation suitable for families. All are equipped with hospitality tray, dressing gowns, TV and many other little luxuries. The front rooms have lovely views of the estuary. Wherever possible, local produce goes into the enjoyable breakfasts which include a well-regarded fruit compôte along with a cooked breakfast. Breakfasts are served at a relaxed pace in the elegant dining room. Woodlands also caters for vegetarians and other dietary needs. Delicious three-course dinners are available by arrangement. Woodlands has on-site parking. The area offers spectacular cliff and country walks but if you prefer to sit and relax while enjoying spectacular views then take a trip on the scenic Looe to Liskeard railway – the river views are best at high tide. Looe also offers shark and sea fishing, horse riding, tennis and several championship golf courses within easy reach. Looe railway station is just a short walk from Woodlands.

Recommended in the area

The Eden Project; South West Coast Path; Lanhydrock (NT)

Kallacliff

★★★★ GA

Address: 12 Lusty Glaze Road, NEWQUAY TR7 3AD
Tel: 01637 871704
Email: kallacliffhotel@btconnect.com
Website: www.kallacliffhotel.co.uk
Map ref: 1, SW86
Directions: 0.5m NE of town centre. A3058 to Newquay, right off Henver Rd onto Lusty Glaze Rd, 350yds on right
Rooms: 8 en suite, D £74–£80 Parking: 10
Notes: ⊘ on premises ⊗ on premises ⋔

Set on the cliff top above Lusty Glaze beach, with stunning sea views, this family-owned, guesthouse is in a peaceful location within walking distance of central Newquay. Guests can start the day enjoying the wonderful views over breakfast in the dining room, then return in the evening to watch the sun set over the sea in the conservatory or the lounge and bar (refreshments are available here throughout the day and evening). The bright bedrooms have en suite shower rooms, TV and hospitality trays.

Recommended in the area

Lusty Glaze beach; Blue Reef Aquarium; South West Coast Path.

The Old Mill House

★★★★ GH

Address: PADSTOW, PL27 7QT
Tel: 01841 540388
Fax: 01841 540406
Email: enquiries@theoldmillhouse.com
Website: www.theoldmillhouse.com
Map ref: 1, SW97
Directions: 2m S of Padstow. In Little Petherick centre on A389
Rooms: 7 en suite, S £80–£120 D £80–£120 Parking: 20
Notes: ⊘ on premises ⊗ on premises ⋔ under 14yrs
Closed: Nov–Mar

You are assured of a warm welcome in this licensed Grade II listed mill house just 2 miles from the popular village of Padstow. The idyllic converted corn mill and millhouse is next to a pretty stream with ducks and a pair of swans – you may even spot a kingfisher. The seven comfortable bedrooms are individually decorated, well equipped and all have good views. An extensive breakfast menu is served in the original mill room.

Recommended in the area

The Eden Project; Lost Gardens of Heligan; Camel Trail Cycle Path

Camilla House

★★★★★ GH

Address: 12 Regent Terrace, PENZANCE TR18 4DW
Tel/Fax: 01736 363771
Email: enquiries@camillahouse.co.uk
Website: www.camillahouse.co.uk
Map ref: 1, SW53
Directions: A30 to Penzance, at railway station follow road along harbour front onto Promenade Rd. Opp Jubilee Bathing Pool, Regent Ter 2nd right
Rooms: 8 (7 en suite), S £35–£39.50 D £70–£79
Parking: 6 **Notes:** ⊘ on premises ⊗ on premises ⋔

The friendly proprietors of this attractive Grade II listed terrace house – Simon Chapman was a finalist for AA friendliest 'Landlady' of the Year award 2007 – do their utmost to ensure a comfortable stay. On arrival, guests are served with tea and coffee with 'Thunder and Lightning', a real Cornish treat. Bedrooms and bathrooms are attractively furnished, providing many added extras, such as fluffy towels and bathrobes, refreshment trays with Fairtrade products and Cornish mineral water, flatscreen Freeview TV/DVD, hairdryer, magazines and sweets. Some bedrooms and the dining room also provide delightful sea views over Mount's Bay. Wireless internet connection is available throughout, and there is also access to computers in the stylish, high-ceilinged lounge, which stocks a library of DVDs as well as Cornish monopoly. A range of breakfast options is on offer in the dining room, home to a well-stocked residents' bar, using home-made or fresh local produce; options include traditional cooked breakfast, fruit, yoghurt, Cornish cheese platters, and smoked haddock and pollock from nearby Newlyn. Evening meals are available by prior arrangement. Camilla House has been registered and inspected by the Green Tourism Business Scheme award since 2006 and is committed to operating in an environmentally responsible fashion.

Recommended in the area

Land's End; Lizard Peninsula; South West Coast Path

The Summer House

★★★★★ ⊚⊚ GA

Address: Cornwall Terrace, PENZANCE TR18 4HL
Tel: 01736 363744
Email: reception@summerhouse-cornwall.com
Website: www.summerhouse-cornwall.com
Map ref: 1, SW53
Directions: A30 to Penzance, at railway station follow road along harbour front onto Promenade Rd, pass Jubilee Pool, right after Queens Hotel, Summer House 30yds on left
Rooms: 5 en suite, S £85–£120 D £95–£125 **Parking:** 6
Notes: ⊘ ⊗ ⋈ under 13yrs **Closed:** Nov–Feb

The philosophy of the Summer House is to combine great food and beautiful surroundings with a happy, informal atmosphere, making it the perfect seaside retreat. Close to the seafront and harbour, this stylishly converted, stunning Grade II listed Regency house features bold decor, polished wood, bright colours, and a curving glass-walled tower that fills the building with light. Fresh flowers are among the thoughtful extras provided in the twin and double en suite bedrooms, which all have evocative names such as Sunshine, Pinstripe and Sea-checks. Each of the spacious rooms is light, airy and individually decorated, and is enhanced by interesting family pieces and collectables, as well as a range of home comforts to help you relax, such as TV, radio, DVD player, hairdryer, books and magazines. Fresh local food and regional produce is simply prepared to provide memorable dining from a weekly changing menu, with dishes distinctly Mediterranean in feel and good wines on hand to accompany them. The rich Cornish puddings are especially hard to resist. The restaurant opens out onto a walled garden with terracotta pots, sub-tropical planting and attractive blue tables and chairs, where in warmer weather evening drinks and dinner may be enjoyed.

Recommended in the area

St Michael's Mount (NT); Land's End; The Minack Theatre

Ednovean Farm

★★★★★ FH

Address: PERRANUTHNOE TR20 9LZ
Tel: 01736 711883
Email: info@ednoveanfarm.co.uk
Website: www.ednoveanfarm.co.uk
Map ref: 1, SW52
Directions: Off A394 towards Perranuthnoe at
Dynasty Restaurant, farm drive on left on bend
by post box
Rooms: 3 en suite, S £75–£95 D £75–£95
Parking: 4 Notes: ⊘ on premises ⊗ on premises ⋈ under 16yrs Closed: 24–28 Dec & New Year

Spectacular sea views over St Michael's Mount and Mount's Bay are a delightful feature of this converted 17th-century farmhouse which stands high above the village in beautiful grounds. The stylish bedrooms are furnished with comfortable beds and quality pieces, chintz fabrics, and thoughtful extras like flowers, magazines and fruit. Guests can relax in the elegant sitting room, the garden room and on several sunny patios. The coastal footpath and the beach are just three minutes away.

Recommended in the area
St Michael's Mount (NT); Godolphin House; Penlee House Gallery (Newlyn School paintings)

Trenake Manor Farm

★★★★ FH

Address: Pelynt, POLPERRO PL13 2LT
Tel/Fax: 01503 220835
Email: lorraine@cornishfarmhouse.co.uk
Website: www.cornishfarmhouse.co.uk
Map ref: 1, SX25
Directions: 3.5m N of Polperro. A390 onto B3359
for Looe, 5m left at small x-rds
Rooms: 3 en suite £56–£64 Parking: 10
Notes: ⊘ on premises ⋈

Situated midway between the historic fishing ports of Looe and Polperro, this welcoming 15th-century farmhouse is surrounded by 300 acres of its own farmland. It has been owned by the same family for five generations and makes a good base for touring Cornwall. En suite bedrooms, including one family room, are spacious and boast elegant Victorian kingsize bedsteads and a number of thoughtful finishing touches. Breakfast is made from local produce and served in the cosy dining room. Guests are welcome to relax on the sunloungers provided in the large, well-kept garden.

Recommended in the area
The Eden Project; Lost Gardens of Heligan; Polperro

The Corn Mill

★★★★ BB

Address: Port Isaac Road, PORT ISAAC PL30 3HZ
Tel: 01208 851079
Map ref: 1, SW09
Directions: Off B3314, between Pendoggett and Trelill
Rooms: 3 (2 en suite), D £70–£75 Parking: 3
Notes: ⊗ on premises 🐾 allowed in bedrooms ♦♦
Closed: 24 Dec–5 Jan

Dating from the 18th century, this former mill has been lovingly restored to provide a beautiful home packed with character. The delightful garden and charming hostess add to the pleasure of a stay here. Bedrooms are individually styled, and personal touches create a wonderfully relaxed and homely atmosphere. Most rooms have their own shower room, while the twin room uses a bathroom with an enormous Victorian bathtub, and plenty of hot water. Luxury extras such as huge towels and cotton bed linen are pampering touches. Delicious breakfasts with home-made nutty bread are served in the farmhouse kitchen. The Eden Project is only a half-hour drive away.

Recommended in the area

South West Coast Path; Lost Gardens of Heligan; St Michael's Mount (NT)

The Coach House

★★★★ GA

Address: Kuggar, RUAN MINOR, Helston TR12 7LY
Tel: 01326 291044
Email: mjanmakin@aol.com
Website: www.the-coach-house.net
Map ref: 1, SW71
Directions: 1m N of Ruan Minor in Kuggar village
Rooms: 5 (en suite), S £40 D £70
Parking: 10 Notes: ⊗ on premises ⊗ on premises
♦♦ Closed: Xmas

This 17th-century house, close to Kennack Sands and Goonhilly Downs nature reserve, retains many interesting original features. Its location makes it an ideal base for hikers. The friendly proprietors look after their guests well, and they can relax in the spacious lounge-dining room where a fire burns in colder months and which boasts low beamed ceilings and an inglenook fireplace and old bread oven. The en suite bedrooms, two of which are in a converted stable block, are attractively decorated and offer extras such as hairdryer, tea and coffee-making facilities and Sky television.

Recommended in the area

Lizard Peninsula; The Earth Satellite Station; Flambards Theme Park

BioDomes, Eden Project

Smeaton Farm

★★★★ ≜ ⊜ FH

Address: SALTASH, Saltash PL12 6RZ
Tel/Fax: 01579 351833
Email: info@smeatonfarm.co.uk
Website: www.smeatonfarm.co.uk
Map ref: 1, SX45
Directions: 1m N of Hatt and 1m S of St Mellion just off A388
Rooms: 3 en suite, S £40–£50 D £60–£80
Parking: 8 Notes: ⊗ ⊗ in bedrooms ⫯⫯

This elegant Georgian farmhouse is surrounded by 450 acres of rolling Cornish farmland, situated within the Duchy of Cornwall. It provides a wonderfully peaceful place to stay, and the atmosphere is relaxed and hospitable, with every effort made to ensure guests have a comfortable and rewarding break. The bedrooms, including two family rooms, are spacious, light and airy and well equipped. Enjoyable dinners often feature seasonal vegetables and home-reared meats – the farm is now fully organic – and the sausages and home-cured bacon at breakfast come highly recommended.

Recommended in the area

Saltash Town Museum; Churchdown Farm Community Nature Reserve; trips on the River Tamar

Anchorage House

★★★★★ GA

Address: Nettles Cnr, Tregrehan Mills,
ST AUSTELL PL25 3RH
Tel: 01726 814071
Fax: 01726 813462
Email: info@anchoragehouse.co.uk
Website: www.anchoragehouse.co.uk
Map ref: 1, SX05
Directions: 2 m E of town centre off A390, opposite St Austell
Garden Centre
Rooms: 4 en suite, S £75–£115 D £100–£160 Parking: 6
Notes: ⊗ on premises ⊗ on premises ⊀ under 16yrs
Closed: Dec–Feb

Jane and Steve Epperson have created a very special place to stay here, with the utmost luxury and pampering in a perfect location near the Cornish coast. Little wonder that it makes it into *Britain's Best Bed and Breakfast* once again. The modern brick building has a charming conservatory at the rear, overlooking the new swimming and leisure complex. The hospitality and delightful informality offered by this English/Texan couple is outstanding, the rooms are impeccably fitted out, with extra-large beds, satellite TV and lots of other extras, and the sparkling bathrooms have everything you would expect of such a highly-rated establishment. But that's not all. Facilities here include a spa with various treatments on offer, plus a hot tub, a 15metre lap pool and a small but well-equipped gym. When guests have finished working out or being pampered in the spa, they can enjoy a bistro supper (by arrangement 24 hours in advance), served in the glass room, using the finest local fresh produce. Breakfast is also a special occasion, with an extensive cooked menu and delicious buffet to choose from.

Recommended in the area

The Eden Project; Wheal Martyn Heritage Centre; Lost Gardens of Heligan

Highland Court Lodge

★★★★★ GA

Address: Biscovey Road, Biscovey, Par,
ST AUSTELL PL24 2HW
Tel: 01726 813320
Fax: 01726 813320
Email: enquiries@highlandcourt.co.uk
Website: www.highlandcourt.co.uk
Map ref: 1, SX05
Directions: 2m E of St Austell. A390 E to St Blazey Gate, right onto Biscovey Rd, 300yds on right
Rooms: 3 en suite, S £95 D £90–£170 Parking: 12
Notes: ⊗ on premises ⊗ on premises ⚹

There is a definite 'wow' factor to this excellent Cornish retreat, where an inspirational setting, with views over St Austell Bay and excellent walking nearby, is combined with a truly relaxing atmosphere. The bedrooms here are impressive, with quality furnishings, luxurious fabrics, fresh flowers, a beverage tray, minibar, TV, DVD and VCR players and broadband internet access. Each has a private patio and a spacious en suite bathroom, some with spa baths, where luxury toiletries, aromatherapy candles and bathrobes are all provided. For extra pampering, a range of spa treatments are available. Guests can also make use of the lounge with deep sofas, and a fire is lit to create a cosy and welcoming ambience on chillier evenings. As well as a charming dining room, Highland Court boasts a terrace with fine views, where dinner is served on summer evenings. Local Cornish fish and seafood, as well as organic produce, feature strongly in the freshly prepare dinners. Like breakfast – which might include energy shakes, full Cornish hearty breakfast and smoked salmon with free-range scrambled eggs – dining here is not to be missed. Self-catering accommodation is also available, as are photography workshops.

Recommended in the area

The Eden Project; Lost Gardens of Heligan; South West Coast Path.

Truro Cathedral

Hunter's Moon

★ ★ ★ ★ GH

Address: Chapel Hill, Polgooth,
ST AUSTELL PL26 7BU
Tel/Fax: 01726 66445
Email: enquiries@huntersmooncornwall.co.uk
Website: www.huntersmooncornwall.co.uk
Map ref: 1, SX05
Directions: 1.5m SW of town centre. Off B2373 into
Polgooth, pass village shop on left, 1st right
Rooms: 4 en suite, S £40–£47 D £56–£70
Parking: 5 Notes: ⊘ on premises ⊗ on premises ♨ under 14yrs

A friendly welcome and pot of tea or coffee in the conservatory awaits you on arrival at Hunter's Moon. The guest rooms are decorated and furnished to a high standard and two of these have super king-size beds, which can be converted into twin beds. There is ample private car parking, and plenty of space to sit, relax and enjoy the garden and countryside views. The Polgooth Inn is five minutes' walk from Hunter's Moon and there are many more restaurants within a few miles.

Recommended in the area

The Eden Project; Lost Gardens of Heligan; Charlestown harbour

Lower Barn

★★★★★ GA

Address: Bosue, St Ewe, ST AUSTELL PL26 6EU
Tel: 01726 844881
Email: janie@bosue.co.uk
Website: www.bosue.co.uk
Map ref: 1, SX05
Directions: 3.5m SW of St Austell. Off B3273 at x-rds signed Lost Gardens of Heligan, Lower Barn signed 1m on right
Rooms: 4 (3 en suite) **Parking:** 7 **Notes:** ⊘ on premises ⊗ in bedrooms ♥ **Closed:** Jan

Tucked away down a meandering country lane yet with easy access to local attractions, this converted barn has huge appeal and proprietors Mike and Janie Cooksley fully deserved the award AA Guest Accommodation of the Year for England 2005/2006. The warm colours and decoration create a Mediterranean feel that is complemented by informal and genuine hospitality. It is the attention to detail that places Lower Barn a cut above the rest. The three en suite bedrooms are equipped with a host of extras from daily fresh towels and fridges to tea and coffee-making facilities. Breakfast is chosen from an extensive menu and served round a large table or on the patio deck overlooking the garden, which also has a luxurious hot tub. You can even collect your own free-range eggs for breakfast. A candlelit dinner, available most nights of the week, is served in the conservatory or on the terrace – and you can bring your own wine. After exploring the many attractions the area has to offer, including Mevagissey, where a bustling harbour shelters a fishing fleet and the narrow streets are lined with colour-washed old houses, galleries and gift shops, you can unwind with some gorgeous massage and therapy treatments to make your experience at Lower Barn memorable.

Recommended in the area

The Eden Project; Lost Gardens of Heligan; Mevagissey; cliff walks; Roseland Peninsula

Penarwyn House

★★★★★ GA

Address: ST BLAZEY, Par PL24 2DS
Tel/ Fax: 01726 814224
Email: stay@penarwyn.co.uk
Website: www.penarwyn.co.uk
Map ref: 1, SX05
Directions: A390 W through St Blazey, left at 2nd speed camera, house past school
Rooms: 3 en suite, S £65–£99 D £85–£120
Parking: 6 **Notes:** ⊘ on premises ⊗ on premises 🐾under 10yrs **Closed:** 21 Dec–9 Jan

True Cornish hospitality and memorable breakfasts complement this spacious Victorian residence which is set in tranquil surroundings, yet close to main routes. Since 2003, owners Mike and Jan Russell – who have many years experience successfully running bed and breakfast establishments – have been painstakingly restoring Penarwyn House to its original glory. Many of the old features have been faithfully restored alongside luxury new en suites, which include a bath by candlelight for romantics and a separate shower. The bedrooms are most impressive, spacious, delightfully appointed, and equipped with a host of extras including tea and coffee facilities, hairdryers, flat-screen colour TV and DVD/CD player. Treffry is a kingsize double room, looking out over the front garden, with a large corner bath and fluffy bath sheets. Prideaux, the largest room, has large comfy chairs and an en suite with a slipper bath and a separate shower, while Caerhayes, although smaller than the other bedrooms, offers the same comfort and style. There is a panelled snooker room with a $^3/_4$ size snooker table and wireless internet access is available for use on guest laptops. Breakfast is another highlight at Penarwyn House, and along with the friendly and attentive service, this all makes for a pleasurable stay.

Recommended in the area

The Eden Project; Lanhydrock (NT); Lost Gardens of Heligan

Edgar's

★★★★ GA

Address: Chy-an-Creet, Higher Stennack,
ST IVES TR26 2HA
Tel: 01736 796559
Fax: 01736 796559
Email: stay@chy.co.uk
Website: www.chy.co.uk
Map ref: 1, SW54
Directions: 0.5m W of town centre on B3306, opp
Leach Pottery
Rooms: 7 en suite, S £39 D £58 **Parking:** 8 **Notes:** ⊗ on premises ⊗ in bedrooms ⋔
Closed: Nov–Feb

Also known as Chy an Creet, Edgar's was built in the 1920s and is today a family-run guest house with lots of character and plenty of space. Away from but within easy reach of the bustling town centre, harbour and golden sandy beaches, the property nestles in its own gardens near to where the edge of town meets the Penwith Moors. On-site parking is available to guests, and many coach tours exploring the local area stop right outside. Inside the house, owners Judith and David have refurbished to a high standard. Public areas are homely and spacious, and include a well-stocked bar with a real fire and a relaxing lounge, where plenty of reading material is provided. The en suite bedrooms, some on the ground floor and some available as family rooms, are well equipped, including TV, a complimentary drinks tray, toiletries and fluffy towels. Meals are cooked on the bright red Aga – bar snacks are available and breakfast, served in the dining room, features home-made preserves. The owners are happy to help with recommendations and reservations for evening dining, and David is particularly knowledgeable about the local area.

Recommended in the area

Land's End; Penzance; Tate St Ives

Tate Gallery, St Ives

The Old Count House

★★★★ GH

Address: 1 Trenwith Square, ST IVES TR26 1DQ
Tel: 01736 795369
Fax: 01736 799109
Email: counthouse@btconnect.com
Website: www.theoldcounthouse-stives.co.uk
Map ref: 1, SW54
Directions: Follow signs to St Ives, located between leisure centre and school
Rooms: 10 (9 en suite), S £35–£38 D £70–£84
Parking: 9 **Notes:** ⊘ on premises ⊗ in bedrooms ⊁ **Closed:** 20–29 Dec

This granite stone house built in 1825 is situated in a quiet residential area with private parking, yet is just a five-minute walk from town, with its many restaurants. Bedrooms here vary in size and all are comfortably furnished and most enjoy magnificent views over the harbour and bay. One luxurious room has a four-poster bed and Jacuzzi-style bath. Breakfast offers extensive choices made from fresh local produce, including kippers. Guests are welcome to relax in the conservatory, garden and sauna.

Recommended in the area

Tate St Ives; Porthmeor Beach; St Ives town

The Regent

★★★★ GA

Address: Fernlea Terrace, ST IVES TR26 2BH
Tel: 01736 796195
Fax: 01736 794641
Email: keith@regenthotel.com
Website: www.regenthotel.com
Map ref: 1, SW54
Directions: In town centre, near bus & railway station
Rooms: 9 (7 en suite), S £33.50–£34.50
D £72–£92 Parking: 12 Notes: ⊗ on premises
⊗ on premises ✢ under 16yrs

The Regent Hotel was established 78 years ago when a local architect purchased Penwyn House from a retired sea captain and converted it to provide an interest for his wife and daughter. In 1972 the late Mr and Mrs SH Varnals bought the property and in due course passed it on to Keith and Sandi Varnals, the present proprietors. Sandi, a former lingerie designer, has worked her magic on the interior of the old building, while Keith, an engineer turned chef, has modernised the facilities to appeal to today's modern traveller. Bedrooms are well equipped with colour TV, radio alarm clocks and tea and coffee-making facilities. Seven rooms have facilities en suite, and most benefit from spectacular sea views. The breakfast menu offers a good choice of hot dishes, cooked to order, and an extensive buffet of cereals, yoghurts, pastries, fruit and juice. The oak-smoked fish and bacon is sourced locally. Also on offer are espresso, cappuccino, and cafetière coffee, hot chocolate and a choice of teas. There is a lounge and bar for evening relaxation, and parking is provided for all rooms. If you prefer not to drive, the hotel is situated close to the local bus, coach and rail stations. The Regent is Ideally located to explore the local area, being just a short stroll from the narrow cobbled streets and harbour in St Ives.

Recommended in the area

South West Coast Path; Tate St Ives; Penzance on Cornwall's south coast

St Ives Bay

The Rookery

★★★★ GA

Address: 8 The Terrace, ST IVES TR26 2BL
Tel: 01736 799401
Email: therookerystives@hotmail.com
Website: www.rookerystives.com
Map ref: 1, SW54
Directions: A3074 through Carbis Bay, right fork at Porthminster Hotel, The Rookery 500yds on left
Rooms: 6 en suite, S £37.50–£40 D £60–£80
Parking: 6 **Notes:** ⊘ on premises ⊗ on premises
🚫 under 7yrs

Ron and Barbara Rook's friendly establishment stands on an elevated position overlooking the harbour, sandy beaches and St Ives Bay, near the town's train and bus stations, and only a short walk to the shops, galleries and restaurants in St Ives. The rooms are attractively decorated, and are well equipped with considerate extras such as a chiller to keep soft drinks and wines cool. A choice of full English, continental or vegetarian breakfast is served in the dining room.

Recommended in the area

Tate St Ives; Barbara Hepworth Museum; The Minack Theatre

Woodside

★★★★ GA

Address: The Belyars, ST IVES TR26 2DA
Tel: 01736 795681
Email: woodsidehotel@btconnect.com
Website: www.woodside-hotel.co.uk
Map ref: 1, SW54
Directions: A3074 to St Ives, left at Porthminster Hotel onto Talland Rd, 1st left onto Belyars Ln, Woodside 4th on right
Rooms: 10 en suite, S £40–£55 D £80–£120
Parking: 12 Notes: ⊘ on premises ⊗ on premises ⊮ under 5yrs

Suzanne and Chris Taylor are welcoming hosts who diligently attend to their beautiful property. They promise personal attention, ensuring an enjoyable holiday here. Woodside stands in peaceful grounds above St Ives Bay, with fantastic views from most bedrooms and all of the public rooms. Just a 5-minute walk away in St Ives are lovely stretches of golden beaches for bathing and surfing, the picturesque harbour with its traditional fishing fleet, and the narrow cobbled streets lined with artists' studios, galleries and craft shops. The comfortable, spacious en suite bedrooms range from single, double and twin to family rooms, and all are well equipped with colour TV, a radio-alarm clock, hairdryer and a hospitality tray. Guests can relax in the comfortable lounge with a TV and games area, enjoy a drink at the bar, or relish the sea views from the attractive gardens or terrace. A heated outdoor swimming pool is open from May to September. Breakfast is another delight, you'll find a hearty choice of full English, continental or vegetarian dishes prepared from fresh local produce where possible. A short hole golf course and a leisure centre with a superb gym and indoor pool are both within a short distance of Woodside.

Recommended in the area

Tate St Ives; Land's End; The Eden Project

Bodrean Manor Farm

★★★★ FH

Address: Trispen, TRURO TR4 9AG
Tel: 01872 273227
Fax: 01872 273225
Website: www.bodreanmanorfarm.co.uk
Map ref: 1, SW84
Directions: 3m NE of Truro. A30 onto A39 towards
Truro, left after Trispen village signed Frogmore &
Trehane, farm driveway 100yds
Rooms: 3 (2 en suite), S £35–£40 D £50–£55
Parking: 6 Notes: ⊘ on premises ⊗ on premises ♦♦

This friendly farmhouse lies in countryside with splendid views, yet is only minutes from the city of Truro. It has been restored to a high standard and the spacious, luxurious bedrooms, all with facilities en suite, are thoughtfully equipped. The bathrooms are well provisioned with soft towels and a host of toiletries. Original features in the dining room include a beamed ceiling and an inglenook fireplace, while the full English breakfast, using local and home-grown produce, is certainly not to be hurried.

Recommended in the area

The Eden Project; Lost Gardens of Heligan; Trelissick Garden (NT)

Oxturn House

★★★★ BB

Address: Ladock, TRURO TR2 4NQ
Tel: 01726 884348
Email: oxturnhouse@hotmail.com
Website: www.oxturnhouse.co.uk
Map ref: 1, SW84
Directions: 6m NE of Truro. B3275 into Ladock, onto
lane opp Falmouth Arms, up hill 200yds, 1st right
after end 30mph sign, Oxturn on right
Rooms: 2 (1 en suite and 1 with pb. Both rooms can
be twin or kingsize), D £56–£64 Parking: 4 Notes: ⊘ ⊗ ♦♦ under 12yrs Closed: Dec–Jan

Bedrooms at this large family house are spacious and come with lovely southerly views of the garden and beyond to parkland. Guests are provided with colour TV, hairdryer and welcome tray. The pleasant lounge has deep sofas, and in summer the French doors are opened out onto the patio. Hearty breakfasts are served in the dining room, which overlooks the large garden and the local birdlife. The whole county is easily accessible from here and the owners are happy to advise on planning itineraries.

Recommended in the area

Truro; St Just in Roseland; boat trips down the River Fal to Falmouth

Rhododendron, Trelissick Gardens

The New Inn

★★★★ INN

Address: VERYAN, Truro TR2 5QA
Tel: 01872 501362
Fax: 01872 501078
Email: jack@newinn-veryan.fsnet.co.uk
Website: www.newinnveryan.co.uk
Map ref: 1, SW93
Directions: In village centre
Rooms: 3 (2 en suite), S £35 D £70 **Notes:** ⊗ in
bedrooms ⊗ on premises ⋦ under 14yrs

Popular with visitors and locals alike, the New Inn is based on a pair of 16th-century cottages and is situated in the pretty Cornish village of Veryan, set in the Roseland peninsula. The bedrooms here are brightly decorated and well equipped, with extras such as colour TV, tea and coffee-making facilities and hairdryer thoughtfully provided. Dining in the bar area is an enjoyable experience; breakfast is chosen from an extensive menu made as much as possible from local produce and featuring stewed fruit, smoked fish and full English, while lunches, dinners and snacks come from a wide-ranging menu.

Recommended in the area

The Eden Project: Lost Gardens of Heligan; Carne and Pendower beaches

CUMBRIA

Ullswater, Lake District National Park

Elterwater Park

★★★★ GH

Address: Skelwith Bridge, AMBLESIDE LA22 9NP
Tel: 015394 32227
Email: enquiries@elterwater.com
Website: www.elterwater.com
Map ref: 5, NY30
Directions: A593 from Ambleside to Coniston, 1m past Skelwith Bridge Hotel, layby on right fronts estate road to Elterwater Park, signed at gate
Rooms: 5 en suite, S £40–£46 D £60–£72
Parking: 10 Notes: ⊗ on premises ⊗ in bedrooms ✖ under 10yrs

Set on the hills above Langdale, this stone house is full of traditional features. All the attractive bedrooms are en suite and are furnished with radios, hairdryers, hospitality trays and fresh flowers – one room has easier access. Breakfast and dinner are served in the spacious lounge-dining room. Your hosts hold a full residential licence with a wine list chosen for quality and value to go with the freshly prepared dinners. There is a terrace for fine days – and a drying room for those other days.
Recommended in the area
Ambleside; Coniston Water; Cumbrian Way

Kent House

★★★★ GH

Address: Lake Road, AMBLESIDE LA22 0AD
Tel: 015394 33279
Email: mail@kent-house.com
Website: www.kent-house.com
Map ref: 5, NY30
Directions: From town centre, by Post Office on one-way system 300yds on left on terrace above main road
Rooms: 5 (4 en suite), S £38–£45 D £60–£90 Parking: 2
Notes: ⊗ on premises 🐾 allowed in bedrooms ♦♦

Kent House, an elegant Victorian Guest House retaining many original features, has offered a friendly welcome to guests from all over the world since the mid 1800s. Sandra and Simon continue this tradition offering spacious guest rooms (featuring Wi-fi access) and a full English Lakeland breakfast prepared using fresh local produce. Breakfasts can be tailored from the extensive menu and if you are feeling a liitle more self-indulgent – breakfast in bed is also available.
Recommended in the area
Lake Windermere; Dove Cottage & The Wordsworth Museum; Hill Top (Beatrix Potter's home) NT

Riverside

★ ★ ★ ★ GH

Address: Under Loughrigg, AMBLESIDE LA22 9LJ
Tel: 015394 32395
Fax: 015394 32440
Email: info@riverside-at-ambleside.co.uk
Website: www.riverside-at-ambleside.co.uk
Map ref: 5, NY30
Directions: A593 from Ambleside to Coniston, over stone bridge, right onto Under Loughrigg Ln, Riverside 150yds left

Rooms: 6 en suite, S £65–£82 D £82–£98 (special mid-week breaks and discount for longer stays)
Parking: 15 **Notes:** ⊗ on premises ⊗ on premises 🚼 under 5yrs **Closed:** Xmas & New Year

Built in 1866 and situated on a quiet country lane, alongside the River Rothay, Riverside is an award-winning bed and breakfast in a beautiful rural riverside location. Both traditional English and vegetarian breakfasts are offered using local ingredients with freshly prepared home-made breads and preserves. Bedrooms, all with lovely views of the river or the garden, are very comfortable, stylishly furnished and feature homely extras such as hospitality trays and colour TV; some have luxurious spa baths. The house has extensive landscaped gardens with views of the surrounding fells which guests are welcome to use as well as the lounge which is warmed by a log burning stove in the winter months. Here you'll find a good collection of local maps, guides and books to help you discover all the area has to offer. There is ample parking in the grounds and from the house there is access nearby to Loughrigg Fell, which offers spectacular views of Windermere, Rydal Water, Grasmere and many of the high mountains.

Recommended in the area

Grasmere; Dove Cottage & The Wordsworth Museum; The World of Beatrix Potter; Ambleside; walk to the waterfall Stock Ghyll Force

Wanslea Guest House

★★★★ GH

Address: Low Fold, Lake Rd, AMBLESIDE LA22 0DN
Tel/Fax: 015394 33884
Email: information@wanslea.co.uk
Website: www.wanslea.co.uk
Map ref: 5, NY30
Directions: On S side of town, opp garden centre
Rooms: 8 en suite, S £30–£45 D £64–£90
Notes: ⊗ on premises 🐾 allowed in bedrooms 👶
under 6yrs Closed: 23–26 Dec

Located at the foot of Wansfell, on the quieter south side of Ambleside village, this Victorian house
is an ideal base for exploring the Lake District. Guests can relax in the comfortable bedrooms, some
of which are individually themed, such as the Arabian Nights Room with its canopied bed and starry
ceiling or the Rock and Roll Room, with a retro feel. Rooms are well equipped with colour TV, hairdryer
and tea and coffee-making facilities; and the themed rooms have spa baths and widescreen TV.
Comprehensive breakfasts are served in the spacious dining room, and there's a cosy lounge.
Recommended in the area
Hill Top (Beatrix Potter's home) (NT); Lakeside Railway; Dove Cottage & The Wordsworth Museum

Hall Croft

★★★★ BB

Address: Dufton, APPLEBY-IN-WESTMORLAND
CA16 6DB
Tel: 017683 52902
Email: r.walker@leaseholdpartnerships.co.uk
Map ref: 6, NY62
Directions: 3m N of Appleby. In Dufton by village grn
Rooms: 3 (2 en suite), S £31 D £52 Parking: 3
Notes: ⊗ on premises 🐾 allowed on premises 👪
Closed: 24–26 Dec

Located in a tranquil village, this large Victorian house stands at the foot of the Pennines with
spectacular views in all directions. The substantial gardens are a joy to explore as are the surrounding
network of paths and walks from the village. Proprietors Frei and Ray Walker provide high quality
facilities that include two spacious bedrooms with en suite and a third that has a large private
bathroom. Substantial cooked breakfasts include a varied range of home-made produce and are served
in the period lounge/dining room. Afternoon tea and cakes and packed lunches are available.
Recommended in the area
North Pennines AONB; Northern Lake District; Appleby-in-Westmorland

Dove Cottage, Grasmere

Hazel Bank Country House

★★★★★ ◉ GH

Address: Rosthwaite, BORROWDALE, CA12 5XB
Tel: 017687 77248
Email: enquiries@hazelbankhotel.co.uk
Website: www.hazelbankhotel.co.uk
Map ref: 5, NY21
Directions: A66 Keswick, follow B5289 signed Borrowdale, turn left before Rosthwaite over humped back bridge
Rooms: 8 en suite, S £65–£95 D £130–£190
Parking: 12 **Notes:** ⊘ on premises ⊗ on premises ⚺ under 12yrs

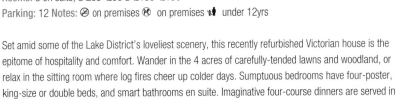

Set amid some of the Lake District's loveliest scenery, this recently refurbished Victorian house is the epitome of hospitality and comfort. Wander in the 4 acres of carefully-tended lawns and woodland, or relax in the sitting room where log fires cheer up colder days. Sumptuous bedrooms have four-poster, king-size or double beds, and smart bathrooms en suite. Imaginative four-course dinners are served in the delightful dining room. The Cumbrian breakfast is a great way to start your day out.

Recommended in the area

Lakeland's central fells; Scafell, Great Gable and Glaramara

The Wheatsheaf

★★★★ ≙ ⊜ INN

Address: BRIGSTEER, Kendal LA8 8AN
Tel: 015395 68254
Email: wheatsheaf@brigsteer.gb.com
Website: www.brigsteer.gb.com
Map ref: 6, SD48
Directions: Off A591 signed Brigsteer, Wheatsheaf
at bottom of hill
Rooms: 3 en suite Parking: 25 Notes: ⊗ on premises
⊗ on premises ♦♦

A family-owned free house dating from 1762, when it was three
cottages and a shoeing room for horses, the Wheatsheaf is
very much a traditional dining inn with accommodation. Lying in the peaceful little hamlet of Brigsteer,
just three miles to the west of Kendal, it was once the focal point for the local hunt but today makes a
perfect base for exploring the Lake District and Yorkshire Dales. Inside all is welcoming and fresh. The
well-equipped en suite bedrooms have all been refurbished to offer modern comforts. Award-winning
food is served throughout with the option of dining in the cosy, well-stocked bar or the charming dining
rooms. Major refurbishment here too has resulted in a contemporary feel, with polished oak floors
and handcrafted bistro-style tables and chairs. Home-made dishes made by chef Gareth Webster
range from traditional Cumbrian bar snacks to gourmet meals based on locally sourced produce,
meat and game, such as breast of local pheasant with a wild mushroom farce. Vegetarian meals are
also available, as are fine dining evenings, with a selection of real ales and a good wine selection as
accompaniment. Well-behaved children are welcome and there is a special child menu available. The
Wheatsheaf provides ample parking.

Recommended in the area

Levens Hall; Lakeland Wildlife Oasis; Holme Park Fell (NT)

Swaledale Watch Farm House

★★★★ GA

Address: Whelpo, CALDBECK CA7 8HQ
Tel/Fax: 016974 78409
Email: nan.savage@talk21.com
Website: www.swaledale-watch.co.uk
Map ref: 5, NY33
Directions: 1m SW of Caldbeck on B5299
Rooms: 4 en suite, S £28 D £50 Parking: 8
Notes: ⊗ on premises ⊗ on premises ♦♦
Closed: 24–26 Dec

This busy farm is set in idyllic surroundings, with views of the fells and mountains. Just a mile away is the village of Caldbeck, once renowned for its milling and mining, or take a walk through The Howk, a beautiful wooded limestone gorge with waterfalls. Nan and Arnold Savage work hard to make their hospitality seem effortless and to put you at ease. The lounges have TVs, books and games while the bedrooms have bath and shower en suite. Two bedrooms and a lounge are in the converted cowshed, ideal for a group of four. Nan's hearty Cumbrian breakfasts are delicious.

Recommended in the area

100-acre nature reserve on site; Northern Fells; Howk Walk to Caldbeck village

Crosthwaite House

★★★★ GH

Address: CROSTHWAITE, Kendal LA8 8BP
Tel: 015395 68264
Fax: 015395 68264
Email: bookings@crosthwaitehouse.co.uk
Website: www.crosthwaitehouse.co.uk
Map ref: 6, SD49
Directions: A590 onto A5074, 4m right to Crosthwaite, 0.5m turn left
Rooms: 6 en suite, S £27.50–£29.50 D £55–£59
Parking: 10 Notes: ⊗ on premises ✈ allowed on premises ♦♦ Closed: mid Nov–Dec

A sturdy mid 18th-century house, this establishment is in the village of Crosthwaite, at the northern end of the Lyth valley, famous for its damson orchards. You can see across the valley from the lounge, and from the dining room, where an imaginative menu of traditional home cooking is freshly cooked on the kitchen Aga. The spacious bedrooms have showers and toilets en suite, plus tea and coffee facilities. The owners create a relaxed atmosphere in which it is easy to feel at home.

Recommended in the area

Lake Windermere; Sizergh Castle and Garden (NT); three golf courses within 4 miles

Hawkshead, Lake District

Moss Grove Organic

★★★★★ GA

Address: GRASMERE, Ambleside LA22 9SW
Tel: 015394 35251
Fax: 015394 35306
Email: enquiries@mossgrove.com
Website: www.mossgrove.com
Map ref: 5, NY30
Directions: M6, junct 36, follow A591, turn left
Rooms: 11 en suite, S D £125–£250 Parking: 11
Notes: ⊘ ⌂ ⚹ Closed: 24–25 Dec

Located in the centre of Grasmere, this impressive Victorian house has been refurbished using as many natural products as possible, with ongoing dedication to causing minimal environmental impact. The bedrooms – two are on the ground floor – are decorated with beautiful wallpaper and natural clay paints and feature handmade beds and furnishings. Home entertainment systems, flatscreen TVs and luxury bathrooms add further comfort. Extensive continental breakfasts are served in the spacious kitchen, where guests can help themselves and dine at the large wooden dining table in the guest lounge.

Recommended in the area

Grasmere Lake; Rydal Water; Dove Cottage & The Wordsworth Museum

Sawrey Ground

★★★★ ≜ GA

Address: Hawkshead Hill, HAWKSHEAD LA22 0PP
Tel: 015394 36683
Email: mail@sawreyground.com
Website: www.sawreyground.com
Map ref: 5, SD39
Directions: B5285 from Hawkshead, 1m to Hawkshead Hill, sharp right after Baptist chapel, signs to Tarn Hows for 0.25m. Sawrey Ground on right

Rooms: 3 en suite, D £70–£82 **Parking:** 6 **Notes:** ⊘ on premises ⊗ on premises ⁑ under 8yrs

Built by Anthony Sawrey in 1627, this picturesque oak-beamed farmhouse has a magical setting on the edge of the Tarn Hows Forest, a peaceful location in the centre of the Lake District just above Hawkshead village. Mike and Gill O'Connell offer guests a warm welcome to their home, with its friendly, relaxed atmosphere and popular home-made cakes which are served each afternoon. They have been highly rated by the AA for their care and hospitality, and will do all they can to make your stay enjoyable and memorable. The centuries of occupation have created a comfortable and lived-in feeling, from the entrance hall, lounge and dining room, to the three attractive south-facing bedrooms – all are en suite with colour TV and tea and coffee-making facilities. Many walks are possible from the front door, leading to Coniston, Windermere and Langdale, and including the beautiful lake of Tarn Hows. The area is good for birdwatching and wildlife, and also for cycling and fishing. The central location is ideal for touring the Lakeland region, and there are some excellent places to eat within easy driving distance.

Recommended in the area

Great walks from the front door; Blackwell (The Arts & Crafts House), Bowness-on-Windermere; Brantwood (Ruskin's house), Coniston

West Vale Country House

★★★★★ ◎◎ GH

Address: Far Sawrey, HAWKSHEAD,
Ambleside LA22 0LQ
Tel: 015394 42817
Fax: 015394 45302
Email: enquiries@westvalecountryhouse.co.uk
Website: www.westvalecountryhouse.co.uk
Map ref: 5, SD39
Directions: Cross Windemere by car ferry at Bowness, B5285
for 1.25m to Far Sawrey, West Vale on left leaving village
Rooms: 7 en suite, S £70–£78 D £100–£160 Parking: 8
Notes: ⊘ on premises ⊗ on premises ❦ under 12yrs

West Vale is a lovely country house, built in the 1890s as a Victorian gentleman's residence, where
you can forget all your cares. It is surrounded by the stunning countryside of the Lake District National
Park on the edge of the pretty village of Far Sawrey, with views of Grizedale Forest and the Old Man of
Coniston beyond the vale. Beautiful gardens have been cultivated around the property, and there
is a delightful spot by the large pond to sit and soak up the sun. Yours hosts Dee and Glynn Pennington
have left nothing to chance in their desire to create a perfect retreat. The bedrooms are impeccably
decorated, furnished and equipped to a very high standard, and the bathrooms are also stylish. After
a long journey you can anticipate a welcoming decanter of sherry in the bedroom. Elegant lounges,
with a roaring log fire in the winter months, help you to unwind, and excellent dinners are served in
the dining room which is also open to non-residents. Afternoon Tea can be taken in the lounge or, in
warmer weather, on the terrace. The traditional breakfasts (there are also vegetarian and continental
options) are equally delicious.

Recommended in the area

Hill Top, (Beatrix Potter's home) (NT); Brantwood; Dove Cottage & The Wandsworth Museum

Dalegarth House

★★★★  GA

Address: Portinscale, KESWICK CA12 5RQ
Tel: 017687 72817
Email: allerdalechef@aol.com
Website: www.dalegarth-house.co.uk
Map ref: 5, NY22
Directions: Off A66 to Portinscale, pass Farmers Arms, 100yds on left
Rooms: 10 en suite, S £35–£40 D £70–£80 **Parking:** 14
Notes: ⊗ on premises ⊗ on premises 🌵under 12yrs
Closed: Dec–1 Mar

The views from this spacious Edwardian house, in the village of Portinscale, just south of Keswick, are nothing short of stunning. It sits on high ground, with a panoramic vista that takes in Derwent Water (just 400 metres from the door), Skiddaw, Catbells and the expanse of the fells of the northern Lakeland. It would be hard to find a better location for a walking holiday, and the full meal service here is a real bonus for hungry hikers. A full English breakfast starts the day, packed lunches are available on request and guests can return to a daily-changing four-course table d'hote dinner, prepared by the resident chef-proprietors Pauline and Bruce Jackson. Traditional and contemporary dishes feature, many of which have a regional emphasis, and there's an extensive wine list. Their appetites thus sated, guests can stroll in the gardens or relax in the comfortable lounge bar, furnished, like the rest of the house, with many antiques. The bedrooms at Dalegarth vary, with double, twin, family and single rooms all available. Each has an en suite bathroom, TV radio and tea and coffee-making facilities. The Jacksons have also embued the house with a charming family atmosphere while providing the most professional of standards.

Recommended in the area

Cars of the Stars, Keswick; Theatre by the Lake, Keswick; Mirehouse

The Grange Country House

★★★★★ GH

Address: Manor Brow, Ambleside Road,
KESWICK CA12 4BA
Tel: 017687 72500
Email: info@grangekeswick.com
Website: www.grangekeswick.com
Map ref: 5, NY22
Directions: M6 junct 40, A66 13m. A591 for 0.5m,
turn right onto Manor Brow
Rooms: 10 en suite S £65–£91 D £82–£106
Parking: 10 Notes: ⊘ on premises ⊗ in bedrooms ⬥under 10yrs Closed: Jan

This stylish Victorian residence stands in beautiful gardens just a stroll from the lovely market town of Keswick. It offers a relaxed atmosphere and professional service. The spacious bedrooms are well equipped with hairdryer, colour TV, hospitality tray and mineral water; some have beams and mountain views. Breakfast is a hearty affair made with local farmed meats and free-range eggs and featuring Fairtrade products where possible. The proprietors are keen to give advice on walks and local activities.

Recommended in the area

The Cumberland Pencil Museum; Castlehead Viewpoint; Keswick town

Honister House

★★★★ BB

Address: 1 Borrowdale Road,
KESWICK CA12 5DD
Tel: 017687 73181
Email: honisterhouse@btconnect.com
Website: www.honisterhouse.co.uk
Map ref: 5, NY22
Directions: 100yds S of town centre, off Market Sq
onto Borrowdale Rd
Rooms: 3 en suite £70–£75 Notes: ⊘ ⊗ ⬥⬥

This charming family home is one of the oldest properties in Keswick, dating back to the 18th century. It retains many interesting original features, including timber beams and wood-burning fires, and boasts attractive and well-equipped en suite bedrooms that feature prints by local artists, hospitality trays and colour TV with video player or DVD. John and Susie Stakes are the friendly proprietors, and the hearty breakfasts they serve utilise high-quality local, organic and Fairtrade produce wherever possible and include dishes such as kedgeree and a vegetarian breakfast alongside the full English option.

Recommended in the area

Theatre by the Lake; Trotters World of Animals; Hill Top, (Beatrix Potter's Home) (NT)

Howe Keld

★★★★ GH

Address: 5/7 The Heads, KESWICK
CA12 5ES
Tel: 017687 72417
Fax: 017687 72417
Email: david@howekeld.co.uk
Website: www.howekeld.co.uk
Map ref: 5, NY22
Directions: From town centre towards Borrowdale, right opp main car park, 1st on left
Rooms: 15 en suite, S £38–£40 D £70–£80 Parking: 9 Notes: ⊘ on premises 🐾 allowed in bedrooms ♦♦ Closed: Xmas & Jan

This friendly establishment has a cosy first-floor lounge with spectacular fell views and easy access to the facilities in Keswick and to Derwent Water. Breakfast in the dining room is a delight, whether you stick to the impressive buffet or order from the varied cooked selection. The bedrooms are smartly decorated – the two ground floor rooms are particularly popular.

Recommended in the area

Keswick; walking in the fells; Castlerigg Stone Circle

Sunnyside Guest House

★★★★ GH

Address: 25 Southey Street, KESWICK CA12 4EF
Tel: 017687 72446
Email: enquiries@sunnysideguesthouse.com
Website: www.sunnysideguesthouse.com
Map ref: 5, NY22
Directions: 200yds E of town centre. Off A5271 Penrith Rd onto Southey St, Sunnyside on left
Rooms: 7 en suite, D £60–£70 Parking: 8
Notes: ⊘ ⊗ in bedrooms ♦♦ under 12yrs

Sunnyside is a stylish Victorian guest house set in a quiet area close to the town centre. The bedrooms, including a family room, have all been refurbished to a high standard and come well equipped with refreshment-making facilities, hairdryer and colour TV. For special occasions, you can arrange in advance to have chocolates, flowers or champagne in the room. There is a spacious and comfortable lounge with plenty of books and magazines, and the owners serve a hearty breakfast at individual tables in the airy and attractive dining room using fresh Cumbrian produce and offering vegetarian options.

Recommended in the area

Derwentwater; Borrowdale; Keswick's Theatre by the Lake

New House Farm

★★★★★ 🛎 ☕ FH
Address: LORTON, Cockermouth
          CA13 9UU
Tel: 01900 85404
Fax: 01900 85478
Email: hazel@newhouse-farm.co.uk
Website: www.newhouse-farm.com
Map ref: 5, NY12
Directions: 6m S of Cockermouth on B5289 between Lorton
& Loweswater
Rooms: 5 en suite, S £75–£100 D £150 Parking: 30 Notes: ⊗
on premises 🐾 allowed on premises 👶 under 6yrs

Hazel Thompson bought New House Farm in 1990 and has completely renovated it to its present de luxe standard. Located in the north-west corner of the Lake District National Park, this Grade II listed house dates from 1650. The restoration discovered original oak beams and rafters, flagstone floors, and fireplaces where blazing log fires now crackle on colder days. There are lovely views from all the stylish rooms, and these views can also be enjoyed by taking a relaxing Hot Spring Spa in the beautifully maintained garden. The appealing en suite bedrooms are richly furnished and equipped with many thoughtful extras including home-baked biscuits or a champagne tray and flowers for special occasions – two rooms have a magnificent oak four poster. The delicious three- or five-course dinner menu uses local ingredients whenever possible and changes daily – traditional puddings are a speciality. Hearty breakfasts are another highlight. Stabling is available for guests who wish to bring their own horses. Guests are welcome to wander around the 15 acres of open fields, woods, streams and ponds.

Recommended in the area

Keswick; Cockermouth; Buttermere lake

The Old Vicarage

★★★★ ⌂ ⊜ GH

Address: Church Lane, LORTON
CA13 9UN
Tel: 01900 85656
Email: enquiries@oldvicarage.co.uk
Website: www.oldvicarage.co.uk
Map ref: 5, NY12
Directions: B5292 onto B5289 N of Lorton. 1st left
signed Church, house 1st on right
Rooms: 8 (7 en suite), S £43–£55 D £86–£100
Parking: 10 Notes: ⊘ on premises ⊗ in bedrooms

Set in the beautiful Lorton Vale in a quiet, unspoilt corner of the Lake District National Park, The Old Vicarage enjoys sensational views of the surrounding fells of Grasmoor, Grisedale Pike and Whinlatter. This charming country guest house is surrounded by fields and set in over an acre of lovely wooded gardens. The Old Vicarage is a wonderful Victorian property with antiques, log fires and quaint charm, an ideal place to relax and unwind. Amongst the eight tastefully-furnished guest bedrooms are a luxurious four-poster bedroom - the perfect setting for a romantic weekend - and a comfortable ground floor room with en suite bathroom. The converted coach-house offers two welcoming rooms with exposed stone walls and en suite shower rooms and is ideal for families. A hearty breakfast menu is served every morning in the elegant dining room, and a delicious home-cooked dinner is available in the evenings, if desired. The Old Vicarage, with its reputation for providing a warm, friendly and relaxed atmosphere, is perfectly situated for exploring the nearby lakes of Buttermere and Crummock Water. The nearby historical market town of Cockermouth is the site of the original Jennings brewery which offers enjoyable tours.

Recommended in the area

Buttermere lake; Grisedale Pike; Crummock Water; Cockermouth

Winder Hall Country House

★★★★★ GA

Address: LORTON CA13 9UP
Tel: 01900 85107
Fax: 01900 85479
Email: nick@winderhall.co.uk
Website: www.winderhall.co.uk
Map ref: 5, NY12
Directions: A66 W from Keswick, at Braithwaite onto B5292 to Lorton, left at T-junct signed Buttermere, Winder Hall 0.5m on right

Rooms: 7 en suite, S £49.95–£97 D £74–£134 Parking: 10 Notes: ⊗ on premises ⊗ on premises
👫 Closed: 2–31 Jan

Winder Hall, an impressive former manor house dating from the 14th century, is set in the peaceful village of Low Lorton, near Buttermere. Inside, it retains a real sense of history, yet has an informal, family-run atmosphere and provides thoughtful service. The evocatively named bedrooms, such as Greystones and Whinlatter, are smart and individually styled, some featuring luxurious furnishing such as Georgian and Tudor four-posters. All rooms are en suite and thoughtfully equipped, and all enjoy stunning fell views. The lounge is also richly furnished and the oak-panelled dining room is the perfect setting for skilfully prepared meals made using local seasonal produce – organic wines and locally produced organic ingredients all feature. The leisurely breakfast includes fresh Fairtrade coffee, croissants, fruit salad, home-cured bacon and organic Cumberland sausage. Guests are invited to wander around the garden, and they can collect their own eggs for breakfast from the free-range hens, or even help feed the pigs. For wetter days, a selection of games is on hand, and there are laundry and drying facilities available. Guests can also make sure of the hot tub and spa bath in the Summer House.

Recommended in the area

Buttermere; Keswick; beaches of west Cumbria

Muncaster Castle, Lake District.

Underwood Country Guest House

★★★★★ GH

Address: The Hill, MILLOM
LA18 5EZ
Tel: 01229 771116
Fax: 01229 719900
Email: enquiries@underwoodhouse.co.uk
Website: www.underwoodhouse.co.uk
Map ref: 5, SD18
Directions: A595 onto A5093 through village, The
Green & The Hill, Underwood 0.5m after The Hill

Rooms: 5 en suite, S £40–£60 D £80–£120 **Parking:** 20 **Notes:** ⊘ on premises ⊗ in bedrooms
🚼 under 14yrs

This beautiful Victorian vicarage stands in 8 acres of mature grounds overlooking the Duddon Estaury
and Whicham Valley. The bedrooms feature a king-size bed and bathrooms with power shower, all have
colour TV and bathrobes. Guests can relax in one of the two lounges, swim in the heated pool
or play tennis. The food is of a high quality, using the best of local fresh produce.
Recommended in the area
Lake District National Park; Windermere; Muncaster Castle and Gardens

The Knoll Country House

★★★★★ GA

Address: Lakeside, NEWBY BRIDGE,
            Ulverston LA12 8AU
Tel: 015395 31347
Fax: 015395 30850
Email: info@theknoll-lakeside.co.uk
Website: www.theknoll-lakeside.co.uk
Map ref: 5, SD38
Directions: A590 W to Newby Bridge, over rdbt,
signed right for Lake Steamers, house 0.5m on left

Rooms: 8 en suite, S £57–£92 D £80–£124 **Parking:** 8 **Notes:** ⊗ on premises ⊗ in bedrooms
★ under 16yrs **Closed:** 24–26 Dec

Jenny Meads escaped from corporate life in 2001 and found the Knoll, a small Victorian country house set in a leafy dell on the west side of Windermere. Jenny knew this was the place to create a tranquil oasis offering fabulous food and quality accommodation. All rooms have been refurbished, including new bathrooms, and some are de luxe. They are all well equipped with flat screen TV and DVD player, alarm clock radio and bath robes, while hospitality trays provide fruit and leaf teas, coffee and hot chocolate, and hand-baked biscuits. The beautifully furnished lounge has an open fire for chillier evenings. There is also a well-stocked bar. Food is the real feature here. Jenny and her team passionately support local businesses, using excellent Cumbrian produce including daily fresh fish and meat. The hot breakfast is a hearty traditional affair complemented by a healthy buffet option and home-made preserves. If you are out walking the fells, then a packed lunch can be provided. Their formula for the Knoll clearly works – more than half of the bookings come from people who have stayed here before.

Recommended in the area

Aquarium of the Lakes; World of Beatrix Potter; Holker Hall and Gardens

'Lady of the Lake', Ullswater

Lyndhurst Country House

★★★★ GH

Address: NEWBY BRIDGE, Ulverston LA12 8ND
Tel: 015395 31245
Email: chris@lyndhurstcountryhouse.co.uk
Website: www.lyndhurstcountryhouse.co.uk
Map ref: 5, SD38
Directions: On the junct of A590 and A592 at Newby Bridge rdbt
Rooms: 3 en suite, S £40 D £60–£65 **Parking:** 3
Notes: ⊘ on premises ⊗ in bedrooms 🚼 under 8yrs **Closed:** 23–28 Dec

Situated at the southern tip of beautiful Lake Windermere and set in its own lovely gardens, this 1920s house is well located within easy reach of a host of local amenities, such as hotels, restaurants and country inns. The comfortable bedrooms are well equipped and tastefully decorated. Evening meals (by arrangement) and hearty breakfasts here feature local produce as much as possible and are served in the pleasant dining room, which also has a lounge area that opens out onto the garden.

Recommended in the area

Windermere Lake Cruises; Hill Top (Beatrix Potter's home) (NT); Holker Hall Gardens and Motor Museum

Brooklands Guest House

★★★★ GH

Address: 2 Portland Place, PENRITH CA11 7QN
Tel/Fax: 01768 863395
Email: enquiries@brooklandsguesthouse.com
Website: www.brooklandsguesthouse.com
Map ref: 6, NY53
Directions: From town hall onto Portland Place, 50yds on left
Rooms: 7 en suite, S £35 D £65–£75 Parking: 2
Notes: ⊗ on premises ⊗ on premises ♦♦

Charming and elegant, Brooklands Guest House is situated in the heart of the bustling market town of Penrith with its many attractions. This beautiful, refurbished Victorian terrace house is an excellent base for exploring the many delights of the Lake District National Park while convenient for the attractive Eden Valley. Debbie and Leon ensure you have a most enjoyable stay and that you will be keen to make a return visit. The traditional hearty breakfast, designed to satisfy the largest of appetites, offers a choice of fruit juices, fresh fruit, yoghurt, cereals, oat cakes and cheese followed by such delights as Cumberland sausage, back bacon and eggs cooked to your liking; there's also a vegetarian option. All bedrooms are furnished to the highest standard and have nice touches such as colour television and tea and coffee-making facilties. For a romantic escape with a touch of luxury, the Brooklands' suite has a locally handcrafted four-poster bed, a sofa, television, DVD, radio-alarm clock, hairdryer, luxury branded toiletries, bath robes and a choice of light refreshments in a mini-fridge. If you intend to explore the area on two wheels then Brooklands has secure storage for your bicycle. Ullswater, one of the areas lovliest lakes, is just a short distance southwest of Penrith and can be enjoyed at leisure aboard a 19th-century steamer.

Recommended in the area

Penrith; Coast to Coast cycle route; Ullswater lake; Rheged Discovery Centre

Glenfield Guest House

★★★★ GH

Address: Back Corkickle, WHITEHAVEN CA28 7TS
Tel: 01946 691911
Email: glenfieldgh@aol.com
Website: www.glenfield-whitehaven.co.uk
Map ref: 5, NX91
Directions: 0.5m SE of town centre on A5094
Rooms: 6 en suite, S £35 D £55 Notes: ⊗ ♞ allowed in bedrooms ♦♦ Free Wi-fi available

Glenfield is an imposing family-run Victorian town house, with traditional large rooms and high ceilings, set in a conservation area close to the town centre and harbour. The house has been lovingly restored while retaining Victorian features such as open fires in the guest lounge and dining room. Emphasis is placed on real home cooking and baking, incorporating local and organic ingredients whenever possible and optional, menu-driven evening meals are available. Guests can enjoy a drink in the residents' lounge, dining room or in the landscaped garden. Glenfield has earned a reputation for its unobtrusive, home-from-home atmosphere, with many guests making return visits.

Recommended in the area

Cockermouth; Lake District National Park; Ennerdale Water; Crummock Water

The Coach House

★★★★ GA

Address: Lake Road, WINDERMERE
LA23 2EQ
Tel: 015394 44494
Email: enquiries@lakedistrictbandb.com
Website: www.lakedistrictbandb.com
Map ref: 6, SD49
Directions: A591 to Windermere house 0.5m on right opp St Herbert's Church
Rooms: 5 (en suite), S £35–£60 D £50–£75 Parking: 5 Notes: ⊗ on premises ⊗ in bedrooms ♦♦ under 5yrs
Closed: 24–26 Dec

The property was originally a Victorian coach house, but now the interior is more chic and minimalist, achieved through the bold use of bright colours and contemporary furnishings. The modern decor continues in the bedrooms, with stylish iron beds, showers, and a host of amenities such as radios, alarm clocks and hairdryers. The breakfasts are a special feature.

Recommended in the area

Windermere lake cruises; Blackwell (The Arts & Crafts House); Holehird Gardens

Wast Water, Lake District National Park

The Coppice

★★★★ ☕ GH

Address:	Brook Road, WINDERMERE LA23 2ED
Tel:	015394 88501
Fax:	015394 42148
Email:	chris@thecoppice.co.uk
Website:	www.thecoppice.co.uk
Map ref:	6, SD49
Directions:	0.25m S of village centre on A5074

Rooms: 9 en suite, S £40–£45 D £62–£80
Parking: 10 Notes: ⊘ on premises 🐾 allowed on premises 👥

This traditional Lakeland vicarage retains all its character and charm. Built of local stone, The Coppice sits in an elevated position between the villages of Windermere and Bowness, perfectly placed for touring or walking in the Lake District National Park. Hosts Chris and Barbara promise a memorable experience and can provide extras such as flowers, chocolates and champagne on arrival or the chance to upgrade to a four-poster bed. The en suite bedrooms, some with bath, some with shower, have been individually designed so each has its own distinctive feel. All have colour TV and complimentary tea and coffee trays. The renowned Lakeland breakfast and dinner are enjoyed in the light and airy dining room and a pre-dinner drink can be taken in the spacious lounge which has an open fire. Dinner is served most evenings and the restaurant has an excellent reputation in the area with locally sourced seasonal ingredients used in the dishes. This includes championship sausages and fine cured bacon, fell-bred beef, pork and lamb and fish from Fleetwood. The dinner menu also features vegetarian options, together with home-made bread and desserts. Additional facilities at The Coppice include private car park, local leisure club membership and fishing. Dogs are welcome in some of the rooms.

Recommended in the area

Hill Top Farm (Beatrix Potter's home) (NT); Wordsworth's homes Rydal Mount and Dove Cottage

The Fairfield Garden Guest House

★★★★ GH

Address: Brantfell Road, Bowness-on-Windermere,
WINDERMERE LA23 3AE
Tel/Fax: 015394 46565
Email: tonyandliz@the-fairfield.co.uk
Website: www.the-fairfield.co.uk
Map ref: 6, SD49
Directions: Into Bowness town centre, turn opp St
Martin's Church & sharp left by Spinnery restaurant,
house 200yds on right
Rooms: 10 (9 en suite), S £27–£49 D £54–£78 Parking: 10 Notes: ⊘ on premises 🐾 allowed on premises 👶 under 6yrs

Situated close to Bowness Bay, Fairfield Garden Guest House is the perfect place to take a tranquil break. Owners Tony and Liz Blaney offer genuine hospitality and high standards of personal service at their 200-year-old home, which is set in half an acre of its own beautifully landscaped gardens. The bedrooms – single, twin, double, four-poster, deluxe and family rooms are available – are well equipped with lots of useful extras such as hospitality tray, assorted toiletries and a hairdryer. Options are available for guests to have sparkling wine or Belgian chocolates in their room on arrival and, for special occasions, to have rose petals scattered on the bed. The four-poster room has its own wet room with heated floor for that added touch of luxury. The power shower here is big enough for two, and comes with body jets and massage pebbles on the floor. Special facilities are available for visitors with mobility requirements. Breakfasts come in hearty or healthy versions, each made with the finest ingredients. There is free internet access via a public terminal or for those with their own laptops, a wireless connection is available.

Recommended in the area

Blackwell (The Arts & Crafts House); Windermere lake steamers; Wordsworth House (NT)

Fair Rigg

★★★★ GH

Address: Ferry View, BOWNESS-ON-WINDERMERE LA23 3JB
Tel: 015394 43941
Email: stay@fairrigg.co.uk
Website: www.fairrigg.co.uk
Map ref: 6, SD49
Directions: 0.5m S of village centre at junct A5074 & B5284
Rooms: 6 en suite, S £42–£80 D £66–£88 **Parking:** 6
Notes: ⊘ ⊗ ⋔ under 14yrs

This fine Victorian guest house enjoys a rural setting on the edge of Bowness, with magnificent views up to the lake and fells beyond. The rooms have been carefully refurbished to provide comfort and relaxation in stylish home-from-home surroundings. Bedrooms (three kingsize, two doubles and a twin) are individually designed to create a relaxing ambience and are fully equipped, including TV with video. Most rooms boast lake views. The dining room, with its bay window looking out towards the hills, provides the ideal setting for a relaxing breakfast, and deer are often to be seen outside.

Recommended in the area

Wordsworth House (NT); Lake Windermere; Holker Hall

Glenville House

★★★★ GH

Address: Lake Road, WINDERMERE LA23 2EQ
Tel: 015394 43371
Fax: 015394 48457
Email: mail@glenvillehouse.co.uk
Website: www.glenvillehouse.co.uk
Map ref: 6, SD49
Directions: Off A591 into Windermere, B5074 to Bowness, Glenville 0.5m on right next to Church
Rooms: 6 en suite, S £94 D £102 **Parking:** 6
Notes: ⊘ on premises ⊗ on premises ⋔ **Closed:** 31Oct–Etr

This traditional Lakeland stone house has a relaxing and friendly atmosphere, and stands in well-tended gardens just a short walk from Lake Windermere. Freshly cooked Cumbrian breakfasts made from local ingredients are served in the cosy dining room, while the attractive bedrooms, including one ground-floor and two deluxe rooms, have been refurbished to a high standard. All have kingsize or super-kingsize beds and come with luxury toiletries, flatscreen TV, hairdryer and well-stocked hospitality tray.

Recommended in the area

Lakeside and Haverthwaite Railway; Aquarium of the Lakes; Holker Hall

Lake Windemere, Lake District

Falconwood

★★★★★ ⇔ BB

Address: Moor Road, Stainburn, WORKINGTON CA14 1XW
Tel: 01900 602563
Email: info@lakedistrict-bedandbreakfast.co.uk
Website: www.lakedistrict-bedandbreakfast.co.uk
Map ref: 5, NY02
Directions: 1.5m E of Workington. Off A66 to Stainburn, right onto Moor Rd, premises 750yds
Rooms: 2 en suite, S £50 D £70 **Parking:** 6
Notes: ⊘ on premises ⊗ in bedrooms ⛺ under 14yrs

Enjoying spectacular views over the Solway Firth to Scotland, Falconwood is a perfect base for exploring the Western Lake District. Ian and Dawn Lewis-Dalby are the hosts and Ian's gourmet dinners in the comfortable dining room are worth the trip alone. Pre-dinner drinks can be enjoyed in the relaxing lounge. The bedrooms complete the experience with their perfect combination of luxury with comfort. All, of course, have en suite bathrooms and nicely coordinated décor.

Recommended in the area

Wordsworth House, Cockermouth; Western Lakes; Whitehaven harbour

DERBYSHIRE

Peak District National Park

Chatsworth House, Peak District National Park

Holly Cottage

★★★★ BB

Address: Pilsley, BAKEWELL DE45 1UH
Tel: 01246 582245
Website: www.hollycottagebandb.co.uk
Map ref: 7, SK26
Directions: Follow brown tourist signs for Chatsworth and Pilsley. Holly Cottage next to post office
Rooms: 3 en suite, D £60–£70 Notes: ⊘ on premises ⊗ in bedrooms ✗ under 10yrs

Holly Cottage is a 17th-century mellow-stone cottage, part of a combined post office and shop within the beautifully preserved and tranquil village of Pilsley, at the heart of Chatsworth Estate. This is a good base for exploring the Peak District National Park. Inside, it offers a relaxed and informal atmosphere and genuine hospitality, and features impeccably clean, well-furnished and cosy en suite bedrooms that come with a wealth of thoughtful extras. The comprehensive English breakfasts, prepared using fresh Estate produce from local farmers, are served in the attractive pine-furnished dining room. For other meals, the area abounds in excellent local pubs serving good and varied food.

Recommended in the area

Chatsworth House; Peak District National Park; Bakewell

Dannah Farm Country House

★★★★★ ♨ 🍴 GA

Address: Bowmans Lane, Shottle,
BELPER DE56 2DR
Tel: 01773 550273
Fax: 01773 550590
Email: reservations@dannah.co.uk
Website: www.dannah.co.uk
Map ref: 7, SK26
Directions: A517 from Belper towards Ashbourne,
1.5m right into Shottle after Hanging Gate pub on
right, over x-rds & right

Rooms: 8 en suite, S £75–£100 D £110–£250 **Parking:** 20 **Notes:** ⊗ on premises ⊗ on premises
🚼 **Closed:** 24–26 Dec

Dannah, a Georgian farmhouse on a working farm on the Chatsworth Estate is home to Joan and
Martin Slack and their collection of pigs, hens and cats, and Cracker the very good-natured English
setter. Each bedroom has its own individual character, beautifully furnished with antiques and old pine
and filled with a wealth of thoughtful extras. Some rooms have private sitting rooms, four-poster beds
and amazing bathrooms featuring a double spa bath or Japanese-style tubs – the Studio Hideaway
suite even has its own private terrace with hot tub. All the bedrooms look out onto green fields and
open countryside. The two delightful sitting rooms have open fires on chilly evenings and views over
the gardens. The English farmhouse breakfasts are a true delight, served in relaxed and elegant
surroundings. Dinner is available by arrangement, alternatively there are excellent pubs and restaurants
within easy reach. Footpaths criss-cross the surrounding area in the heart of the Derbyshire Dales,
making it an ideal location for walking enthusiasts.

Recommended in the area

Chatsworth; Dovedale; Alton Towers

The Crescent, Buxton

Grendon Guest House

★★★★★ GH

Address: Bishops Lane, BUXTON SK17 6UN
Tel: 01298 78831
Email: grendonguesthouse@hotmail.com
Website: www.grendonguesthouse.co.uk
Map ref: 7, SK07
Directions: 0.75m from Buxton centre. Off A53 St Johns Rd before Duke of York pub & lights leaving town
Rooms: 5 en suite, S £35–£50 D £65–£88
Parking: 8 **Notes:** ⊘ on premises ⚬ under 10yrs
Closed: 3–20 Jan

Spaciousness distinguishes this detached property set in attractive gardens with glorious Peak District views. Coordinated design and antique furnishings characterise the interior, and is particularly evident in the four-poster suite. All rooms have easy chairs and hospitality trays. Homemade specialities are a feature of the memorable breakfasts and dinner is available by arrangement.

Recommended in the area

Walks to the Goyt Valley from the door; Peak District National Park; Chatsworth

Roseleigh

★★★★ GH

Address: 19 Broad Walk, BUXTON SK17 6JR
Tel/Fax: 01298 24904
Email: enquiries@roseleighhotel.co.uk
Website: www.roseleighhotel.co.uk
Map ref: 7, SK07
Directions: A6 to Morrisons rdbt, onto Dale Rd, right at lights, 100yds left by Swan pub, down hill & right onto Hartington Rd
Rooms: 14 (12 en suite), S £33–£84 D £70–£84 **Parking:** 9
Notes: ⊘ on premises ⊗ on premises 🕯under 6yrs
Closed: 16 Dec–16 Jan

Roseleigh is a comfortable and elegant Victorian property that benefits from a prime location overlooking Buxton's 23-acre Pavilion Gardens – the land on which it stands was once owned by the Duke of Devonshire. Built in 1871 and situated on the pedestrianised Broad Walk, it is just a 5-minute walk from the heart of the town and benefits from its own car park. The quality furnishings and decor throughout highlight the house's many original features. Most of the sympathetically furnished bedrooms in this family-run establishment have smart en suite shower rooms; all have colour TV and tea and coffee-making facilities, and several have good views over the Pavilion Gardens. The comfortable guest lounge, which overlooks the lake, is the place simply to relax or you can plan the next day's itinerary by poring over the many books on the Peak District provided by the hosts, Gerard and Maggi, both of whom had interesting careers prior to opening Roseleigh; they are knowledgeable about the local area and are happy to advise on suitable pubs, restaurants and activities. The elegant dining room offers a range of breakfast choices, including vegetarian options, from a menu that makes use of local produce where possible.

Recommended in the area

Buxton Opera House; Chatsworth; Peak District National Park

The Rising Sun

★★★★ GA

Address: Thornhill Moor, CASTLETON S33 0AL
Tel: 01433 651323
Fax: 01433 651601
Email: info@the-rising-sun.org
Website: www.the-rising-sun.org
Map ref: 7, SK18
Directions: On A625 from Sheffield to Castleton
Rooms: 12 en suite, S £55.50–£69.50 D £60–£140
Parking: 120 **Notes:** ⊗ in bedrooms 🐾 allowed on premises ♦♦

Carefully restored and lovingly presented by Carole and Graham Walker, the 18th-century Rising Sun at Thornhill Moor lies within the Hope Valley in the heart of the Peak District National Park. This family-run property offers spacious luxury bedrooms, ranging from doubles to sumptuous executive suites, all with quality furnishings and efficient modern bathrooms. Some rooms have stunning country views, and nice touches include fresh flowers and antique furniture. The friendly staff attend to your every need in an considerate manner making any stay here truly memorable. A highlight is the excellent and imaginative food served in the pleasant public areas. The lunch and dinner menus are created daily using fresh produce, offering a choice of traditional British food with modern European and Far Eastern influences. Guests can choose from buffet-style menus or individually prepared dishes such as lamb shank braised in onion, soya and red wine gravy or pheasant casserole in port wine jus with a side salad of buttered mash followed by Bakewell Tart and custard or melting chocolate pudding. The good food is complemented by an equally good selection of real ales and fine wines. Well-behaved dogs are welcome in some of the rooms. Weddings and receptions are held at the Rising Sun.

Recommended in the area

Chatsworth; Castleton Caverns; Peveril Castle; Bakewell; Eyam; Derwent and Ladybower reservoirs

Stoney Ridge

★★★★ GA

Address: Granby Road, Bradwell,
CASTLETON S33 9HU
Tel: 01433 620538
Email: toneyridge@aol.com
Website: www.stoneyridge.org.uk
Map ref: 7, SK18
Directions: From N end of Bradwell onto Town Ln,
left at x-rds, left onto Granby Rd
Rooms: 4 (3 en suite), S £45 D £55–£70 Parking: 3
Notes: ⊘ ⇥ allowed on premises ⅶ under 10yrs

Set in the heart of the Peak District National Park, Stoney Ridge sits in an elevated position, overlooking a mature garden and large lawn. Guests can relax in the attractive heated indoor pool, or pass time in the large residents' lounge, which has a balcony. Pretty bedrooms are well equipped with TV, hairdryer, hospitality tray and toiletries, and some have fine views. Wi-fi available. Breakfast comes with a range of options, including full English, vegetarian (on request), and gluten free, all served with tea or coffee.
Recommended in the area
Chatsworth House; Derwent Valley; Castleton Caverns

Underleigh House

★★★★★ ≙ GA

Address: Off Edale Road, HOPE,
Hope Valley S33 6RF
Tel: 01433 621372
Fax: 01433 621324
Email: info@underleighhouse.co.uk
Website: www.underleighhouse.co.uk
Map ref: 7, SK18
Directions: From village church on A6187 onto Edale
Rd, 1m left onto lane
Rooms: 6 en suite, S £50–£55 D £70–£90 Parking: 6 Notes: ⊘ on premises ⊗ on premises
ⅶ under 12yrs Closed: Xmas, New Year & 7–31 Jan

At this ideal base for walkers, Vivienne and Philip Taylor provide thoughtfully furnished bedrooms each with a hairdryer, radio alarm, and tea and coffee facilities. Some rooms have direct access to the gardens, one has its own lounge. Enjoy an evening drink on the terrace in summer, or by the log fire in the lounge in cooler weather. Breakfast is served around one large table in the dining room.
Recommended in the area
Castleton Caverns; Chatsworth; Eyam

Hearthstone Farm

★★★★ FH

Address: Hearthstone Lane, Riber,
MATLOCK DE4 5JW
Tel: 01629 534304
Fax: 01629 534372
Email: enquiries@hearthstonefarm.co.uk
Website: www.hearthstonefarm.co.uk
Map ref: 7, SK35
Directions: A615 at Tansley 2m E of Matlock, turn
opp Royal Oak towards Riber, at gates to Riber Hall
left onto Riber Rd and 1st left onto Hearthstone Ln, farmhouse on left
Rooms: 3 en suite, D £60–£65 Parking: 6 Notes: ⊗ 🐾 allowed on premises ♿
Closed: Xmas & New Year

Set high on the hill above Matlock, this traditional farmhouse is a welcoming home in a lovely rural area. The farm has unrivalled views of the historic village of Riber, dominated by Riber Castle. Beautifully decorated in keeping with its age and character, the stone house has original exposed stone walls and oak beams. The three charming bedrooms are equipped with a host of extras for that home-from-home feel, and all rooms are en suite with modern bathrooms and have farm or valley views. Unwind in the inviting sitting room after a day exploring the area, while the elegant dining room is a stylish setting for breakfast. As a working farm producing eggs, vegetables and organic beef, pork and lamb by traditional environmentally friendly methods, Hearthstone can offer delicious truly local, fresh food, particularly the sausages and bacon that are produced on the premises. The farm overlooks the popular tourist destination of Matlock Bath where a cable car ride to the Heights of Abraham offers a birds eye view of the surrounding area.

Recommended in the area

Peak Railway; Chatsworth; Haddon Hall; Dovedale and the Manifold Valley; Cromford Mill

Pear Tree Farm

★★★★ FH

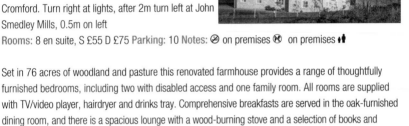

Address: Lea Main Rd, Lea Bridge, MATLOCK DE4 5JN
Tel: 01629 534215
Fax: 01629 534151
Email: sue@derbyshirearts.co.uk
Website: www.derbyshirearts.co.uk
Map ref: 7, SK35
Directions: M1 junct 28, A38 S, A610 Ambergate, A6 Cromford. Turn right at lights, after 2m turn left at John Smedley Mills, 0.5m on left
Rooms: 8 en suite, S £55 D £75 **Parking:** 10 **Notes:** ⊘ on premises ⊗ on premises ⋔

Set in 76 acres of woodland and pasture this renovated farmhouse provides a range of thoughtfully furnished bedrooms, including two with disabled access and one family room. All rooms are supplied with TV/video player, hairdryer and drinks tray. Comprehensive breakfasts are served in the oak-furnished dining room, and there is a spacious lounge with a wood-burning stove and a selection of books and videos/DVDs. Internet access is provided. A separate art studio is available, with art courses on offer.

Recommended in the area
Lea Rhododendron Gardens; Chatsworth; Peak District National Park

Yew Tree Cottage

★★★★ ≙ BB

Address: The Knoll, Tansley, MATLOCK DE4 5FP
Tel: 01629 583862
Email: enquiries@yewtreecottagebb.co.uk
Website: www.yewtreecottagebb.co.uk
Map ref: 7, SK35
Directions: 1.2m E of Matlock. Off A615 into Tansley
Rooms: 3 en suite, S £50–£75 D £65–£85
Parking: 3 **Notes:** ⊘ on premises ⊗ on premises ⋔ under 12yrs

This 18th century cottage, full of original character and charm and with stunning views, is set in pretty, gardens in the village of Tansley. The cottage is a true home from home and ideally situated for all the Peaks and Dales. The Dornans, a well-travelled couple, use their experiences to provide outstanding service and hospitality. The elegantly furnished and decorated bedrooms are very well equipped including well-stocked refreshment trays. Breakfast is a memorable feast of both home-made and local produce and light refreshments are served in the sitting room where log fires cheer up the cooler days.

Recommended in the area
Chatsworth; Crich Tramway Village; Heights of Abraham cable cars

The Smithy

★★★★★ GA

Address: NEWHAVEN, Biggin, Buxton SK17 0DT
Tel/Fax: 01298 84548
Email: thesmithy@newhavenderbyshire.
freeserve.co.uk
Website: www.thesmithybedandbreakfast.co.uk
Map ref: 7, SK16
Directions: 0.5m S of Newhaven on A515. Next to
Biggin Ln, private driveway opp Ivy House
Rooms: 4 en suite, D £37.50–£45 Parking: 8
Notes: ⊘ in bedrooms ⊗ on premises

Welcoming owners Lynn and Gary Jinks have restored this former drovers' inn and blacksmith's shop to a high standard with all modern comforts and a very personal service. The well-decorated good-sized bedrooms are all en suite with hospitality trays and many extras. Tasty breakfasts, including free-range eggs and home-made preserves, are served in the forge, which still has its vast open hearth, and is adjacent to a cosy lounge. The pleasant gardens are set within four acres of meadowland.

Recommended in the area

Chatsworth; Tissington and High Peak Trails (within walking distance); Peak District National Park

Braeside Guest House

★★★★ GH

Address: 113 Derby Road, RISLEY DE72 3SS
Tel: 0115 939 5885
Email: bookings@braesideguesthouse.co.uk
Website: www.braesideguesthouse.co.uk
Map ref: 8, SK43
Directions: W end of village on B5010
Rooms: 6 en suite, S £45 D £60 Parking: 10
Notes: ⊘ on premises ⊗ on premises ♦♦
Closed: 25–26 Dec

Guests here can enjoy an added element of privacy as the bedrooms – doubles and twins – are all located in converted barns close to the house, which was originally part of the Risley Hall Estate and is set in extensive grounds. Each attractively appointed room has original beams and offers many thoughtful extras, such as remote-control colour TV, tea and coffee-making facilities. Two of the rooms have patio doors that open onto a sun terrace. Breakfast, made as far as possible from local ingredients, is served in the main cottage's conservatory, which has superb views over the countryside.

Recommended in the area

Donnington Park Race Track; Peak District National Park; Chatsworth

Lathkill Hill, Peak District National Park

The Old Manor House

★★★★★ BB

Address: Coldwell Street,
WIRKSWORTH,
Matlock DE4 4FB
Tel: 01629 822502
Email: ivan@spurrier-smith.fsnet.co.uk
Map ref: 7, SK25
Directions: On B5035 Coldwell St off village centre
Rooms: 1, S £50–£60 D £80–£85 **Parking:** 1
Notes: ⊗ on premises ⊗ on premises ⚐
Closed: Xmas & New Year

This impressive 17th-century house is located on the edge of the pleasant town of Wirksworth, which is well worth a visit for its period buildings, narrow streets and intricate alleyways. The house and the private bathroom and bedroom, with its four-poster bed and quality furnishings, retains many original features. A full, hearty breakfast is served in the elegant dining room and a spacious drawing room is available to relax in after a day out. There are good restaurants and pubs in the vicinity.

Recommended in the area

Peak District National Park; Chatsworth; Carsington Water

DEVON

Torquay harbour

Gages Mill Country Guest House

★★★★ GA

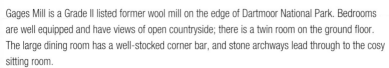

Address: Buckfastleigh Road,
ASHBURTON TQ13 7JW
Tel: 01364 652391
Fax: 01364 652641
Email: richards@gagesmill.co.uk
Website: www.gagesmill.co.uk
Map ref: 2, SX76
Directions: Off A38 turn right at Peartree junct, left at fuel station, Gages Mill 500yds on left
Rooms: 7 en suite, S £45 D £62–£70 Parking: 7 Notes: ⊘ in bedrooms ⊗ on premises 🐾 under 8yrs Closed: 23 Oct–1 Mar

Gages Mill is a Grade II listed former wool mill on the edge of Dartmoor National Park. Bedrooms are well equipped and have views of open countryside; there is a twin room on the ground floor. The large dining room has a well-stocked corner bar, and stone archways lead through to the cosy sitting room.
Recommended in the area
Buckfast Abbey; Dartmoor National Park; South Devon Steam Railway

Greencott

★★★★ GA

Address: Landscove, ASHBURTON TQ13 7LZ
Tel: 01803 762649
Map ref: 2, SX76
Directions: 3m SE of Ashburton. Off A38 at Peartree junct, Landscove signed on slip road, village green 2m on right, opp village hall
Rooms: 2 en suite, S £23 D £46 Parking: 3
Notes: ⊘ in bedrooms ⊗ 🐾 Closed: 25–26 Dec

Modern facilities in a traditional atmosphere are offered at this renovated house in the village of Landscove, which is just 3 miles from Ashburton. Greencott stands in a garden with lovely country views. The bedrooms are carefully furnished and well equipped with baths and showers en suite, central heating, and tea and coffee amenities. Television, books, maps and local information are provided in the comfortable sitting room, and traditional country cooking is served around the oak dining table. The full English breakfast includes home-made bread, and dinner is available on request. Older children are welcome, but pets cannot be accommodated, with the exception of assist dogs.
Recommended in the area
Dartington; Buckfast Abbey; riding, fishing and golf nearby

Sladesdown Farm

★★★★ FH

Address: Landscove, ASHBURTON TQ13 7ND
Tel/Fax: 01364 653973
Email: sue@sladesdownfarm.co.uk
Website: www.sladesdownfarm.co.uk
Map ref: 2, SX76
Directions: 2m S of Ashburton. Off A38 at Peartree junct, Landscove signed on slip road, left at 2nd x-rds, farm 100yds right
Rooms: 4 (2 en suite)
Notes: ⊗ ⊗ ⚤

Convenient for the A38, this modern farmhouse offers very spacious, attractive accommodation. There's a friendly atmosphere, with relaxation assured whether you're in the cheerful bedrooms, the lounge, with its exposed beams and open fireplace, or on the terrace in finer weather. A hearty breakfast featuring delicious local and home-made produce is the perfect start to the day, served in the breakfast room.

Recommended in the area
Buckfast Abbey; Newton Abbot Racecourse; Stover Country Park

Kerrington House

★★★★★ GA

Address: Musbury Road, AXMINSTER EX13 5JR
Tel: 01297 35333
Fax: 01297 35345
Email: jreaney@kerringtonhouse.com
Website: www.kerringtonhouse.com
Map ref: 2, SY29
Directions: 0.5m from Axminster on A358 towards Seaton, house on left
Rooms: 5 en suite, S £69–£75 D £90–£110
Parking: 6 Notes: ⊗ ⊗ in bedrooms ⚤

Be prepared for a very warm welcome and genuine pampering at this lovingly-restored period house set in landscaped gardens. Bedrooms are beautifully decorated and feature quality furniture, coordinated fabrics and many extras while antique pieces and well-loved treasures create a personal atmosphere in the drawing room. Kerrington is renowned for its delicious food served at breakfast. Groups of families and friends are welcome to use the accommodation for small house parties.

Recommended in the area
Lyme Regis; Dorchester; East Devon Heritage Coast

Buckfast Abbey, Buckfastleigh, Dartmoor National Park

Halmpstone Manor

★★★★★ 🛏 🍽 GA

Address: Bishop's Tawton, BARNSTAPLE EX32 0EA
Tel: 01271 830321
Fax: 01271 830826
Email: jane@halmpstonemanor.co.uk
Website: www.halmpstonemanor.co.uk
Map ref: 2, SS52
Directions: 3m SE of Barnstaple. Off A377 E of river & rail bridges
Rooms: 4 en suite, S £70 D £100–£140 **Parking:**
12 **Notes:** ⊗ on premises 🐾 allowed on premises 👫 **Closed:** Xmas & New Year

A place to seriously relax, this gracious 1700s house has its origins in the 12th century. It has been praised for its hospitality for hundreds of years, a tradition that owners Jane and Charles Stanbury happily continue. It stands in tranquil grounds, and offers a memorable stay with squashy sofas, crackling fires and quality bedrooms. One room has a four-poster bed – just the thing for a luxury break.

Recommended in the area

RHS Rosemoor and Marwood Hill; North Devon Heritage Coast; Tarka Trail

Prehistoric Postbridge, Dartmoor National Park

The Pines at Eastleigh

★★★★ GA

Address: The Pines, Eastleigh, BIDEFORD EX39 4PA
Tel: 01271 860561
Fax: 01271 861689
Email: pirrie@thepinesateastleigh.co.uk
Website: www.thepinesateastleigh.co.uk
Map ref: 2, SS42
Directions: A39 onto A386 signed East-The-Water.
1st left signed Eastleigh, 500yds next left, 1.5m to
village, house on right
Rooms: 6 en suite, S £40–£45 D £75–£95 Parking: 20 Notes: ⊘ on premises 🐾 allowed on premises 🚼 under 9yrs

From its magnificent hilltop position overlooking the Torridge estuary and Lundy Island, this Georgian house, standing in 7 acres of gardens, is perfect for a relaxing break. Most of the comfortable bedrooms are in converted stables around a charming courtyard. There are two rooms in the main house. The tasty breakfasts are made from local and home-made produce.
Recommended in the area
Instow and Clovelly; cycling and walking on The Tarka Trail; Hartland Heritage Coast

Kilbury Manor

★★★★ 📧 ☕ GA

Address: Colston Road, BUCKFASTLEIGH
          TQ11 0LN
Tel: 01364 644079
Email: info@kilburymanor.co.uk
Website: www.kilburymanor.co.uk
Map ref: 2, SX76
Directions: Off A38 onto B3380 to Buckfastleigh,
left onto Old Totnes Rd, at bottom turn right, Kilbury
Manor on left
Rooms: 4 (3 en suite), S £40–£50 D £60–£75 **Parking:** 5
Notes: ⊘ on premises ⊗ on premises ♦♦

A fine example of a 17th-century longhouse, Kilbury Manor is a charming Grade II listed building situated in the tranquil surroundings of the Dart Valley, which offers access to the river across the meadow. The owners pride themselves on creating a relaxed atmosphere just a mile away from the quaint village of Buckfastleigh. Rooms here, located in either the main house or in adjacent converted barns with their own access, are full of character and have been tastefully furnished in keeping with the period of the house. Rooms in the barn can make use of a fridge and a drying area, ideal after a wet or muddy walk, while all rooms benefit from colour TV, hairdryer, and a hospitality tray stocked with Fairtrade products. Kilbury Manor serves an excellent breakfast, as well as dinner by prior arrangement, in its elegant dining room, and guests are welcome to bring their own wine to have with dinner. The emphasis is on freshly cooked local produce throughout, and breakfast includes interesting options, such as piquant devilled tomatoes on granary toast or creamy scrambled egg served on an English muffin with organic smoked salmon, as well as more traditional offerings.

Recommended in the area

South Devon Steam Railway; Dartmoor National Park; Buckfast Abbey

Downderry House

★★★★★ GA

Address: 10 Exmouth Road,
BUDLEIGH SALTERTON EX9 6AQ
Tel/Fax: 01395 442663
Email: info@downderryhouse.co.uk
Website: www.downderryhouse.co.uk
Map ref: 2, SY08
Directions: From M5 signed for Budleigh Salterton. From A303 exit at Daisy Mount and follow B3180
Rooms: 5 en suite, S £69–£79 D £79–£99
Parking: 9 Notes: ⊘ on premises ⌐ allowed in 1 bedroom ⌖ under 10yrs

This refurbished 1920s house set in an acre of beautiful gardens. The spacious and stylish bedrooms offer impressive levels of comfort, with rich fabrics, comfortable armchairs, Wi-fi and fresh flowers. In addition, the luxurious bathrooms come with robes and fluffy towels. Most rooms have good views, while one twin suite enjoys its own separate sitting room. Breakfast provides a taste of the local area, served in the dining room overlooking the gardens.

Recommended in the area

Jurassic Coast; Exeter Cathedral; Bicton Park Botanical Gardens

Hansard House

★★★★ GA

Address: 3 Northview Road,
BUDLEIGH SALTERTON EX9 6BY
Tel: 01395 442773
Fax: 01395 442475
Email: enquiries@hansardhotel.co.uk
Website: www.hansardhousehotel.co.uk
Map ref: 2, SY08
Directions: 500yds W of town centre
Rooms: 12 en suite, S £36–£42 D £75–£89
Parking: 11 Notes: ⊘ on premises ⌖

Set in an ideal situation a short walk from central Budleigh Salterton, Hansard House is just five minutes from the beach and the cliff path of this beautiful part of the East Devon coast. The tastefully decorated en suite bedrooms have TV, tea and coffee making facilities and hair dryers, and most have views across the town, to the countryside and estuary beyond. The hearty breakfast, and also dinner by arrangement, is served in the light and airy dining room. Children and pets are welcome.

Recommended in the area

Otter Estuary Bird Sanctuary; Bicton Park BotanicalGardens

Palm house and orangery, Bicton Park, Botanical Gardens

Easton Court

★★★★ GA

Address: Easton Cross,
CHAGFORD TQ13 8JL
Tel: 01647 433469
Email: stay@easton.co.uk
Website: www.easton.co.uk
Map ref: 2, SX78
Directions: 1m NE of Chagford at junct A382 &
B3206
Rooms: 5 en suite, S £45–£65 D £60–£80
Parking: 5 **Notes:** ⊘ on premises ✱ allowed on premises ✸ under 10yrs

Debra and Paul Witting's impressive thatched Tudor farmhouse stands in acres of gardens and
paddocks in the Teign valley. Evelyn Waugh was charmed by the place and wrote Brideshead
Revisited here, and you too should find it inspiring. An Edwardian extension houses the en suite
bedrooms with fabulous views of the countryside - four rooms are superior, and there is a mixture
of showers and bathrooms.

Recommended in the area

Castle Drogo (NT); Fingle Bridge; Dartmoor National Park

Tor Cottage

★★★★★ GA

Address: CHILLATON, Tavistock PL16 0JE
Tel: 01822 860248
Fax: 01822 860126
Email: info@torcottage.co.uk
Website: www.torcottage.co.uk
Map ref: 1, SX48
Directions: A30 Lewdown exit through Chillaton towards Tavistock, 300yds after Post Office right signed Bridlepath No Public Vehicular Access to end

Rooms: 4 en suite, S £94 D £140 Parking: 8 Notes: ⊘ ⊗ Closed: 17 Dec–7 Jan

This romantic cottage offers tranquillity and seclusion in 18 acres of grounds. Nothing is too much trouble for Maureen Rowlatt, who has equipped the en suite bed-sitting rooms with everything you could desire. Each one is individually designed, from the warmth and style of the Art Deco Room to the blue and cream elegance of The Craftsman's Room – both converted from an original craftsman's workshop. One room is in the cottage wing and the others are in converted barns – each has a private terrace/garden and a log fire. Laughing Waters, the garden retreat, is nestled in its own private valley and is also available on a self-catering basis during Christmas and New Year. Breakfast is an imaginative range of dishes, and can be taken in the conservatory-style dining room or on the terrace in fine weather. The gardens are a feature in their own right with many private corners, a stream, and in summer, a heated swimming pool. Woodlands cloaking the hillside behind the cottage are home to a variety of wildlife including badgers, pheasants and deer that enjoy the cover of the gorse, while buzzards and the occasional heron can be seen overhead. Children cannot be accommodated. Autumn and spring breaks are available – 3 nights for the price of 2.

Recommended in the area

Dartmoor; The Eden Project; National Trust houses and gardens

Lower Orchard

★★★★ BB

Address: Swan Hill Road, COLYFORD EX24 6QQ
Tel: 01297 553615
Email: robin@barnardl.demon.co.uk
Map ref: 2, SY29
Directions: On A3052 in Colyford, between Lyme Regis & Sidmouth
Rooms: 2 (1 en suite), S £40–£50 D £50–£60
Parking: 3 **Notes:** ⊘ ↑ allowed on premises ↯

The modern ranch-style family house has uninterrupted rural views across the Axe Valley. The two very spacious bedrooms are on the ground floor, one with a bathroom en suite and the other with adjacent private shower facilities. Breakfast is served in the lounge-dining room with patio doors leading to a sun terrace. A splash pool in the garden is tempting in warm weather. Lyme Regis is only 6 miles away, and the unspoiled towns of Honiton and Sidmouth are also within easy reach. Owner Lorrie Barnard breeds Tibetan Terriers, so the establishment is pet friendly. The owners also own the Motoring Memories museum situated at the top of their drive.

Recommended in the area

Forde Abbey and Gardens; Seaton Tramway; Jurassic Coast World Heritage Site

Nonsuch House

★★★★★ 🛎 ☕ GA

Address: Church Hill, Kingswear,
DARTMOUTH TQ6 0BX
Tel: 01803 752829
Fax: 01803 752357
Email: enquiries@nonsuch-house.co.uk
Website: www.nonsuch-house.co.uk
Map ref: 2, SX85
Directions: A379 2m before Brixham. Left onto B3205. Left up Higher Contour Rd, down Ridley Hill, house on bend on left hand side at top of Church Hill

Rooms: 4 en suite, S £70–£100 D £95–£135 **Parking:** 3 **Notes:** ⊘ ⊗ in bedrooms ↯ under 10yrs

Kit and Penny Noble's lovely Edwardian house is set on a south-facing hill in Kingswear, with panoramic views of both the Dart estuary and the sea. The accommodation is of a very high quality – the spacious bedrooms are comfortable with lots of little extras. Meals are prepared from fresh, local ingredients whenever possible and you can also be assured of a wonderful breakfast.

Recommended in the area

Dartmouth; Brixham; South West Coast Path

The Edwardian

★★★★ GH

Address: 30–32 Heavitree Road, EXETER EX1 2LQ
Tel: 01392 276102
Email: michael@edwardianexeter.co.uk
Website: www.edwardianexeter.co.uk
Map ref: 2, SX99
Directions: M5 junct 29, right at lights signed city centre, on left after Exeter University School of Education
Rooms: 13 en suite, S £55 D £70–£75 **Parking:** 5
Notes: ⊘ on premises 🖈 allowed on premises ♦♦

Built in 1912, the Edwardian started life as two separate houses that were joined together in the 1970s. The property has been refurbished showing attention to detail, which is evident in the furnishings, and the antiques and china lovingly collected over the years. Situated in the city of Exeter and within easy access of the M5 motorway, the guest house is ideally located for both business and pleasure. The twelve bedrooms are decorated in different styles using original period furniture that complements the modern comforts. All are en suite and include telephone, TV, hair dryers and tea and coffee making facilities. The larger rooms have four-poster beds and two rooms have sleigh beds. Sofa beds in some rooms make them suitable for families. Other bedrooms have antique brass, wrought iron or period wooden bedsteads – one with a canopy over. Those south facing are bright with lovely views to the distant hills. A relaxing lounge provides the perfect place to unwind at the end of an exhausting day and the freshly prepared full English, vegetarian or continental breakfast is taken in a pretty dining room. Proprietors, Michael and Jackie Scott-Hake, are happy to advise on the abundance of excellent restaurants nearby.

Recommended in the area

Exeter Cathedral; Exeter quayside; Dartmoor National Park

A sundial on a building on Cathedral Close, Exeter

Mill Farm

★★★★ FH

Address: Kenton, EXETER EX6 8JR
Tel: 01392 832471
Website: www.millfarmstay.co.uk
Map ref: 2, SX99
Directions: A379 from Exeter towards Dawlish, over minirdbt by Swans Nest, farm 1.75m on right
Rooms: 5 (en suite), S £35 D £50 Parking: 12
Notes: ⊗ on premises ⊗ on premises ⊠ under 6yrs Closed: Xmas

Just a short drive from the Powderham Estate and outside the pretty village of Kenton, this charming working farmhouse is surrounded by peaceful pastureland and streams. Inside the decor is carefully coordinated, with stencil designs on the walls and lots of antique furniture. The spacious bedrooms are sunny with wide country views. Hearty farmhouse breakfasts served in the bright dining room are an appetising start to the day, and there are plenty of local places serving evening meals. There is also lounge. The owner is very friendly, and keen to welcome you to her well-managed home.

Recommended in the area

Powderham Castle; Dartmoor; Exe Estuary Nature Reserve

The Barn

★★★★ 🏠 ⬭ GA

Address: Foxholes Hill, Marine Drive,
EXMOUTH EX8 2DF
Tel: 01395 224411
Fax: 01395 225445
Email: info@barnhotel.co.uk
Website: www.barnhotel.co.uk
Map ref: 2, SY08
Directions: M5 junct 30, take A376 to Exmouth, then
signs to seafront. At rdbt last exit into Foxholes Hill.
Located on right
Rooms: 11 en suite, S £35–£52 D £70–£104 **Parking:** 30 **Notes:** ⊘ on premises
⊗ in bedrooms ⋔ **Closed:** 23 Dec–10 Jan

Close to miles of sandy beaches, this Grade II listed establishmen is set in an impeccable and stunning 2-acre garden, which is sea facing and with spectacular views of the East Devon Heritage Coast. There is a terrace and a swimming pool for summer. The building is a leading example of the Arts and Crafts movement and was built in the early 1900s by Edward Prior, a contemporary of William Morris. The Barn has been sympathetically modernised and furnished in keeping with its architectural design and creates an atmosphere of country-house style. The public rooms and most of the bedrooms have outstanding sea views. The attractively decorated, en suite bedrooms have colour TV, hospitality tray, hairdryer and direct-dial telephone. Breakfast, featuring freshly squeezed juices and local produce, is served in the bright, airy dining room. Exmouth is fifteen minutes walk away along the tree-lined and landscaped Madeira Walk. There are also several rural and coastal walks in the area and the estuary of the River Exe offers opportunities for birdwatching, sailing, fishing and windsurfing.

Recommended in the area

Crealy Adventure Park; Exeter; Bicton Park Botanical Gardens

The Devoncourt

★★★★ GA

Address: 16 Douglas Avenue, EXMOUTH EX8 2EX
Tel: 01395 272277
Fax: 01395 269315
Email: enquiries@devoncourt.com
Website: www.devoncourthotel.com
Map ref: 2, SY08
Directions: M5/A376 to Exmouth, follow seafront to Maer Rd, right at T-junct
Rooms: 10 en suite, S £45–£69 D £70–£115
Parking: 50 **Notes:** ⊘ in dining room ⊗ on premises ♦♦

Subtropical gardens sloping gently towards the sea and sandy beaches give an appealing Mediterranean character to this smart seaside establishment. The Devoncourt has an outdoor pool with sun terrace and loungers or explore the 4 acres of landscaped grounds and find the private access to the beach, tennis courts, croquet, putting greens and golf nets. If it does rain, the leisure complex offers an indoor pool, spa, sauna, steam room, solariums and fitness centre. Another major attraction here is the the snooker room, opened by Ray Reardon, which contains a world championship standard table. The various, well-equipped bedrooms – single, double and spacious family suites – are light and simple, decorated in pastel tones and patterned fabrics. They have tea- and coffee-making facilities, clock radio, telephone and digital colour TV. Guests can choose between eating in the informal bar or in Avenues restaurant, where picture windows frame the fantastic sea views and the cuisine satisfies all tastes. Among the spacious public areas, the sun lounge is a particularly lovely spot to enjoy a pot of tea and while away the day. Or you may even venture out and stroll along the seafront promenade to the mouth of the River Exe.

Recommended in the area

Bicton Park Botanical Gardens; Crealy Adventure Park; Exeter with its cathedral and excellent Maritime

Leworthy Farm House

★★★★ GA

Address: Lower Leworthy, Nr Pyworthy,
HOLSWORTHY EX22 6SJ
Tel: 01409 259469
Fax: 01409 259469
Email: leworthyfarmhouse@yahoo.co.uk
Website: www.leworthyfarmhouse.co.uk
Map ref: 1, SS30
Directions: From Holsworthy onto Bodmin St towards
North Tamerton, 4th left signed Leworthy/Southdown

Rooms: 7 en suite, S £40–£65 D £60–£65 **Parking:** 8 **Notes:** ⊘ on premises No pets ♦♦

Pat and Phil Jennings' passions for the countryside, collecting books, curios and classical music, and meeting new people come together wonderfully at Leworthy Farm House. Spacious public rooms include a softly lit dining room with an oak parquet floor and colourful displays of old china, a peaceful drawing room with comfortable old sofas and armchairs and more displays of pictures and china, and a warmly decorated conservatory. Bedrooms, some with window seats, are beautifully furnished with pine or antique pieces and thoughtfully equipped with radio alarms, hairdryers, electric blankets, books and magazines. Hospitality trays are set with bone china, fresh milk, a selection of teas, coffees and chocolate, biscuits and fresh flowers. All the rooms are en suite and have ample supplies of soft towels and toiletries. A good choice of dishes is served at breakfast, and picnics are available by arrangement. Evening meals are not served here, but there are plenty of cafés, pubs and restaurants to choose from in the area. Leworthy is an ideal base for exploring Dartmoor and Bodmin Moor and the lovely villages of Clovelly, Tintagel, Boscastle and Padstow. Bude and its wonderful four-mile sweep of golden sand is also within easy driving distance.

Recommended in the area

Rosemoor Gardens; South West Coast Path; Dartington Glass

Courtmoor Farm

★★★★ FH

Address: Upottery, HONITON EX14 9QA
Tel: 01404 861565
Email: courtmoor.farm@btinternet.com
Website: www.courtmoor.farm.btinternet.co.uk
Map ref: 2, ST20
Directions: 4m NE of Honiton off A30
Rooms: 3 en suite, S £35–£37 D £57–£60
Parking: 20 Notes: ⊘ on premises ⊗ on premises
♦♦ Closed: 20 Dec–1 Jan

Rosalind and Bob Buxton welcome you to their spacious farmhouse with marvellous views over the Otter valley and surrounding countryside. The extensive grounds are home to a flock of sheep and three ponies. Accommodation is provided in a family room, double room and twin, all equipped with digital televisions, hairdryers, electric blankets, clock radios as well as tea and coffee facilities. The full English breakfast should easily satisfy but special diets can be catered for. A fitness suite and a sauna are also available.

Recommended in the area

Honiton antiques shops and Lace Museum; Lyme Regis; Forde Abbey and Gardens

Collingdale Guest House

★★★★ GH

Address: 13 Larkstone Terrace,
ILFRACOMBE EX34 9NU
Tel: 01271 863770
Fax: 01271 863867
Email: stay@thecollingdale.co.uk
Website: www.thecollingdale.co.uk
Map ref: 2, SS54
Directions: Take A399 E through Ilfracombe, on left past B3230 turning Rooms: 9 (8 en suite),
S £40–£45 D £65–£78 Notes: ⊘ on premises ⊗ on premises ♦♦ (min 8 years)

The Collingdale is beautifully situated directly on the South West coastal path, with miles of uninterrupted views across Ilfracombe harbour. Inside, this Victorian residence is furnished to a high standard throughout, with well-equipped bedrooms, a cosy and well-stocked bar and an elegant dining room serving freshly prepared cuisine made from local Devon produce as available. Guests can also relax on the terrace or in the pleasant garden.

Recommended in the area

Lundy Island, Tunnels Beaches, Chambercombe Manor

Norbury House

★★★★ GH

Address: Torrs Park, ILFRACOMBE EX34 8AZ
Tel: 01271 863888
Email: info@norburyhouse.co.uk
Website: www.norburyhouse.co.uk
Map ref: 2, SS54
Directions: From A399 continue to end of High St/
Church St. At mini rdbt after lights take 1st exit onto
Church Rd. Bear left onto Osbourne Rd. At T-junct
turn left onto Torrs Park, at top of hill on right
Rooms: 6 en suite, D £70–£100 Parking: 6 Notes: ⊘ on premises ↿ allowed on premises ⁑

Norbury House stands in a quiet elevated position with views over the town and the sea. Adam Bess and Paula Newman have refurbished the property, bringing a stylish contemporary twist to this traditional Victorian residence. The well-equipped bedrooms come in a choice of suites, super kingsize, family and superior doubles, many with sea views. Breakfast is served in the sunny dining room and dinner is available by arrangement. Meals are freshly prepared, using local produce whenever possible.

Recommended in the area

Marwood Hill Gardens; Arlington Court (NT); Lundy Island

Strathmore

★★★★ GA

Address: 57 St Brannock's Road, ILFRACOMBE
EX34 8EQ
Tel/Fax: 01271 862248
Email: peter@small6374.fsnet.co.uk
Website: www.the-strathmore.co.uk
Map ref: 2, SS54
Directions: A361 from Barnstaple to Ilfracombe,
Strathmore 1.5m from Mullacot Cross entering
Ilfracombe
Rooms: 8 en suite, S £32–£35 D £60–£76 Parking: 7 Notes: ⊘ on premises ↿ allowed on premises ⁑

There is a warm atmosphere at this charming Victorian property within easy walking distance of Ilfracombe town centre and harbour. Cottage-style, en suite bedrooms with many thoughtful extras provide a restful night's sleep. Set yourself up for the day with a choice of either a light continental breakfast or a generous full English, both served in the relaxed setting of the elegant dining room

Recommended in the area

Bicclescombe Park; Cairn Nature Reserve; Lundy Island; South West Coast Path

Moor View House

★★★★★ 🛏 GA

Address: Vale Down, LYDFORD EX20 4BB
Tel: 01822 820220
Fax: 01822 820220
Map ref: 2, SX38
Directions: 1m NE of Lydford on A386
Rooms: 4 en suite, S £50 D £65–£75
Parking: 15 **Notes:** ⊘ on premises ⊗ in bedrooms
🚼 under 12yrs

Built in 1869, Moor View House is a small licensed Victorian country house situated in large mature grounds on the western slopes of Dartmoor, where guests have enjoyed hospitality for more than a hundred years. The house has a very interesting history: in around 1900 it changed hands over a game of cards whilst in Edwardian times, the writer Eden Phillpotts visited and wrote the famous play A Farmer's Wife and the novel Widecombe Fair. Today, David and Wendy Sharples offer first class accommodation and friendly hospitality. There are four en suite bedrooms, each with TV, radio, hospitality trays and bathrobes amongst other facilities. During 2006, a large conservatory was built, leading from the drawing room to the garden beyond and this offers lovely views towards Cornwall in the distance. Sunsets are a delight to behold. Guests to the house are offered accommodation and a choice of English or continental breakfast. Dinner is available by prior arrangement and Wendy's award-winning cooking uses locally-produced meat, fish, game and vegetables. There are also fine, sensibly-priced wines to compliment the good food. Moor View House is an ideal base from which to tour Devon and Cornwall's heritage sites, coast and, of course, Dartmoor; after which it is a delight to return and relax in Moor View's garden on warm evenings, or, on cooler days, around a blazing log fire in the traditionally-furnished reception rooms.

Recommended in the area

Lydford Gorge (NT); Tavistock; The Eden Project

Bonnicott House

★★★★★ 🛏 🍽 GH

Address: 10 Watersmeet Rd, LYNMOUTH EX35 6EP
Tel: 01598 753346
Email: stay@bonnicott.com
Website: www.bonnicott.com
Map ref: 2, SS74
Directions: A39 from Minehead over East Lyn River Bridge, left onto Watersmeet Rd, 50yds, on right
Rooms: 8 (7 en suite), S £37–£86 D £45–£96
Notes: ⊘ on premises ⊗ on premises ⛷ under 14

In the heart of the lovely village of Lynmouth, on a particularly scenic stretch of the north Devon coast, you will find Bonnicott House, a Grade II listed former rectory of the church opposite. It stands in an elevated location, with unparalleled panoramic views over the village, the East Lyn valley and the sea. This is a lovely house with beautiful terraced gardens, where guests can relax in the sun to the sound of the tinkling water feature. But you don't have to go outside to enjoy the views – inside each of the rooms the eye is drawn to the window and the stunning vista beyond. This house also boasts a beautiful lounge where guests can congregate to chat or quietly enjoy a book, take tea or light afternoon refreshments, or have a drink from the licensed bar. In cooler months, a crackling log fire makes it even more inviting. The dining room, where award-winning breakfasts and cooked-to-order evening meals are served, has a double aspect with more of those terrific views. The bedrooms, each with its own private bathroom, are luxurious and comfortable and guests are not only provided with complimentary tea and coffee-making supplies, but also a decanter of sherry. It is very peaceful here (children under 14 and pets are not accommodated), and the hosts ensure a charming, homely atmosphere. Wi-fi broadband internet access is available.

Recommended in the area

Cliff Railway, Lynmouth; Watersmeet Lodge and tea gardens; Valley of the Rocks, Lynton.

Highcliffe House

★★★★★ 🏠 ⌂ GA

Address: Sinai Hill, LYNTON EX35 6AR
Tel: 01598 752235
Email: info@highcliffehouse.co.uk
Website: www.highcliffehouse.co.uk
Map ref: 2, SS74
Directions: Off A39 into Lynton, signs for Old Village, at Crown pub up steep hill, house 150yds on left
Rooms: 7 en suite, S £70–£90 D £90–£120
Parking: 7 **Notes:** ⊘ on premises ⊗ on premises ♨ under 16yrs **Closed:** Dec–mid Feb

Once a private summer residence, this beautifully restored house is now more widely accessible, thanks to Karen and Michael Orchard. They aim to exceed all expectations of accommodation, facilities and service, and you are unlikely to be disappointed. Highcliffe House stands in grounds with stunning views over the Exmoor hills, and across Lynmouth, the coastline and the Bristol Channel towards South Wales. The elegant en suite bedrooms are very spacious, each one individual in design, and some have beautifully carved king-size beds. Fine furnishings, a welcoming decanter of sherry, and a hospitality tray and colour TV/DVD are among the extras provided for your comfort. There are two inviting lounges, one with a splendid view. There are also fine views from the candlelit conservatory restaurant where imaginative home cooking is served in the evening. This is also the setting for breakfast when the choice includes a West Country breakfast, smoked salmon, and pancakes with bacon and maple syrup – all accompanied by home-made preserves, local honey, fresh coffee and a selection of teas. Plenty of lovely walks begin from outside the house which is just a short walk from the waterpowered cliff railway which links Lynton with Lynmouth.

Recommended in the area

Exmoor National Park; cliff railway between Lynton and Lynmouth; South West Coast Path

Victoria Lodge

★★★★★ GA

Address: 30–31 Lee Road, LYNTON EX35 6BS
Tel: 01598 753203
Email: info@victorialodge.co.uk
Website: www.victorialodge.co.uk
Map ref: 2, SS74
Directions: Off A39 in village centre opp Post Office
Rooms: 8 en suite, S £59.50–£119 D £70–£140 Parking: 6
Notes: ⊘ on premises ⊗ on premises ⊮under 11yrs
Closed: Nov–3 Mar

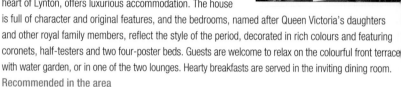

This large, elegant villa, built in the 1880s and located in the
heart of Lynton, offers luxurious accommodation. The house
is full of character and original features, and the bedrooms, named after Queen Victoria's daughters
and other royal family members, reflect the style of the period, decorated in rich colours and featuring
coronets, half-testers and two four-poster beds. Guests are welcome to relax on the colourful front terrace
with water garden, or in one of the two lounges. Hearty breakfasts are served in the inviting dining room.
Recommended in the area
Exmoor National Park; Woolacombe beach; The Tarka Trail

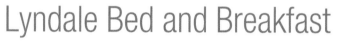

Lyndale Bed and Breakfast

★★★★ BB

Address: Lyndale Leygreen, Teigngrace,
         NEWTON ABBOT TQ12 6QW
Tel: 01626 332491
Email: sue.haddy@btinternet.com
Website: www.lyndale-devon.co.uk
Map ref: 2, SX87
Directions: Going S from Exeter on A38, exit
Teigngrace Lyndale, 1m on right
Rooms: 2 en suite, D £56–£60 Parking: 4
Notes: ⊘ on premises ⊗ in bedrooms ⊮

This modern detached bungalow is surrounded by pleasant countryside and offers fine views. Inside,
the well-decorated and comfortably furnished and spacious ground floor bedrooms come with TV and
beverage tray. Breakfast, including options such as full English, scrambled eggs with smoked salmon,
croissants and fresh coffee, is served in the bright conservatory overlooking the garden, where outdoor
seating is available for sunnier days. All in all, a good base for walkers and lovers of the countryside.
Recommended in the area
Stover Country Park; Templer Way Walk; Dartmouth National Park

Berkeley's of St James

★★★★ GA

Address: 4 St James Place East, The Hoe,
PLYMOUTH PL1 3AS
Tel/Fax 01752 221654
Email: enquiry@onthehoe.co.uk
Website: www.onthehoe.co.uk
Map ref: 1, SX45
Directions: Off A38 towards city centre, left at sign
The Hoe, over 7 sets of lights, left onto Athenaeum
St, right to Crescent Av, 1st left
Rooms: 5 en suite, S £40–45 D £55–£65 **Parking:** 3 **Notes:** ⊘ on premises ⊗ on premises ♦♦
Closed: 23 Dec–1 Jan

This welcoming guesthouse lies in a quiet secluded square on Plymouth Hoe, just a short walk from
the promenade and city centre. Bedrooms are decorated in pastel shades and pretty floral bedspreads,
and equipped with a number of thoughtful extras; a family room is available. The substantial traditional
breakfast uses organic dry cure bacon and sausages and free-range eggs supplied by local farms.

Recommended in the area

National Maritime Museum; Historic Barbican; Dartmoor National Park

Glendevon

★★★★ GH

Address: Cotmaton Road, SIDMOUTH EX10 8QX
Tel: 01395 514028
Email: enquiries@glendevon-hotel.co.uk
Website: www.glendevon-hotel.co.uk
Map ref: 2, SY18
Directions: A3052 onto B3176 to minirdbt. Right, house
100yds on right
Rooms: 8 en suite **Notes:** ⊘ on premises
⊗ on premises ⋈♦

Glendevon is in a peaceful location on the western side of
Sidmouth, just a short walk from the town's leisure facilities
and Esplanade. The bedrooms are all neatly presented with bathrooms en suite. There is a spacious
lounge and a sunny terrace which can be enjoyed by guests. Full English breakfasts are served at
individual tables in the dining room. Evening meals, prepared from fresh local produce, are available by
arrangement.

Recommended in the area

Connaught Gardens; The Byes; Exeter

The Salty Monk

★★★★★ ◎◎ RR

Address: Church Street, Sidford,
SIDMOUTH EX10 9QP
Tel: 01395 513174
Email: saltymonk@btconnect.com
Website: www.saltymonk.biz
Map ref: 2, SY18
Directions: On A3052 in Sidford opp church
Rooms: 5 en suite, S £70–£95 D £110–£180
Parking: 20 Notes: ⊘ on premises ⚞ allowed on
premises ⅋ Closed: 2wks Nov & 3wks Jan

The Salty Monk is an attractive 16th-century property set in lovely countryside in the village of Sidford, just 2 miles from the coast. Some of the well-presented rooms feature spa baths, hydro massage showers or a king size water bed. The restaurant is decorated in country-house style and overlooks the award-winning gardens. Contemporary English cuisine is created with the freshest of ingredients using mainly local produce in season. There is a courtyard patio for summer drinks and cream teas.

Recommended in the area

Exeter; The Donkey Sanctuary; South West Coast Path

Strete Barton House

★★★★ GH

Address: Totnes Rd, STRETE,
Dartmouth TQ6 0RU
Tel: 01803 770364
Fax: 01803 771182
Email: info@stretebarton.co.uk
Website: www.stretebarton.co.uk
Map ref: 2, SX84
Directions: Off A379 into village centre, just below church
Rooms: 6 (5 en suite), S £65–£90 D £75–£100 Parking: 4
Notes: ⊘ on premises ⚞ under 3yrs

This beautifully refurbished manor house is only a short distance from some of south Devon coast's finest beaches – the coastal path is 200 yards from the garden. The spacious double rooms all have king-size beds, one even has a super king-size four-poster, and all have private bathrooms, five of which are en suite. The bedooms also have TV and DVD players, clock-radios, hair dryer and a hospitality tray.

Recommended in the area

Blackpool Sands; Woodlands Adventure Park; Dartmouth.

Thomas Luny House

★★★★★ GA

Address: Teign Street, TEIGNMOUTH TQ14 8EG
Tel: 01626 772976
Email: alisonandjohn@thomas-luny-house.co.uk
Website: www.thomas-luny-house.co.uk
Map ref: 2, SX94
Directions: A381 to Teignmouth, at 3rd lights turn right to quay, 50yds turn left onto Teign St, after 60yds turn right through white archway
Rooms: 4 en suite, S £62–£68 D £72–£94 **Parking:** 8
Notes: ⊘ on premises ⊗ on premises ⚲under 12yrs

This delightful late 18th-century house is run by John and Alison Allan whose relaxed yet attentive approach is much appreciated by their guests. The large drawing room and dining room are beautifully furnished and have French doors opening onto a walled garden. The bedrooms are well equipped and very comfortable. Home-made dishes and a full cooked breakfast are a speciality.

Recommended in the area

Tuckers Maltings; Powderham Castle; Cockington village

The Colindale

★★★★ GA

Address: 20 Rathmore Road, Chelston,
          TORQUAY TQ2 6NY
Tel: 01803 293947
Email: rathmore@blueyonder.co.uk
Website: www.colindalehotel.co.uk
Map ref: 2, SX96
Directions: From Torquay station 200yds on left in Rathmore Rd
Rooms: 8 (6 en suite), S £40–£45 D £65–£70
Parking: 6 **Notes:** ⊘ on premises ⊗ on premises ⚲ under 12yrs **Closed:** Dec

Barry Greenwood-Smith has worked as a butler for the rich and famous in Beverley Hills, Bermuda and Chelsea since the 1970s. Now he loves to share his home with visitors to Torquay. Well-kept grounds surround the elegant Victorian house set close to the sea. The bedrooms, some with views over Torbay, are mainly en suite and thoughtfully equipped to make you feel at home. Evening drinks are served in a snug bar, and there's a wonderful selection of books and videos in the pleasant sitting room.

Recommended in the area

Torre Abbey; Cockington village; Living Coasts Zoo

Hartland Point lighthouse

Headland View

★★★★ 🛏 GA

Address: 37 Babbacombe Seafront, TORQUAY TQ1 3LN
Tel: 01803 312612
Email: reception@headlandview.com
Website: www.headlandview.com
Map ref: 2, SX96
Directions: A379 S to Babbacombe, off Babbacombe Rd left onto Portland Rd & Babbacombe Downs Rd & seafront
Rooms: 6 (4 en suite) D £64 **Parking:** 4 **Notes:** ⊘ ⊗ 🚭 under 4yrs **Closed:** Dec–Feb

Every comfort is thought of in this delightful little guesthouse by the sea. There are spectacular views over the World Heritage Coast of Lyme Bay from the sun lounge and most of the bedrooms have balconies. Those without sea views have four poster beds for your luxury. Colin and Sue Jezard and a professional team will ensure that you have a memorable stay. The excellent breakfast includes kedgeree, fresh fruit pancakes, home-made yoghurt and bread. Lovely beaches, and a good choice of pubs and restaurants are all nearby.

Recommended in the area

Torquay; South-West Coastal Path; Oddicombe beach

Linden House

★★★★ GA

Address: 31 Bampfylde Road,
TORQUAY TQ2 5AY
Tel: 01803 212281
Email: lindenhouse.torquay@virgin.net
Website: www.lindenhousetorquay.co.uk
Map ref: 2, SX96
Directions: Onto A3022, 1st left opposite playing fields
Rooms: 7 en suite **Parking:** 7 **Notes:** ⊘ on premises
🐾 allowed in bedrooms 🚸 under 10yrs

Built around the 1880s, this elegant Victorian villa, ideally located for a stay in the English Riviera, has stood the test of time, and its delightful entrance and hallway give guests a taste of a bygone age. To the front of the house is a good-sized floral garden, in which guests are welcome to relax with morning coffee and home-made cheese scones or a Devonshire cream tea, weather permitting. Inside, the property has been refurbished in a classic style using soft, neutral colours and fabrics. Bedrooms are comfortably furnished, using white bed linen and cream duvets for a relaxed feel. All provide hairdryers, TV and complimentary beverages and mineral water. Some of the en suite bathrooms have bath as well as shower, and all come supplied with good-quality toiletries. The garden room has its own private patio, and offers direct access to the garden. Delicious and home-cooked, the four-course breakfast utllises fresh, local and organic produce, and includes delights such as fruit smoothies, organic yoghurt, flat-field mushrooms with scrambled eggs or French toast with organic maple syrup; dinners are available by prior arrangement. Guests can also make use of the pretty, relaxing sitting room, which overlooks the garden.

Recommended in the area

Torre Abbey; Cockington Village; Dartmoor

Bayard's Cove, Dartmouth

The Durant Arms

★★★★ 🍴 INN

Address: Ashprington, TOTNES TQ9 7UP
Tel: 01803 732240
Email: info@thedurantarms.com
Website: www.thedurantarms.com
Map ref: 2, SX85
Directions: A381 from Totnes for Kingsbridge,
1m left for Ashprington
Rooms: 8 en suite, S £50–£55 D £80–£85
Parking: 8 Notes: ⊗ on premises ⊗ on premises
🐾 Closed: 25–26 Dec evenings

Immaculate whitewashed walls and masses of well-tended shrubs and plants make this traditional country inn a focal point in the picturesque village of Ashprington, deep in the heart of Devon's South Hams district. Owners Eileen and Graham Ellis proudly offer their own brand of hospitality and provide attractive accommodation in either the main building or a refurbished annexe. The bedrooms are individually designed to a very high standard, using stylish furnishings, and include a host of thoughtful touches to help ensure a memorable stay. Each room has a luxurious well-appointed en suite bathroom that adds additional comfort. The inn is renowned locally for its delicious food. A blackboard menu of home-cooked food is available in the character bar or the smart dining room, both furnished in rich red velvets. All dishes are freshly cooked to order, offering fresh vegetables and a wide variety of meat and fish; seasonal local produce is used whenever possible. To compliment your meal there is a good choice of real ales, beers and wines, some from the local Sharpham Vineyard, just a 15-minute walk away and open to the public for visiting and wine tasting. There are stunning views of the River Dart from this delightful inn. Packed lunches are available.

Recommended in the area

Historic Totnes; The Eden Project; Sharpham Vineyard

Main street, Totnes

Harrabeer Country House

★★★★ ➞ GA

Address: Harrowbeer Lane,
YELVERTON PL20 6EA
Tel: 01822 853302
Email: reception@harrabeer.co.uk
Website: www.harrabeer.co.uk
Map ref: 2, SX56
Directions: In village. Off A386 Tavistock Rd onto
Grange Rd, right onto Harrowbeer Ln
Rooms: 6 (5 en suite), S £48–£80 D £64.99–£95
Parking: 10 **Notes:** ⊘ on premises ⚑ allowed on premises ♙
Closed: 3rd wk Dec, 2nd wk Jan

This lovely Devon longhouse on the edge of Dartmoor has a relaxing lounge, a bar for a convivial
evening drink and well-equipped comfortable bedrooms. Breakfast is a leisurely affair served in the
dining room, and dinner can be served by arrangement. The Harrabeer provides an excellent base for
exploring the beautiful surrounding countryside. Two self-catering units are available.

Recommended in the area

The Garden House; The Eden Project; Dartmoor National Park

DORSET

The Dorset coast near Durdle Door

Cransley

★★★★ GA

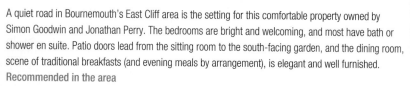

Address: 11 Knyveton Road, East Cliff,
BOURNEMOUTH BH1 3QG
Tel: 01202 290067
Fax: 07092 381721
Email: info@cransley.com
Website: www.cransley.com
Map ref: 3, SZ09
Directions: Off A338 at St Pauls rdbt by ASDA store,
over next rdbt, Knyveton Rd 1st left
Rooms: 11 (10 en suite), S £30–£35 D £60–£70 **Parking:** 8
Notes: ⊗ on premises ⊗ on premises ⚹under 14yrs

A quiet road in Bournemouth's East Cliff area is the setting for this comfortable property owned by Simon Goodwin and Jonathan Perry. The bedrooms are bright and welcoming, and most have bath or shower en suite. Patio doors lead from the sitting room to the south-facing garden, and the dining room, scene of traditional breakfasts (and evening meals by arrangement), is elegant and well furnished.

Recommended in the area

New Forest National Park; Thomas Hardy Country; Poole Harbour and Brownsea Island

---

Westcotes House

★★★★ GH

Address: 9 Southbourne Overcliff Drive,
Southbourne, BOURNEMOUTH BH6 3TE
Tel/Fax: 01202 428512
Website: www.westcoteshousehotel.co.uk
Map ref: 3, SZ09
Directions: 2m E of town centre. A35 onto B3059,
turn down Grand Av continue to end and turn right
Rooms: 6 en suite, S £44–£48 D £64–£74
Parking: 6 Notes: ⊗ ⊗ in bedrooms ⚹ under 10

Overlooking Poole Bay from the cliff top at Southbourne, this small establishment is elegantly decorated and has private parking. The conservatory-lounge leads onto a sunny sea-facing terrace, and a zigzag path and cliff lift give easy access to the promenade and sandy beach. All the rooms are en suite and your friendly hosts Brenda and Christopher Burrell have added numerous extras including bathrobes, tissues and toiletries. One of the bedrooms is on the ground floor. Excellent home cooking is served in the well-presented dining room, which has sea views. Dinner is available by arrangement.

Recommended in the area

Poole Harbour; Thomas Hardy Country; Bournemouth

Bournemouth, Poole Bay

The Roundham House

★★★★★ GA

Address: Roundham Gardens, West Bay Road,
BRIDPORT DT6 4BD
Tel: 01308 422753
Email: cyprencom@compuserve.com
Website: www.roundhamhouse.co.uk
Map ref: 2, SY49
Directions: A35 into Bridport, at the Crown Inn rdbt
take exit signed West Bay. 400yds on left
Rooms: 8 (7 en suite), S £46–£57 D £82–£97
(Premiere room £118) **Parking:** 10 **Notes:** ⊗ on premises 🐾 allowed on premises 👶 under 6yrs
Closed: Dec–Feb

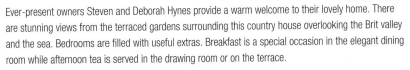

Ever-present owners Steven and Deborah Hynes provide a warm welcome to their lovely home. There
are stunning views from the terraced gardens surrounding this country house overlooking the Brit valley
and the sea. Bedrooms are filled with useful extras. Breakfast is a special occasion in the elegant dining
room while afternoon tea is served in the drawing room or on the terrace.

Recommended in the area

Abbotsbury Swannery and Gardens; Montacute House (NT); Forde Abbey and Gardens

The Lord Bute & Restaurant

★★★★★ ◎◎ GA

Address: 179–181 Lymington Road, Highcliffe
on Sea, CHRISTCHURCH BH23 4JS
Tel: 01425 278884
Fax: 01425 279258
Email: mail@lordbute.co.uk
Website: www.lordbute.co.uk
Map ref: 3, SZ19
Directions: A337 towards Highcliffe
Rooms: 13 en suite, S £75–£95 D £98–£225
Parking: 40 **Notes:** ⊘ on premises ⌒ allowed on premises ⭍

The elegant Lord Bute stands directly behind the original entrance lodges of Highcliffe Castle, close to the beach and the historic town of Christchurch. It was once home to Lord Bute, British Prime Minister from 1762 to 1763. Comfort and impeccable standards are key here. The luxurious and very stylish en suite bedrooms, including some family rooms and some on the ground floor, have all been finished to a very high standard, with many thoughtful extras including spa baths, as well as direct-dial telephones, trouser press, air-conditioning and well-stocked tea and coffee-making facilities. Self-contained suites, some with their own private landscaped garden areas and including a bridal suite, are available in what were once the gatehouses to the castle. Elsewhere, guests can relax in the warm and welcoming lounge, or peruse the menu in the tranquil conservatory-styled orangery. The excellent food makes dining here memorable. Served in the smart, classically furnished restaurant with a friendly ambience, breakfast, lunch and dinner are all available, prepared by award-winning chefs. Special events include cabaret evenings and a jazz diary. Conferences and weddings are also catered for, and a conference suite is available.

Recommended in the area

New Forest; Hengistbury Head; Christchurch Priory

Baytree House Dorchester

★★★★ BB

Address: 4 Athelstan Road,
DORCHESTER DT1 1NR
Tel: 01305 263696
Map ref: 2, SY69
Directions: 0.5m SE of town centre
Rooms: 3 en suite, S £30 D £55 Parking: 3
Notes: ⊗ on premises ⊗ on premises ♦♦

In 2006 owners Nicola and Gary Cutler completely refurbished Baytree House, creating a stylish place to stay, with spacious and light rooms, contemporary décor and luxurious fittings. Although it is set in a quiet residential area, it's just a 10-minute stroll to the historic centre of Dorchester and a short drive to many of rural Dorset's attractions. The bedrooms offer either en suite shower room or a private bathroom, which has shower and bath. The Cutlers also own the Walnut Grove Restaurant and Coffee Shop in the town centre, and employ the same high standards of cooking at Baytree House. Guests are offered a 15 percent discount on meals at the Walnut Grove.

Recommended in the area

Thomas Hardy's Cottage; Monkey World; Dorset's Jurassic coastline

The Casterbridge

★★★★★ GA

Address: 49 High East Street,
DORCHESTER DT1 1HU
Tel: 01305 264043
Fax: 01305 260884
Email: reception@casterbridgehotel.co.uk
Website: www.casterbridgehotel.co.uk
Map ref: 2, SY69
Directions: In town centre, 75yds from town clock
Rooms: 14 en suite, S £55–£75 D £99–£125
Parking: 2 Notes: ⊗ in dining room ⊗ on premises ♦♦ Closed: 24–26 Dec

This well-run establishment provides a traditional English welcome, with cheerful attentive staff and a high standard of accommodation. Public rooms include an elegant dining room, drawing room, and a cosy bar-library. Breakfast in the conservatory is an extensive buffet or individually cooked breakfasts. All bedrooms are en suite with either bath or shower, tea and coffee facilities, direct-dial telephones, and one room is suitable for families. Children are welcome and high chairs are available.

Recommended in the area

Thomas Hardy Museum; Abbotsbury Swannery; Lulworth Cove

Little Court

★★★★★ GA

Address: 5 Westleaze, Charminster,
DORCHESTER DT2 9PZ
Tel: 01305 261576
Fax: 01305 261359
Email: info@littlecourt.net
Website: www.littlecourt.net
Map ref: 2, SY69
Directions: A37 from Dorchester, 0.25m right at
Loders Garage, Little Court 0.5m on right

Rooms: 8 en suite, S £69–£99 D £69–£109 Parking: 10 Notes: ⊘ on premises ⊗ on premises ♦♦

A picture-postcard Edwardian house, Little Court nestles in 4 acres of beautiful grounds and gardens.
The property has been refurbished to a very high standard and the proprietors are on hand to ensure
you have a excellent stay. Bedrooms have a bath and shower en suite, and come with extras such
as an umbrella. A delicious breakfast, including home-grown produce, is served
in the dining room which adjoins a restful lounge with open fires. A pub nearby serves good food.

Recommended in the area

Jurassic Coast World Heritage Coast; Dorchester; Weymouth

Yalbury Cottage & Restaurant

★★★★★ ⊛⊛ GH

Address: Lower Bockhampton,
DORCHESTER DT2 8PZ
Tel: 01305 262382
Email: yalburyemails@aol.com
Website: www.yalburycottage.com
Map ref: 2, SY69
Directions: Off A35 past Thomas Hardys cottage,
over x-rds, 400yds on left, past telephone box, opp
village pump

Rooms: 8 en suite, S £76–£86 D £98–£112 Parking: 16 Notes: ⊘ on premises
↝ allowed on premises ♦♦

Situated in peaceful countryside, thatched Yalbury Cottage dates from the 17th century. The pretty
restaurant serves excellent food, in an atmosphere enhanced by oak beams and inglenook fireplaces.
The cosy lounge, is also in the old part of the building. The spacious, well-equipped cottage-style
bedrooms are in the modern annexe.

Recommended in the area

Thomas Hardy's birthplace; Athelhampton House; walks in a conservation area

The Acorn Inn

★ ★ ★ ★ ◎ INN

Address: EVERSHOT, Dorchester DT2 0JW
Tel: 01935 83228
Fax: 01935 83707
Email: stay@acorn-inn.co.uk
Website: www.acorn-inn.co.uk
Map ref: 2, ST50
Directions: 0.5m off A37 between Yeovil and Dorchester, signed Evershot, Holywell
Rooms: 10 en suite, from S £75 D £100
Parking: 40 **Notes:** ⊘ in bedrooms ⌦ allowed on premises ⁙

This 16th-century coaching inn was immortalised as the Sow and Acorn in Thomas Hardy's *Tess of the D'Urbervilles*. It stands at the heart of the village of Evershot, in an area of outstanding natural beauty, with walking, fishing, shooting and riding all nearby. Inside are two oak-panelled bars – one flagstoned, one tiled – with logs blazing in carved hamstone fireplaces, and a cosy restaurant. There's also a skittle alley in what was once the stables, and it's rumoured that the residents' sitting room was once used by Hanging Judge Jeffreys as a court room. The en suite bedrooms are all individually styled, and each named after a character from Hardy's novel – several feature interesting four-poster beds. All of the rooms, including two family rooms, have a colour TV, telephone with modem and beverage tray. Hairdryers and irons are available on request. Fresh, local produce is included on the varied and interesting menu, with most of the food sourced from within a 15-mile radius, including local fish and game, and bolstered by blackboard specials. Bar snacks and lighter meals are also available, accompanied by a selection of real ales and a comprehensive wine list. Plenty of parking spaces are available.

Recommended in the area

Evershot village; Forde Abbey; Lyme Regis

Farnham Farm House

★★★★★ GA

Address: FARNHAM, Blandford Forum DT11 8DG
Tel: 01725 516254
Fax: 01725 516306
Email: info@farnhamfarmhouse.co.uk
Website: www.farnhamfarmhouse.co.uk
Map ref: 2, ST91
Directions: Off A354 Thickthorn x-rds into Farnham, continue NW from village centre T-junct, 1m bear right at sign

Rooms: 3 en suite, S £50–£70 D £80 Parking: 7 Notes: ⊘ ⊗ ♦♦ Closed: 25–26 Dec

Farnham Farm House, with its flagstone floors, open log fires and magnificent views, dates back to the 1850s. Guests can walk around the 350-acre working farm, part of a private estate owned by the descendants of archaeologist General Pitt-Rivers. Facilities include a heated outdoor swimming pool, and the Sarpenela Natural Therapy Centre for therapeutic massage. Delicious Aga-cooked breakfasts are served in the attractive dining room. Local produce is used whenever possible.

Recommended in the area

Cranborne Chase; Kingston Lacey (NT); Larmer Tree Gardens

Longpuddle

★★★★ BB

Address: 4 High Street, PIDDLEHINTON DT2 7TD
Tel: 01300 348532
Email: ann@longpuddle.co.uk
Website: www.longpuddle.co.uk
Map ref: 2, SY79
Directions: From Dorchester (A35) take B3143, after village 1st on left
Rooms: 2 en suite, S £45–£50 D £70–£90
Parking: 3 Notes: ⊘ on premises ⌂ allowed in bedrooms ♦♦ Closed: Jan

This 400-year-old thatched cottage is well placed for exploring Thomas Hardy's Dorset. The house overlooks the small River Piddle, which runs between the large garden and the paddocks. Bedrooms are located in the recently refurbished purpose-built annexe and are spacious and tastefully decorated, with extras such as a mini-fridge thoughtfully provided. Breakfast features freshly cooked local produce served in the dining room of the main house, and there is a guest lounge with calming garden views.

Recommended in the area

Cerne Abbas Giant; Maiden Castle, near Dorchester; Sherborne town

The Piddle Inn

★★★★ INN

Address: PIDDLETRENTHIDE,
Dorchester DT2 7QF
Tel: 01300 348468
Fax: 01300 348102
Email: piddleinn@aol.com
Website: www.piddleinn.co.uk
Map ref: 2, SY79
Directions: 7m N of Dorchester on B3143 in middle of Piddletrenthide
Rooms: 3 en suite **Parking:** 15 **Notes:** ⊗ in bedrooms ⌇ allowed in bedrooms

In the heart of Thomas Hardy walking country, nestled in the beautiful Piddle Valley and only half an hour from the Jurassic Coast, The Piddle Inn is a traditional family-owned village inn. Dating from the 1760s, it takes its name from the river that flows past the sunny beer garden, creating a picturesque foreground for a stunning view of the countryside beyond. There are three beautifully refurbished en suite rooms, two of which have views over the River Piddle and the countryside beyond. All of the comfortable rooms have tea and coffee-making facilities, direct-dial telephones, Wi-fi, televisions, DVD players, clock radios and electric safes, and the bathrooms have high-powered electric showers. Fresh flowers are regularly placed in each room, and for special occasions you can arrange in advance to have wine or champagne in the room on arrival. The restaurant here seats 50 and offers daily specials, an a la carte menu sourced straight from local farmers, fish and produce markets, with home-made puddings and a bar and children's menu. Real ales are served straight from the barrel and there's an extensive choice of wine and other beverages. Guests can take time out to relax by the open fire while playing traditional pub games. Well-behaved dogs are welcome.

Recommended in the area

Salisbury Cathedral; Cerne Abbas Giant; Poole

The Greyhound Inn

★★★★ ⬭ INN

Address: 26 High Street, SYDLING ST NICHOLAS,
Dorchester DT2 9PD
Tel: 01300 341303
Email: info@thegreyhounddorset.co.uk
Website: www.thegreyhounddorset.co.uk
Map ref: 2, SY69
Directions: Off A37 into village centre
Rooms: 6 en suite, D £70–£90 Parking: 30
Notes: ⊘ on premises ⊗ on premises ⋔

Situated in the traditional English village of Sydling St Nicholas, the Greyhound Inn is well located for exploring Hardy Country. The inn has a range of stylish, well-equipped en suite bedrooms, three of which are at ground-floor level. Elsewhere, flagstone floors and attractive, relaxed surroundings make this inn a popular place for dining. An interesting and wide choice of meals made from top-quality local produce, and often including fresh game, is offered in either the restaurant, which has a well as its central feature, the bar or the conservatory. Lights snacks are also available.

Recommended in the area

Keep Military Museum; Purbeck; Yeovil

The Esplanade

★★★★ GA

Address: 141 The Esplanade, WEYMOUTH DT4 7NJ
Tel: 01305 783129
Fax: 01305 783129
Email: theesplanade@o2email.co.uk
Website: www.theesplanadehotel.co.uk
Map ref: 2, SY67
Directions: E end of Esplanade, opp pier bandstand
Rooms: 11 en suite, S £33–£50 D £56–£90 Parking: 9
Notes: ⊘ on premises ⊗ on premises ⋔ Open: All year

You are assured of a warm welcome from owners Rob and Terri Cole at this Georgian seafront terrace situated just yards from

the beach and promenade. The front-facing public rooms all have fabulous views of beautiful Weymouth Bay. The good-sized en suite rooms are particularly well furnished and attractively decorated, with many thoughtful extras. There are ground-floor bedrooms too and parking is available. The town centre, harbour, railway station and other local attractions are all within easy walking distance.

Recommended in the area

Abbotsbury Swannery; Dorset beaches; Sea Life Park; Portland Bill; Jurassic Coastline

ortland Bill

The Heritage

★★★ GA

ddress: 8 East St, Chickerell, WEYMOUTH DT3 4DS
el: 01305 783093
ax: 01305 786668
mail: mail@the-heritage.co.uk
Vebsite: www.the-heritage.co.uk
lap ref: 2, SY67
irections: In village centre
ooms: 6 en suite, S £59 D £79 **Parking:** 10
otes: ⊘ on premises 🐾 allowed on premises 👫

his Grade II listed stone building (formerly The Turk's Head Hotel and Restaurant) in the village of
hickerell just outside Weymouth provides high-quality, family-run accommodation. It has been
ympathetically restored to retain many original features. The individually decorated, spacious
edrooms – two of which are family rooms – come with plentiful accessories such as hospitality tray,
olour TV/video and the modern en suite bathrooms all feature both baths and showers. Hearty English
reakfasts are served in the popular restaurant, which is also open for lunch and dinner.

ecommended in the area

urassic Coastline; Portland Bill; Deep Sea Adventure

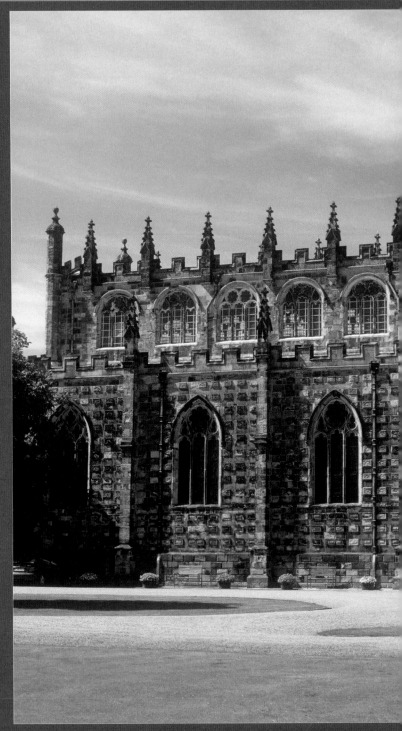

Auckland Castle, Bishop Auckland

Number 34

★★★★ GA

Address: 34 The Bank, BARNARD CASTLE DL12 8PN
Tel: 01833 631304
Email: evasreid@aol.com
Website: www.number34.com
Map ref: 7, NZ01
Directions: 3m from A66, on l after Butter Market rdbt
Rooms: 3 (1 en suite), S £40–£50 D £55–£75
Notes: ⊘ on premises ⊗ in bedrooms 🐾

This delightful house has enjoyed a rich history, and boasts a dining room dating back to Elizabethan times. Set among antique shops in the old quarter of Barnard Castle, it was itself an antique shop until recently. Bedrooms here are generally spacious, well equipped and very stylish, with TV, bathrobes and a decanter of sherry provided. Guests can relax in the lounge or use the garden in warmer weather. Breakfasts are a real treat, with home-made and local produce featuring, and may include fresh fruit platter or scrambled eggs with smoked trout. For evening meals, Barnard Castle's oldest restaurant is next door, and there are many other options nearby.

Recommended in the area

Bowes Museum; High Force and Low Force waterfalls; Rokeby Park Manor House

Clow Beck House

★★★★★ 🛏 🍴 GA

Address: Monk End Farm, Croft-on-Tees,
DARLINGTON DL2 2SW
Tel: 01325 721075
Fax: 01325 720419
Email: heather@clowbeckhouse.co.uk
Website: www.clowbeckhouse.co.uk
Map ref: 7, NZ21
Directions: 3m S of Darlington. In Croft-on-Tees on A167 follow brown tourist signs to Clow Beck House
Rooms: 13 en suite, S £85 D £130 **Parking:** 15 **Notes:** ⊘ ⊗ 🐾 **Closed:** Xmas & New Year

Clow Beck House gets its name from the beck that winds its way through the grounds of the farm to meet the River Tees, providing a perfect opportunity for trout fishing. The bedrooms, decorated to give a sense of period style, are in a cottage and in separate chalets in the gardens. The inviting lounge and the beamed dining room, where imaginative dishes and a good wine list are available, are in the house itself. Heather and David Armstrong are dedicated to making you feel at home.

Recommended in the area

Raby Castle; Beamish Open Air Museum; Yorkshire Dales and Moors

ESSEX

The Pier, Clacton-on-Sea

Chudleigh

★★★★ GA

Address:	13 Agate Road, Marine Parade West, CLACTON-ON-SEA CO15 1RA
Tel:	01255 425407
Fax:	01255 470280
Email:	reception@chudleighhotel.com
Website:	www.tiscover.co.uk/chudleigh-hotel
Map ref:	4, TM11
Directions:	250yds W of pier off Marine Parade West
Rooms:	10 en suite, S £42.50–£45 D £60–£65
Parking:	7 **Notes:** 🐾 allowed in bedrooms 🚼 under 1 yr

With its unique architecture, its front terrace with outdoor furniture and its masses of flowers spilling out of window boxes, tubs and hanging baskets, Chudleigh is a distinctive landmark near the Clacton sea front. The pier and the main shopping centre are both within a short distance, making this an ideal spot for both business and leisure visitors to the town, but it is nevertheless a peaceful place to stay. For more than three decades it has been run with dedication and enthusiasm by Carol and Peter Oleggini, who, as might be surmised from their name, can converse fluently with Italian-speaking guests. Service here is pleasantly informal, but attention to detail and high standards of housekeeping are paramount. It's a delicate balance, perfectly achieved, which brings many guests back time and time again. The bedrooms are very attractive, with coordinating décor, comfortable beds and chairs, en suite bathrooms and facilities such as televisions, direct-dial telephones and tea and coffee-making supplies. There are also spacious family rooms. Downstairs there's a residents' lounge with a television, and an extensive breakfast menu is on offer in the dining room, where the separate tables are dressed with linen tablecloths.

Recommended in the area

Sandy beaches of the Essex coast; Colchester; Beth Chatto Gardens

Colchester Castle Museum

The Old Manse

★★★★ GA

Address: 15 Roman Road, COLCHESTER CO1 1UR
Tel: 01206 545154
Email: wendyanderson15@hotmail.com
Website: www.theoldmanse.uk.com
Map ref: 4, TL92
Directions: In town centre, 250yds E of castle. Off High St-East Hill onto Roman Rd
Rooms: 3 (2 en suite), S £40–£50 D £63–£70
Parking: 1 Notes: ⊗ ⊗ ⅙ under 6yrs
Closed: 23–31 Dec

This elegant and spacious Victorian house is in a quiet location, yet is just a short walk from the castle and the town centre. The bedrooms here are carefully decorated with coordinated soft furnishings, and equipped with many thoughtful touches. Breakfast is served seated at a large communal table in the attractive dining room and there is a comfortable lounge. Famous for its warm welcome and friendly atmosphere, Wendy Anderson was a finalist for AA Friendliest Landlady of the Year 2007.

Recommended in the area

Colchester Castle; Colchester Zoo; Beth Chatto Gardens

The River Eye, Upper Slaughter

Sudeley Castle, Winchcombe

Badger Towers

★★★★ GA

Address: 133 Hales Road, CHELTENHAM GL52 6ST
Tel: 01242 522583
Fax: 01242 574800
Email: mrbadger@badgertowers.co.uk
Website: www.badgertowers.co.uk
Map ref: 2, SO92
Directions: Off A40 London Rd onto Hales Rd, 0.5m on right
Rooms: 7 en suite, S £55–£65 D £70–£120
Parking: 7 Notes: ⊗ on premises ✝ allowed on premises ♦♦ Closed: Xmas & New Year

A comfortable, relaxed atmosphere is felt as soon as you enter this impressive Victorian property, set in a quiet residential area. Owners Claire and Peter Christensen offer elegantly decorated and furnished bedrooms, including two on the ground floor. The breakfast room, where a full English breakfast is freshly cooked from locally sourced produce, is bright and cheerful, and there is a spacious sitting room.

Recommended in the area

Sudeley Castle; Prestbury Park; Cheltenham Promenade and Montpellier

Beaumont House

★ ★ ★ ★ ★ GA

Address: 56 Shurdington Road,
CHELTENHAM GL53 0JE
Tel: 01242 223311
Fax: 01242 520044
Email: reservations@bhhotel.co.uk
Website: www.bhhotel.co.uk
Map ref: 2, SO92
Directions: S side of town on A46 to Stroud
Rooms: 16 en suite, S £62–£178 D £79–£193
Parking: 16 **Notes:** ⊘ on premises ⊗ on premises 🚼 under 5yrs

Built as a private residence, this popular establishment, which is managed by the owner, exudes a genteel charm. Public areas at Beaumont House include a large lounge and an elegant dining room that overlooks the mature gardens, where pre-dinner drinks may be taken or lazy afternoons whiled away. Many improvements have taken place under the Bishop family, who combine a friendly welcome with professional standards. New bedrooms have been added to the top floor and are particularly suited to business travellers, with their king and super-king size beds and wired broadband connection. These compliment the themed 'Out of Asia' and 'Out of Africa' bedrooms, which are also luxuriously furnished and very well equipped, and include whirlpool baths. All bedrooms have flatscreen television, and those situated to the rear of the building have views over Leckhampton Hill; there are also bedrooms on the lower ground floor. In the morning, guests are treated to sumptuous freshly cooked breakfasts made from finest ingredients, including Cotswolds free-range eggs, locally sourced pork sausages, and renowned Craster kippers and smoked haddock from Northumberland, all served in the dining room. For those who prefer it, cold European-style breakfasts are also available.

Recommended in the area

Sudeley Castle; Gloucester Cathedral; Corinium Museum, Cirencester

Cleeve Hill House

★★★★★ GA

Address: Cleeve Hill, CHELTENHAM GL52 3PR
Tel: 01242 672052
Fax: 01242 679969
Email: info@cleevehill-hotel.co.uk
Website: www.cleevehill-hotel.co.uk
Map ref: 2, SO92
Directions: 3m N of Cheltenham on B4632
Rooms: 8 en suite, S £45–£65 D £80–£110
Parking: 10 Notes: ⊘ ⊗ ⛄ under 6yrs

Set on an elevated location north of Cheltenham, and in an ideal spot for visiting the Cotswolds and surrounding area, this elegant Edwardian house offers individually styled bedrooms, including one with a four-poster and a ground-floor room. Attention to detail is evident in the carefully chosen homely extras, such as tea and cake provided on arrival. The deep sofas, superb decor and soft furnishings in the spacious lounges provide a relaxed atmosphere. A bar service is available, and quality breakfasts are served in a conservatory that looks out over the surrounding countryside to the Malvern Hills.

Recommended in the area

National Hunt Racecourse; Stratford-upon-Avon; Bath

Georgian House

★★★★★ BB

Address: 77 Montpellier Terrace,
           CHELTENHAM GL50 1XA
Tel: 01242 515577
Email: penny@georgianhouse.net
Website: www.georgianhouse.net
Map ref: 2, SO92
Directions: M5 junct 11, A40 into town centre & onto
Montpellier Ter, Georgian House on right after park
Rooms: 3 en suite, S £58–£70 D £80–£95
Parking: 2 Notes: ⊘ on premises ⊗ in bedrooms ⛄ under 16yrs Closed: Xmas & New Year

Dating from 1807 and one of the earliest terraced houses in Cheltenham, this elegant Georgian establishment is only a few minutes' stroll from the Promenade. Careful renovation has resulted in delightful accommodation that offers high levels of quality and comfort throughout. Bedrooms here are individually styled, with contemporary features such as remote-control Freeview TV, mini-fridge, ironing facilities, trouser-press and Wi-fi connection cleverly interwoven with period furnishings to great effect.

Recommended in the area

Cheltenham's Regency buildings and gardens; Slimbridge; the Cotswolds

The Moda House

★★★ GA

Address: 1 High Street, CHIPPING SODBURY BS37 6BA
Tel: 01454 312135
Fax: 01454 850090
Email: enquiries@modahotel.com
Website: www.modahotel.com
Map ref: 2, ST78
Directions: In town centre
Rooms: 10 en suite, S £58.50–£62 D £78–£90 Notes: ⊗ ⊮ ⅰ

This imposing three-storey Grade II Georgian house, conveniently situated on the High Street, is a fine guest house, where Jo and Duncan MacArthur have created a warm and welcoming atmosphere in which guests can fully relax. The modern bedrooms of various shapes and sizes have their own distinctive character, all with well-appointed bathrooms, satellite television and magnificent views of the town and countryside beyond. The superb breakfasts are sourced from local suppliers and cooked on an Aga. Chipping Sodbury is an excellent base from which to explore the local area.

Recommended in the area

Bath; Westonbirt Arboretum; Dyrham Park (NT)

Hare & Hounds

★★★★ ◉ INN

Address: Fosse-Cross, Chedworth,
CIRENCESTER GL54 4NN
Tel: 01285 720288
Email: stay@hareandhoundsinn.com
Website: www.hareandhoundsinn.com
Map ref: 3, SP00
Directions: 4.5m NE of Cirencester. On A429 by speed camera
Rooms: 10 en suite, S £60–£70 D £90–£125
Parking: 40 Notes: ⊗ on premises ⊗ in bedrooms ⅰ

This country inn is close to the historic Fosse Way and perfectly situated for visiting nearby Cirencester and the Cotswolds. The smart bedrooms surround a peaceful courtyard and have full disabled access. Guests can dine outside on warm summer days, in the orangerie, or in one of the three elegant dining areas in the main pub. The delicious home-cooked food is highly regarded, chef Gerry Ragosa, an advocate of Cotswold produce, creates superb results using local ingredients where possible.

Recommended in the area

Chedworth Roman Villa (NT); Cheltenham; Cotswold Wildlife Park

The Plough Inn

★★★★ ⬚ INN

Address: FORD, Temple Guiting GL54 5RU
Tel: 01386 584215
Fax: 01386 584042
Email: info@theploughinnatford.co.uk
Website: www.theploughinnatford.co.uk
Map ref: 3, SP02
Directions: On B4077 in village
Rooms: 3 en suite, D £70 Parking: 50 Notes: ⊗ in
bedrooms ⊗ on premises ⋔

The Plough Inn, popular with locals and the racing fraternity, is a charming 16th-century inn, well located for visiting the Cotswolds. Inside it retains many original features including Cotswold stone walls, open fires and beamed ceilings, while the en suite bedrooms are located across a courtyard in a quaint cobble-stoned building – once a hayloft with stabling, it has now been restored to provide comfortable, modern accommodation. Home-cooked food featuring local produce is a highlight here, as are the well-kept Donnington ales, which can be enjoyed in the delightful beer garden.
Recommended in the area
Cheltenham Racecourse; Bourton-on-the-Water; Chipping Campden

Guiting Guest House

★★★★ GH

Address: Post Office Lane, GUITING POWER,
          Cheltenham GL54 5TZ
Tel: 01451 850470
Email: info@guitingguesthouse.com
Website: www.guitingguesthouse.com
Map ref: 3, SP02
Directions: In village centre
Rooms: 7 (5 en suite), S £40 D £76–£80 Parking: 3
Notes: ⊗ on premises ⋔ allowed on premises ⋔

Guiting is an engaging family home at one with its surroundings in a beautiful Cotswold village. Bedrooms are individually decorated and full of charm. Most have facilities en suite and four-poster beds, and all of them are equipped with hairdryers, bathrobes, quality toiletries, and hospitality trays with biscuits, fresh fruit and flowers. Exposed beams, inglenook fireplaces, solid elm floorboards and candlelight provide character in the inviting public rooms. Breakfast and evening meals, based on fresh local produce, are served in the dining room. Please give at least 24 hours notice for a dinner booking.
Recommended in the area
Cotswold Farm Park; Sudeley Castle; Blenheim Palace

Cambrai Lodge

★★★★ GA

Address: Oak Street, LECHLADE ON THAMES
GL7 3AY
Tel: 01367 253173
Email: www.cambrailodge@btconnect.com
Website: www.cambrailodgeguesthouse.co.uk
Map ref: 3, SU29
Directions: From High St onto A361 Oak St
Rooms: 5 en suite, S £45–£65 D £55–£75
Parking: 12 **Notes:** ⊘ on premises 🐾 allowed on
premises ♦♦

This attractive house, on the edge of the market town of Lechlade, is only a stroll from a number of recommended pubs serving food. The bedrooms are all carefully decorated and furnished. Some rooms are in a pretty cottage across the garden and include a king-size bed and corner bath, and there are two ground-floor bedrooms. All the rooms are en suite, have tea and coffee facilities and central heating. Hearty breakfasts are served in the conservatory overlooking the large gardens.

Recommended in the area

Cirencester; Oxford; the Cotswolds

Hyde Wood House

★★★★ BB

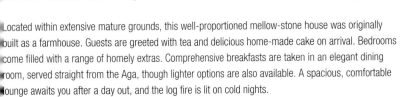

Address: Cirencester Road,
MINCHINHAMPTON GL6 8PE
Tel: 01453 885504
Email: info@hydewoodhouse.co.uk
Website: www.hydewoodhouse.co.uk
Map ref: 2, SO80
Directions: From Stroud A419 to Cirencester, after village of Chalford, turn right at top of hill signed Minchinhampton & Aston Down. House 1m on right
Rooms: 3 en suite, D £60 **Parking:** 6 **Notes:** ⊘ on premises ⊗ in bedrooms ♦♦ under 14yrs

Located within extensive mature grounds, this well-proportioned mellow-stone house was originally built as a farmhouse. Guests are greeted with tea and delicious home-made cake on arrival. Bedrooms come filled with a range of homely extras. Comprehensive breakfasts are taken in an elegant dining room, served straight from the Aga, though lighter options are also available. A spacious, comfortable lounge awaits you after a day out, and the log fire is lit on cold nights.

Recommended in the area

Westonbirt Arboretum; WWT Slimbridge; Cirencester

Northfield Guest House

★★★★ GA

Address: Cirencester Road,
NORTHLEACH GL54 3JL
Tel/Fax: 01451 860427
Email: northfield@loving.orangehome.co.uk
Website: www.northfieldbandb.co.uk
Map ref: 3, SP11
Directions: Signed off A429 Northleach-Cirencester road, 1m from Northleach lights
Rooms: 3 en suite, S £45–£65 D £65–£75
Parking: 10 Notes: ⊘ on premises ⊗ on premises ♦♦ Closed: Dec–Feb

Animals graze in the fields around this Cotswold stone house set in immaculate gardens. Indoors there is a clear commitment to presentation and the bedrooms are a pleasure to stay in – two rooms have direct access to the gardens. The relaxing atmosphere extends to the lounge. The friendly dining room is the scene of delicious country breakfasts including eggs from the resident hens. Northleach is convenient for Cirencester and Gloucester.

Recommended in the area

Chedworth Roman Villa (NT); Keith Harding's Musical Museum; Cheltenham; Stow-on-the-Wold

Aston House

★★★★ BB

Address: Broadwell, STOW-ON-THE-WOLD GL56 0TJ
Tel: 01451 830475
Email: fja@netcomuk.co.uk
Website: www.astonhouse.net
Map ref: 3, SP12
Directions: A429 from Stow-on-the-Wold towards Moreton-in-Marsh, 1m right at x-rds to Broadwell, Aston House 0.5m on left
Rooms: 3 (2 en suite), D £60–£64 Parking: 3
Notes: ⊘ on premises ⊗ on premises ♦♦ under 10yrs Closed: Nov–Feb

The enthusiastic owner ensures that the accommodation has every comfort, with armchairs in all the rooms, electric blankets and fans. Other amenities include quality toiletries in the en suite bathrooms, televisions, radios and hairdryers, tea-making facilities and bedtime drinks and biscuits. Although rooms are not suitable for wheelchair-bound visitors, the stair lift is a boon for those with limited mobility. A full English breakfast is served and there is a good pub within walking distance.

Recommended in the area

Cotswolds villages; Blenheim Palace; Hidcote Manor Gardens

Kings Head Inn & Restaurant

★★★★ ® INN

Address: The Green, Bledington,
STOW-ON-THE-WOLD OX7 6XQ
Tel: 01608 658365
Fax: 01608 658902
Email: kingshead@orr-ewing.com
Website: www.kingsheadinn.net
Map ref: 3, SP12
Directions: 4m SE off B4450
Rooms: 12 en suite, S £55–£60 D £70–£125
Parking: 24 **Notes:** ⊘ in bedrooms ⊗ on premises ♦♦ **Closed:** 25–26 Dec

Located next to the picturesque village green with a brook running past, this classic English country pub is well worth seeking out. In the 16th century it was used as a cider house, and its timeless interior, full of charm and character, has low ceilings, beams, exposed stone walls and open fires. Nicola Orr-Ewing was once a milliner in London, and she has used her creative talents to transform the accommodation. Husband Archie, born in the next village, helps to maintain a relaxed but efficient atmosphere. The stylish bedrooms are individually decorated and each has a modern bathroom. Some rooms are above the inn (these are full of character and have standard double beds), while others are in a quiet courtyard annexe set well back from the pub. These annexe rooms have king-size beds and are more spacious than those in the main building. All rooms have wireless Internet access and televisions. Tasty meals, using locally sourced and organic produce where possible, are served in the smart restaurant. The Aberdeen Angus beef comes from the family's own farm in a neighbouring village and the vegetables from the Vale of Evesham. The interesting breakfast menu offers a choice of delicious and sustaining dishes.

Recommended in the area

Blenheim Palace; Cotswold Farm Park; Cheltenham Races

1 Woodchester Lodge

★★★★ BB

Address: Southfield Road, North Woodchester, STROUD GL5 5PA
Tel: 01453 872586
Email: anne@woodchesterlodge.co.uk
Website: www.woodchesterlodge.co.uk
Map ref: 2, SO80
Directions: A46 onto Selsley Rd, take 2nd left, 200yds on the left
Rooms: 2 (1 en suite), S £35–£40 D £35–£65
Parking: 4 Notes: ⊗ in bedrooms ⊗ in bedrooms Closed: Xmas

This large, late Victorian house, which was once the home of a timber merchant, is set in the peaceful village of North Woodchester, just a short drive from Stroud. Set in landscaped gardens, it has been sympathetically restored to make the most of its unusual features, and the central hallway has a barrel-vaulted ceiling, a grand stairway, oak-turned banisters and etched glass doors. The spacious bedrooms offer king-size beds, television and hospitality tray, and comfortable chairs have been provided from which to enjoy the peaceful, countryside views. Bathrooms come with large baths, heated towel rails and good toiletries. The colourful gardens here have been well-tended, and guests can sit in the sun on the patio or find a spot in the shade from which to enjoy the tranquil setting; otherwise, the comfortable lounge/dining room offers an open fire and satellite television. Guests are greeted on arrival with home-made cakes and tea, and meals, made by a fully qualified chef, often using fruit and vegetables from the garden, are not to be missed. The delicious dinners are served by candlelight, while the freshly prepared breakfasts might include smoked salmon and scrambled egg made from newly laid eggs.

Recommended in the area

Woodchester Mansion and grounds; WWT Slimbridge; Westonbirt Arboretum

Flamingos at WWT Slimbridge

Beaufort House

★★★★★ BB

Address: Willesley, TETBURY GL8 8QU
Tel: 01666 880444
Email: beauforthouseuk@aol.com
Map ref: 2, ST89
Directions: 4m SW of Tetbury. A433 to Willesley,
House set back from road
Rooms: 4 en suite, S £75 D £89
Parking: 8
Notes: ⊗ on premises ⊗ on premises

Located near the market town of Tetbury, within easy reach of Bath and Bristol, this former staging post and inn built from beautiful local stone, dates back to the 17th century. The bedrooms, all with spacious en suite bathrooms, are elegantly furnished and thoughtfully equipped with colour TV, beverage-making facilities and radio alarm. There is also a deeply comfortable guest lounge. Breakfast, featuring organic items (when available), is served in the dining room around one grand table. A delightful walled garden may be enjoyed in warmer weather throughout the stay.

Recommended in the area

Worcester Cathedral; Blenheim Palace; Berkeley Castle; Westonbirt Arboretum (opposite)

Wesley House

★★★★ ◎◎ RR

Address: High Street, WINCHCOMBE GL54 5LJ
Tel: 01242 602366
Email: enquiries@wesleyhouse.co.uk
Website: www.wesleyhouse.co.uk
Map ref: 3, SP02
Directions: On High Street B4632 between Cheltenham and Broadway
Rooms: 5 en suite, S £65 D £80–£95
Notes: ⊘ ⊗ ♦♦

At the heart of Winchcombe, one of the prettiest little towns in the Cotswolds, Wesley House is an timber-framed house that has been sympathetically restored. Its name recalls the fact that John Wesley, the leader of the Methodist movement, stayed at the house in 1755 and 1779. The double rooms are named after the fields surrounding nearby Sudeley Castle and one has a private terrace overlooking the North Cotswold Edge. All of the bedrooms are individually designed and combine the charm of exposed beams and antique furniture with a stylish décor that features richly coloured fabrics and modern comforts such as en suite bathrooms, TV and telephones. The public areas, too, are pleasing and harmonious, with a unique lighting system that changes colour to suit the mood and stunning floral arrangements created by a world-renowned flower arranger. Another contemporary touch is the air-conditioned glass atrium that now covers the terrace. The food has won a well-deserved reputation that extends far beyond the bounds of the town. The menu is varied and exciting, featuring such complex dishes as grilled noisette of Cornish lamb, merguez, sweet potato purée, piquillo pepper and coriander jus, and the excellent award-winning wine list has a bias towards South Africa. A wine bar, also offering food, is adjoined to the Restaurant and Bed & Breakfast.

Recommended in the area

Broadway; Cotswold Heritage Centre, Northleach; Cheltenham Racecourse; Hailes Abbey (NT)

Wigan Pier

Ash Farm Country House

★★★★ GA

Address: Park Ln, Little Bollington,
ALTRINCHAM WA14 4TJ
Tel: 0161 929 9290
Email: ashfarmbb@yahoo.co.uk
Website: www.ashfarm.co.uk
Map ref: 6, SJ28
Directions: Off A56 beside The Home Pub, 5.5miles
M6 from junct 19
Rooms: 4 (3 en suite), S £60 D £85 **Parking:** 6
Notes: ⊗ on premises ⊗ on premises ✖ under 12yrs
Closed: 22 Dec–5 Jan

This charming 18th century Cheshire farmhouse, set in the heart of National Trust countryside, offers a warm and friendly welcome to its guests. A variety of walks can be enjoyed including the nearby Bridgewater Canal, and Dunham Massey Park, former home of the Earl of Stamford. There are four bedrooms: two doubles and a double/twin room offering en suite bathroom/shower and a double room with private bathroom. All are equipped with toiletries and soft fluffy towels and bath robes, as well as flat-screen digital television with digital Freeview and free Wi-fi internet connection. There are a variety of teas, coffees and fresh fruit available to guests. Breakfasts, freshly cooked to order, range from full English breakfast to continental. There are two local pub/restaurants within walking distance, where guests can benefit from a 10 per cent discount. Both offer a warm, friendly atmosphere and excellent service. Ash Farm Country House is ideally located for the M56 (junction 7), Manchester International Airport and Manchester city centre.

Recommended in the area

Manchester City Centre; Trafford Centre; Dunham Massey (NT); Tatton Park (NT)

Dunham Massey, Altrincham, National Trust

Rock Tavern

★★★★ INN

Address: Rock Tavern, Glossop Road, Marple
Bridge, MARPLE SK6 5RX
Tel: 01457 899354
Email: info@rocktavern.co.uk
Website: www.rocktavern.co.uk
Map ref: 7, SJ98
Directions: Situated midway between Glossop and
Marple on A626
Rooms: 5 en suite, S £45 D £55 **Parking:** 80
Notes: ⊘ on premises ⊗ in bedrooms ♦♦

Situated in an elevated position with splendid views over the valley of the River Etherow, this comfortable inn has been serving thirsty travellers since 1857. Today this family-run business has a popular reputation in the area thanks to its extensive menu featuring local produce and carefully prepared dishes. A choice of bedrooms is available and, although the rooms are compact, all are modern and well equipped. A hearty breakfast is provided.

Recommended in the area

Marple Hall; Stockport Hat Works; Etherow Country Park

The Moorfield Arms

★★★★ INN

Address: Shiloh Road, MELLOR, Stockport SK6 5NE
Tel: 0161 427 1580
Fax: 0161 427 1582
Email: info@moorfieldarms.co.uk
Website: www.moorfieldarms.co.uk
Map ref: 7, SJ98
Directions:1m NE of Mellor. Off A6015 towards
Mellor, right onto Shiloh Rd, 0.3m on left
Rooms: 4 en suite Parking: 100 Notes: ⊗ on
premises ⊗ in bedrooms ♦♦

This 400-year-old farmhouse is located in an elevated position on the border of Cheshire and
Derbyshire and benefits from stunning views over the surrounding countryside and Kinder Scout. It has
been renovated and extended to provide spacious, comfortable public areas and carefully furnished
modern bedrooms in a converted barn. The Moorfield Arms is perfectly placed for visiting the nearby
Peak District National Park, for superb walking and for the numerous attractions in the area. The en
suite boutique bedrooms are equipped with tea-and coffee-making facilities and have a flat screen
colour TV. One room has a four-poster bed and there is also a family room. There is a choice of a
traditional full English or continental breakfast to set you up for the day. The excellent restaurant, a
combination of traditional country inn and gastropub, is open all year round. During the summer months
the garden terrace with fine views is the perfect place to have your meal. Diners can choose from an
extensive à la carte menu, a regularly changing specials board and a lunchtime three-course board.
Local ingredients are used in the preparation of meals where possible. On Sundays a carvery is set up
in the function room. This room is also used for private parties, conferences and special occasions.
Recommended in the area
Pennine Way; Blue John Cavern and Mine, Castleton; Chatsworth; Lyme Park (NT); Buxton

HAMPSHIRE

HMS Victory, Portsmouth

Beech Barns Guest House

★★★★ GA

Address: 61 Wellhouse Road, Beech,
ALTON GU34 4AQ
Tel/Fax: 01420 85575
Email: timsiggs@yahoo.com
Website: www.beechbarns.co.uk
Map ref: 3, SU73
Directions: 1.5m W of Alton. Off A339 towards
Beech, 2nd right onto Wellhouse Rd, 0.5m on left
Rooms: 9 en suite, S £55–£80 D £80–£110
Parking: 12 **Notes:** ⊗ in bedrooms ⋔ allowed on premises ⅰⅼ

This rambling house and barn conversion, believed to date from the early 18th century, is set in its own grounds on the outskirts of Alton, where there are plenty of opportunities for walking and cycling in glorious countryside. The en suite bedrooms are attractively decorated with a blend of contemporary and traditional styles. There is a games and TV room and a separate lounge. Outside a large patio area is perfect for relaxing when enjoying tea and home-made cakes. Dinner is available on request.
Recommended in the area
Jane Austen's House; Gilbert White's House and The Oates Museum; Winchester

The Cottage Lodge

★★★★★ GA

Address: Sway Road, BROCKENHURST SO42 7SH
Tel: 01590 622296
Fax: 01590 623014
Email: enquiries@cottagelodge.co.uk
Website: www.cottagelodge.co.uk
Map ref: 3, SU30
Directions: Off A337 opp Careys Manor Hotel onto
Grigg Ln, 0.25m over x-rds, cottage next to war
memorial
Rooms: 12 en suite, S £50–£120 D £50–£170 **Parking:** 14 **Notes:** ⊗ on premises ⋔ allowed on premises ⅰⅼunder 10yrs **Closed:** Xmas & New Year

Owners David and Christina welcome guests to their cosy 17th-century Cottage Lodge with tea or coffee, served in front of the roaring fire. Brockenhurst is one of the few New Forest settlements where grazing ponies and cattle still have right of way. Conveniently close to the high street and the open forest. The individually furnished bedrooms are en suite and a local New Forest breakfast is served.
Recommended in the area
National Motor Museum, Beaulieu; Exbury Gardens; walking, cycling and horse riding

36 on the Quay

★★★★ ◉◉◉ RR

Address: 47 South Street, EMSWORTH PO10 7EG
Tel: 01243 375592
Website: www.36onthequay.co.uk
Map ref: 3, SU70
Directions: On A259. From A3(M) take junct 2
Rooms: 5 en suite, S £70–£90 D £95 **Parking:** 6
Notes: ⊘ on premises ⊀ allowed in bedrooms ⅙
Closed: 3wks Jan & 1wk late Apr–early May

Located in a picturesque fishing village, this 16th-century house occupies a prime position with far-reaching views over the bay. It is the ideal setting to experience some accomplished and exciting cuisine. The stylish en suite rooms are a joy to relax in with their muted colours and sense of space. Charmingly named Nutmeg, Vanilla, Clove and Cinnamon they have great views and come equipped with colour TV, bathrobes, hospitality tray and toiletries. The lounge and summer terrace are perfect for breakfast or a drink. Centre stage goes to the elegant restaurant with its peaceful pastel shades where you can enjoy expertly cooked dishes, using fresh produce to create flavoursome, quality cuisine.
Recommended in the area
Chichester; Weald and Downland Open Air Museum; Portsmouth Historic Dockyard

Wisteria House

★★★★ BB

Address: 14 Mays Lane, Stubbington,
FAREHAM PO14 2EP
Tel: 01329 511940
Email: info@wisteria-house.co.uk
Website: www.wisteria-house.co.uk
Map ref: 3, SU50
Directions: Exit M27 junct 9, take A27 to Fareham.
Turn right onto B3334, at rdbt turn left onto Mays Ln
Rooms: 2 en suite, S £47 D £62 **Parking:** 2
Notes: ⊘ on premises ⊗ in bedrooms ⅙ under 8yrs

Wisteria House, a comfortable and tastefully decorated guest house, is just a short walk from local amenities and a mile from the beach at Lee-on-the-Solent, with its stunning panoramic views of the Isle of Wight. The charming and comfortable bedrooms, both on the ground floor, are packed with homely touches such as kingsize bed, Freeview colour TV with video recorder, radio alarm, hairdryer and well-stocked hospitality tray. A full English breakfast is served in the pretty dining room.
Recommended in the area
Portsmouth Historic Dockyard; The New Forest; Winchester

Tudorwood Guest House

★★★★ GH

Address: 164 Farnborough Road,
FARNBOROUGH GU14 7JJ
Tel: 01252 541123
Email: info@tudorwood.net
Website: www.tudorwood.net
Map ref: 3, SU85
Directions: Off A325 Farnborough Rd onto Sycamore Rd, next 3 left turns onto Cedar Rd, right onto Old Farnborough Rd
Rooms: 6 en suite, S £45–£55 D £60–£70 **Parking:** 7 **Notes:** ⊗ on premises ⊗ on premises ♦♦
Closed: 24–29 Dec

Melanie and Peter offer a warm, welcome to their 1920s Tudor character property in the centre of town. All rooms have en suite bathrooms, tea and coffee facilities, fridge, hair dryer and TV with video or DVD. Apart from the great breakfast, a wide variety of evening meals or snacks are served in the dining room on request. There is wireless Internet available free of charge.
Recommended in the area
London; Farnborough Air Show; RHS Garden Wisley; Thorpe Park

Alderholt Mill

★★★★ GA

Address: Sandleheath Road,
FORDINGBRIDGE SP6 1PU
Tel: 01425 653130
Fax: 01425 652868
Email: alderholt-mill@zetnet.co.uk
Website: www.alderholtmill.co.uk
Map ref: 3, SU11
Directions: 1m W from Fordingbridge, left at x-rds in Sandleheath, 0.5m over bridge on right
Rooms: 5 (4 en suite), S £27–£32 D £40–£75 **Parking:** 10 **Notes:** ⊗ on premises ♠ allowed on premises ♥♦ under 8yrs

This picturesque group of brick buildings beside a working watermill, is perfectly placed for exploring the New Forest. The rooms all have en suite bathrooms, television, tea and coffee-making facilities and there's a residents' lounge. Delicious home-cooked dinners are served and breakfasts feature bread that's freshly baked using flour from the mill. Three self-catering apartments are also available.
Recommended in the area
Rockbourne Roman Villa; Breamore House; Salisbury Cathedral

Ravensdale

★★★★ BB

Address: 19 St Catherines Road,
HAYLING ISLAND PO11 0HF
Tel: 023 9246 3203
Email: phil.taylor@tayloredprint.co.uk
Website: www.ravensdale-hayling.co.uk
Map ref: 3, SU70
Directions: A3023 at Langstone, cross Hayling
Bridge & continue 3m until mini rdbt, right onto
Manor Rd 1m. Right by Barley Mow onto Station Rd,
2nd left onto St Catherines Rd
Rooms: 3 (2 en suite), S £36–£40 D £58–£66 **Parking:** 4 **Notes:** ⊘ on premises ⊗ on premises
🐾 under 8yrs **Closed:** last 2 wks Dec

A relaxed and friendly environment is created here by hosts Jane and Phil Taylor. The attractive
bedrooms are very comfortable and have thoughtful extras. Food is a highlight, the breakfast is excellent
and you can book a delicious evening meal. Ravensdale is not far from the beach and golf course.
Recommended in the area
Chichester Cathedral; Portsmouth Historic Dockyard; walking on the South Downs

The Rufus House

★★★ GA

Address: Southampton Rd, LYNDHURST SO43 7BQ
Tel: 023 8028 2930
Email: stay@rufushouse.co.uk
Website: www.rufushouse.co.uk
Map ref: 3, SU30
Directions: From Lyndhurst centre onto A35
Southampton Rd, 300yds on left
Rooms: 11 en suite, S £30–£55 D £60–£140
Parking: 15 **Notes:** ⊘ ⊗ 🐾 under 5yrs

Located on the edge of Lyndhurst village, and with acres of exceptional woodland and open heaths for
a front garden, this delightful family-run Victorian property, immaculately maintained and with friendly
staff, is an ideal place from which to explore the New Forest. The brightly decorated bedrooms, two of
which are on the ground floor, are appointed and equipped to a high standard. For special occasions
you can stay in one of the four-poster turret suites. Golf courses, equestrian centres, spas, swimming
pools and the beaches of the South Coast are all within easy reach.
Recommended in the area
New Forest; National Motor Museum Beaulieu; Exbury Gardens; New Forest Otter & Wildlife Park

Temple Lodge

★★★★ GA

Address: 2 Queens Road,
LYNDHURST SO43 7BR
Tel: 023 8028 2392
Fax: 023 8028 4910
Email: templelodge@btinternet.com
Website: www.templelodge-guesthouse.com
Map ref: 3, SU30
Directions: M27 junct 2/3 onto A35 to Ashurst/
Lyndhurst, Temple Lodge on 2nd corner on right,
opposite forest
Rooms: 6 en suite, D £80–£120 Parking: 6 Notes: ⊘ ⊗ in bedrooms ⚄ under 12yrs Wi-fi

Temple Lodge is a beautiful Victorian residence, lovingly restored by its present owners and retaining
many original features, such as the large entrance hall with its fine wooden staircase and beautiful
stained-glass window. The six spacious bedrooms here, including a family suite and a family room,
all have en suite facilities, generous hospitality trays, colour TVs and mini fridges, and there's a
comfortable guest lounge where you can relax and enjoy the surround-sound TV and selection of books
and magazines. Breakfasts are freshly prepared, using local ingredients and offering a wide range
of choices, and are served in the elegant dining room, with its high ceiling and period fireplace and
overlooking the well-stocked gardens. This is an ideal place for a relaxing stay, just a few minutes' walk
from the village of Lyndhurst with its numerous pubs and restaurants, and directly opposite the New
Forest. All in all it makes a superb base for walking, cycling and exploring the surrounding countryside.
The owners, Mike and Teresa, are always pleased to be of service and make every effort to ensure your
stay is a truly memorable experience. Good off-road parking is available.

Recommended in the area

National Motor Museum Beaulieu; Exbury Gardens; Buckler's Hard; Lymington; Bournemouth; Christchurch

Alma Mater

★★★★ BB

Address: 4 Knowland Drive, MILFORD ON SEA, Lymington SO41 0RH

Tel: 01590 642811

Email: bandbalmamater@aol.com

Website: www.newforestalmamater.co.uk

Map ref: 3, SZ29

Directions: A337 at Everton onto B3058 to Milford on Sea. Pass South Lawn Hotel, right onto Manor Rd, 1st left onto Knowland Dr

Rooms: 3 en suite, S £45 D £65–£70 **Parking:** 4 **Notes:** ⊘ ⊗ in bedrooms ⚲ under 15yrs

Eileen and John Haywood enjoy welcoming guests to their beautifully kept home overlooking landscaped gardens in a quiet residential area. It is a good base for exploring the New Forest and coast, the yachting centre of Lymington is close by and the village and the beach are just a walk away. A full four-course or continental breakfast is served in the dining room. The bedrooms are centrally heated and have extras such as radios, tea and coffee provisions, toiletries and bathrobes.

Recommended in the area

Hurst Castle; Exbury Gardens; National Motor Museum, Beaulieu

Quinhay Farmhouse

★★★★ BB

Address: Alton Road, Froxfield, PETERSFIELD GU32 1BZ

Tel: 01730 827183

Fax: 01730 827184

Email: janerothery@hotmail.com

Website: www.quinhaybandb.co.uk

Map ref: 3, SU72

Directions: 4m NW of Petersfield. Off A3 at A272 Junct towards Petersfield, at rdbt exit signed Froxfield/Steep, 3.5m on right

Rooms: 3 (1 en suite), S £30 D £60–£70 **Parking:** 10 **Notes:** ⊘ on premises ⊗ in bedrooms ⚲ under 12yrs **Closed:** 15 Dec–15 Jan

Jane Rothery takes great delight in welcoming you to her delightful farmhouse set in rolling countryside outside Petersfield. The spacious bedrooms have a wealth of thoughtful extras, and the large lounge has comfy sofas and access to a terrace. Quinhay is popular with walkers and cyclists.

Recommended in the area

Winchester; Portsmouth Historic Dockyard; Jane Austen's House, Chawton

Moortown Lodge

★★★★ GA

Address: 244 Christchurch Road,
RINGWOOD BH24 3AS
Tel: 01425 471404
Fax: 01425 476527
Email: enquiries@moortownlodge.co.uk
Website: www.moortownlodge.co.uk
Map ref: 3, SU10
Directions: 1m S of Ringwood. Off A31 at Ringwood
onto B3347, signs to Sopley, Lodge next to David
Lloyd Health Club
Rooms: 7 en suite, S £67.50 D £84–£94 Parking: 9 Notes: ⊗ ✈ in bedrooms ♦♦

Moortown Lodge is a charming, family run Georgian property in the attractive market town of Ringwood, the western gateway to the New Forest, where there is a wide range of unusual shops, traditional pubs and lovely restaurants. It offers guests a warm welcome and luxury grade B&B accommodation with many of the features found in a good class hotel. The seven elegantly furnished non-smoking, en-suite rooms, include one with a romantic four-poster bed and two easy access ground floor rooms. All suites have digital TV and DVD, free broadband connection and free national direct-dial phones. Generous traditional breakfasts are cooked to order with lighter and vegetarian breakfast options available. Wherever possible fresh New Forest produce is used in the cooking. The peace and tranquillity of the open forest as well as the unspoilt water meadows of the River Avon are only minutes away. Moortown Lodge is the ideal stopover for business people as well as an excellent base for touring and leisure visitors. There are special arrangements for guests wishing to use the bar, restaurant and outstanding recreational facilities at the adjacent private David Lloyd Leisure Club.

Recommended in the area

Bournemouth; New Forest National Park; Stonehenge

Valley View

★★★★ BB

Address: Cowpits Lane, North Poulner,
RINGWOOD BH24 3JX
Tel: 01425 475855
Fax: 01425 472542
Email: es-brown@tiscali.co.uk
Map ref: 3, SU10
Directions: A31 E 0.75m, E of Ringwood. Left to
Hangelsley, 1st right 0.5m to x-rds, 75yds on right
Rooms: 2 private facilities, S £30–£32 D £56–£60
Parking: 5 **Notes:** ⊘ in bedrooms ⊗ on premises ⅰ↟

This modern establishment has easy access to the New Forest and the coast. The nearby town of Ringwood is attractive with a lively Wednesday street market and many restaurants and pubs. The house has just two rooms, with only one room let at a time; each is well furnished and decorated. The breakfast, featuring delicious home-made preserves, is served in the family dining room. A home-cooked dinner is available by arrangement and should be ordered before 4pm.

Recommended in the area
New Forest National Park; Salisbury Cathedral; Dorset Heavy Horse Centre

Old Drapery Guesthouse

★★★★ BB

Address: Middle Wallop, STOCKBRIDGE SO20 8HN
Tel/Fax: 01264 781301
Email: amanda@olddraperyguesthouse.co.uk
Website: www.olddraperyguesthouse.co.uk
Map ref: 3, SU33
Directions: A303 onto A343, turn right at x-rds by
George Inn, 2nd on left
Rooms: 4 en suite, S £40 D £80–£90
Parking: 5 **Notes:** ⊘ ⊗ ⅰ↟ under 8yrs
Closed: 24–26 & 31 Dec–1 Jan

This Georgian family home is set just off the main road in mature gardens. Hospitality and service are notable here, and the pretty en suite bedrooms come with Sky television and many other thoughtful extras such as bathrobes. Guests are welcome to leaf through the many books in the guest lounge or take a Drapery cream tea. A host of breakfast choices, including smoked salmon and scrambled eggs, are served in the dining room or, weather permitting, on the patio. Good off-street parking is available.

Recommended in the area
Salisbury Cathedral; The Museum of Army Flying; Hillier's Arboretum

New Forest ponies, New Forest National Park

Dormy House

★★★★ GA

Address: 21 Barnes Lane, Sarisbury, WARSASH,
Southampton SO31 7DA
Tel: 01489 572626
Fax: 01489 573370
Email: dormyhousehotel@warsash.globalnet.co.uk
Website: www.dormyhousehotel.net
Map ref: 3, SU40
Directions: Off A27 at Sarisbury Green onto Barnes Ln, house
1m on right
Rooms: 12 en suite, S £55–£65 D £70–£85 **Parking:** 18
Notes: ⊘ on premises ⊗ on premises ♦♦

Situated not far from the River Hamble and the Solent and with good access to major routes, this tranquil Victorian house has a pretty garden and patio. Indoors are all the expected comforts, including an attractive dining room . All the bedrooms have hospitality trays and some have spacious seating areas. The rooms on the ground floor have access to the garden.

Recommended in the area

New Forest National Park; Isle of Wight; Southampton Boat Show

The Old Vine

★★★ INN

ddress: 8 Great Minster St, WINCHESTER SO23 9HA
el: 01962 854616
mail: reservations@oldvinewinchester.com
/ebsite: www.oldvinewinchester.com
Map ref: 3, SU42
Directions: M3 junct 11 towards St Cross, turn right at Green
Man Pub, left onto Symonds St
Rooms: 5 en suite, S £110–£150 D £120–£160 Notes: ⊘ ⊗ ⫯⫯

Set in the heart of historic Winchester this charming 18th-century inn boasts five guest rooms, offering a superior level of comfort in stylish yet warm and restful surroundings. Taking the unique period features of each room into consideration, the design is an elegant mix of antique and contemporary – finely crafted Arts and Crafts, Georgian and Art Deco furniture sits alongside the opulent fabrics and wallpapers of leading designers. All bedrooms feature ensuite bathrooms with power showers, deep pocket-sprung mattresses, crisp Egyptian cotton bed linen, fluffy towels and bathrobes, digital flat-screen TVs, broadband internet access, mini-fridges, room safes and beverage-making facilities. Relax over a glass of fine wine or a pint of Hampshire real ale in our cosy oak-beamed bar or on the flower-filled patio before enjoying a splendid lunch or supper in the relaxed, informal surroundings of our award-winning restaurant, where the menu ranges from honest, tasty pub food to more elaborate fare, complemented by a specials blackboard featuring fresh fish and seasonal dishes. Come morning, freshly baked bread, free-range eggs, Hampshire sausages, juices, fresh fruit, tempting pastries and locally produced preserves are the ingredients for a breakfast, taken either in your room or in the restaurant – the perfect prelude to a exploration of England's ancient capital city.

Recommended in the area

Winchester Cathedral, King Arthur's Round Table, Jane Austen's House, Winchester Military Museums

Ross-on-Wye

Brick House Farm

★★★★ 🏠 BB

Address: ADFORTON, Leintwardine SY7 0NF
Tel: 01568 770870
Email: info@adforton.com
Website: www.adforton.com
Map ref: 2, SO47
Directions: On A4110 in Adforton village. Opposite St Andrew's Church
Rooms: 2, S £40–£60 D £70–£75 **Parking:** 4
Notes: ⊗ on premises ⊗ in bedrooms 🐾 under 12yrs

Brick House Farm is a luxurious bed and breakfast situated close to Ludlow, in the beautiful Welsh Marches. The house, built in the mid-15th century, was renovated in 2006/7 to create a very comfortable and relaxing environment for a short break. The two bedrooms are off a private landing that has a wealth of original oak beams. Each bedroom has its own modern bathroom, each with a wide deep bath and power shower. Outside are a garden and terrace that enjoy stunning views over the unspoiled Teme Valley and the Welsh Hills. The visitor's book is full of praise for attention to detail in every area of the guest experience. The warmth of the welcome at Brick House Farm is a major strength, while the AA Breakfast Award gives further evidence of the quality and range of produce available here. Being located in the Welsh Marches means that some of the country's finest meats can be presented with the minimum of food miles, and the surrounding 10-acre smallholding is home to a flock of free-range chickens that contribute the eggs for breakfast. All breakfasts are cooked to order, and the extensive menu caters for most dietary preferences, including vegetarian, dairy and wheat free, and even vegan.

Recommended in the area

Ludlow town; Stokesay Castle; many sites of the Roman and Bronze Ages

Linton Brook Farm

★★★★ BB

Address: Malvern Road, Bringsty,
BROMYARD WR6 5TR
Tel: 01885 488875
Fax: 01885 488875
Map ref: 2, SO65
Directions: Off A44 1.5m E of Bromyard onto B4220
signed Malvern. Farm 0.5m on left
Rooms: 3 (2 en suite), S £27.50–£40 D £70–£100
Parking: 12 **Notes:** ⊘ on premises ⊗ in bedrooms
👫 **Closed:** Xmas & New Year

Sheila and Roger Steeds's 400-year old farmhouse stands on an ancient site. With such a history behind it, this charming house is filled with atmosphere, fostered by the inglenook fireplace and enormous beam in the dining room, and the wood-burning stove in the sitting room. Bedrooms are spacious and homely. At breakfast, enjoy Sheila's tasty home-smoked food, and afterwards wander through the 68-acre grassland farm with access to wonderful scenic walks.

Recommended in the area

Brockhampton Estate (NT); Elgar Birthplace Museum; Berrington Hall (NT)

Little Hegdon Farm House

★★★★ BB

Address: Hegdon Hill, Pencombe,
BROMYARD HR7 4SL
Tel: 01885 400263
Email: howardcolegrave@hotmail.com
Website: www.littlehegdonfarmhouse.com
Map ref: 2, SO65
Directions: 4m SW of Bromyard. From Bromyard to
Pencombe, 1.5m towards Risbury, at top of Hegdon
Hill down farm lane for 500yds
Rooms: 2 en suite, S £35 D £60 **Parking:** 4 **Notes:** ⊘ in bedrooms ⊗ in bedrooms 👫

A 17th-century former farmhouse, Little Hegdon lies in the heart of Herefordshire with clear views over farmland, cider orchards and hop yards to the Malvern and Cotswold hills. Restored to provide high standards of comfort, the period character of the house survives in the open fires and plenty of exposed oak beams. Facilities include a drawing room and attractive garden. There is one double and one twin room with hairdryers and tea and coffee facilities. Children and pets are welcome.

Recommended in the area

Lower Brockhampton Estate (NT); historic towns of Hereford and Ledbury; Worcester

Church Farm

★★★★ FH

Address: Coddington, LEDBURY HR8 1JJ
Tel: 01531 640271
Website: www.dexta.co.uk
Map ref: 2, SO73
Directions: Coddington is north of Ledbury off the Bromyard Road
Rooms: 3 (2 en suite) **Parking:** 6 **Notes:** ⊗ 🐾 allowed in bedrooms 👫 **Closed:** 16 Dec–15 Jan

Church Farm provides comfortable and peaceful accommodation at a lovely sixteenth-century Grade II listed farmhouse in the quiet hamlet of Coddington, set in the depths of rural Herefordshire. This small working farm boasts a beautiful garden and rural views. Inside, there is a comfortable TV lounge with an inglenook fireplace – log fires are lit on chilly days – and the comfortable bedrooms are maintained to a high standard. Aga-cooked breakfasts are served around the shared kitchen table or in the dining room, and as much as possible is home-made. There is much to do here, with many fine walks around the hamlet, and places of interest just a short drive away.

Recommended in the area

Malvern Hills; Eastnor Castle; Hampton Court Gardens, Leominster

Hills Farm

★★★★★ 🏠 FH

Address: Leysters, LEOMINSTER HR6 0HP
Tel: 01568 750205
Email: j.conolly@btconnect.com
Website: www.thehillsfarm.co.uk
Map ref: 2, SO45
Directions: Off A4112 Leominster to Tenbury Wells, on edge of Leysters
Rooms: 3 en suite, S £35–£45 D £66–£72
Parking: 8 **Notes:** ⊗ on premises ⊗ on premises 👫 under 12yrs **Closed:** Nov–Feb

On high ground, with panoramic views over the Teme Valley, this 15th-century farmhouse is a splendid base for exploring the Welsh Marches. The accommodation is located in beautifully converted barns; each room has its own front door, en suite bathroom, TV, radio and hospitality tray. Guests head to the main farmhouse for breakfast, which is served at separate tables. There's also a pleasant sitting room with lots of reading matter, including maps and guidebooks for planning the next day out.

Recommended in the area

Berrington Hall (NT); Hereford Cathedral and city; Burton Court

Cwm Craig Farm

★★★★ FH

Address: LITTLE DEWCHURCH HR2 6PS
Tel: 01432 840250
Fax: 01432 840250
Map ref: 2, SO53
Directions: Off A49 into Little Dewchurch, turn right in village, Cwm Craig 1st farm on left
Rooms: 3 en suite, S £27–£29 D £50–£54
Parking: 6 Notes: ⊘ ⊗ ♦♦

Cwm Craig Farm is midway between Hereford and Ross-on-Wye and stands on the edge of a village surrounded by superb countryside. The Georgian property retains many original features and offers spacious accommodation furnished with fine period pieces. The bedrooms are all en suite and include two doubles and a family room. Guests have access to their rooms all day, and hospitality trays are provided. Home-cooked breakfasts are served in the dining room and morning room around large tables, and you can relax in the sitting room or the games room with its three-quarter-size snooker/pool table and dartboard. Pets cannot be accommodated.

Recommended in the area

Hereford Cathedral and city; Forest of Dean; Wye Valley

Lea House

★★★★ GA

Address: Lea, ROSS-ON-WYE HR9 7JZ
Tel/Fax: 01989 750652
Email: enquiries@leahouse.co.uk
Website: www.leahouse.co.uk
Map ref: 2, SO52
Directions: 4m SE of Ross on A40, in Lea village
Rooms: 3 (2 en suite), S £37–£45 D £60–£70
Parking: 4 Notes: ⊘ ♦ ♦♦

This sixteenth-century home and former coaching inn makes a good base for exploring the Forest of Dean and the Wye Valley. The atmosphere is relaxed and the house has been beautifully refurbished, with exposed oak beams, inglenook fireplace, imaginative decor, and eclectic pieces from owner Caroline's previous life in the film industry, all adding to the charm. The pretty bedrooms have en suite bathrooms and provide a selection of toiletries and fluffy towels. Tasty, locally sourced breakfasts include freshly squeezed orange juice, home-made breads and imaginative vegetarian options. Dinner can be taken with prior notice. Guests are welcome to make use of the charming walled garden.

Recommended in the area

The Forest of Dean; Dean Forest Steam Railway; Hereford Cathedral

Lumleys

★★★★ BB

Address: Kern Bridge, Bishopswood,
ROSS-ON-WYE HR9 5QT
Tel: 01600 890040
Email: helenmattis@tiscali.co.uk
Website: www.thelumleys.co.uk
Map ref: 2, SO52
Directions: Off A40 onto B4229 at Goodrich, over Kern Bridge, right at Inn On The Wye, 400yds opp picnic ground
Rooms: 3 en suite, D £65–£75 **Parking:** 15
Notes: ⊗ on premises ⌘ allowed on premises ⬦

Its setting, on the banks of the River Wye, makes Lumleys a favourite with those who appreciate the unspoilt countryside of this corner of Herefordshire. The mellow stone Victorian house retains much of its original character, aided by the period pieces and ornaments that adorn the public areas. These include two sitting rooms and a dining room where breakfasts and early evening meals are served.

Recommended in the area

Symonds Yat; Forest of Dean; Goodrich Castle

Thatch Close

★★★★ GA

Address: Llangrove, ROSS-ON-WYE HR9 6EL
Tel: 01989 770300
Email: info@thatchclose.co.uk
Website: www.thatchclose.com
Map ref: 2, SO52
Directions: Off A40 at Symonds Yat West/Whitchurch junct to Llangrove, right at x-rds after Post Office, Thatch Close 0.6m on left
Rooms: 3 en suite, S £40–£45 D £70–£80 **Parking:** 8 **Notes:** ⊗ on premises ⌘ allowed in bedrooms ⬦

The sturdy farmhouse, dating from 1760, is full of character and has a welcoming atmosphere. It stands in 13 acres of colourful gardens, ancient hedges and mature trees, the habitat of badgers, foxes, owls and an African Grey parrot named Aku. The homely bedrooms are individually furnished, and are all en suite. A wholesome breakfast and dinner are served in the dining room, and the leather sofas in the lounge are a pleasant place to retire after dinner.

Recommended in the area

Symonds Yat; Forest of Dean; Monmouth

Trecilla Farm

★★★★★ BB

Address: Llangarron, ROSS-ON-WYE
HR9 6NQ
Tel: 01989 770647
Email: info@trecillafarm.co.uk
Website: www.trecillafarm.co.uk
Map ref: 2, SO52
Directions: A40 onto A4137 to Hereford. 2m x-rds, left signed Llangarron. 1m Llangarron sign, Trecilla Farm 2nd drive on right

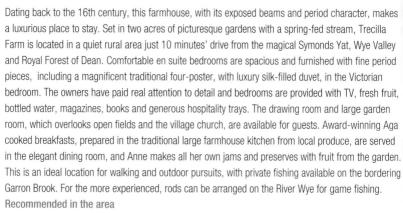

Rooms: 3 en suite, D £80–£110 **Parking:** 7 **Notes:** ⊘ on premises ⊗ on premises ♦ under 16yrs
Closed: 23 Dec–2 Jan

Dating back to the 16th century, this farmhouse, with its exposed beams and period character, makes a luxurious place to stay. Set in two acres of picturesque gardens with a spring-fed stream, Trecilla Farm is located in a quiet rural area just 10 minutes' drive from the magical Symonds Yat, Wye Valley and Royal Forest of Dean. Comfortable en suite bedrooms are spacious and furnished with fine period pieces, including a magnificent traditional four-poster, with luxury silk-filled duvet, in the Victorian bedroom. The owners have paid real attention to detail and bedrooms are provided with TV, fresh fruit, bottled water, magazines, books and generous hospitality trays. The drawing room and large garden room, which overlooks open fields and the village church, are available for guests. Award-winning Aga cooked breakfasts, prepared in the traditional large farmhouse kitchen from local produce, are served in the elegant dining room, and Anne makes all her own jams and preserves with fruit from the garden. This is an ideal location for walking and outdoor pursuits, with private fishing available on the bordering Garron Brook. For the more experienced, rods can be arranged on the River Wye for game fishing.

Recommended in the area

Symonds Yat; Wye Valley; Forest of Dean

The River Wye at Symonds Yat

Garth Cottage

★ ★ ★ ★ GA

Address: SYMONDS YAT (EAST),
Ross-on-Wye HR9 6JL
Tel/Fax: 01600 890364
Email: val.eden@virgin.net
Website: www.garthcottage-symondsyat.com
Map ref: 2, SO51
Directions: Off A40 at Little Chef, Whitchurch, signs
for Symonds Yat East
Rooms: 4 en suite D £72 **Parking:** 9 **Notes:** ⊘ on
premises ⊗ on premises 🧒 under 12yrs **Closed:** Nov–Mar

The Eden family's warm hospitality and attention to the comfort of their guests is evident in this attractive and well-maintained 18th-century house on the banks of the River Wye. As well as its own boat mooring, it offers views over three counties, and provides an ideal base from which to enjoy the local countryside and wildlife; for the more energetic, canoeing, climbing and riding are all available. The bedrooms are well equipped, and breakfast and dinner are served in the conservatory-dining room.
Recommended in the area
Hereford, Worcester and Gloucester cathedrals; Welsh Marches; Black Mountains

Norton House

★★★★ 🏛 🍽 GA

Address: Whitchurch, SYMONDS YAT [WEST] HR9 6DJ
Tel: 01600 890046
Email: su@norton.wyenet.co.uk
Website: www.norton-house.com
Map ref: 2, SO51
Directions: 0.5m N of Symonds Yat. Off A40 into Whitchurch village and left onto Old Monmouth Rd
Rooms: 3 en suite, S £45–£50 D £60–£80 **Parking:** 5
Notes: ⊗ 🐎 allowed on premises 👶 under 12yrs
Closed: 25–26 Dec

Su and Richard Jackson provide a home from home for their guests here at Norton House, who return time and again to enjoy the hospitality and personal attention they receive. Situated in the Wye Valley, this listed building, over 300 years old and built from locally quarried stone, has oak beams, inglenook fireplaces, wood-burning stoves, flagstone floors and heaps of period charm, yet it provides all the modern comforts guests could want, including internet access in the reading lounge. New arrivals are greeted with tea, coffee and home-made cakes. The bedrooms, including a four-poster room, are individually styled and furnished for maximum comfort, with mineral water and fresh flowers in each. Excellent and imaginative meals, as well as packed lunches if requested, are prepared from local or home-grown produce where possible, and guests are invited to enter the spirit of the sustainable approach during their stay. Optional evening meals are served by candlelight, creating a wonderfully romantic atmosphere. The Norton House Speciality Breakfast menu includes choices such as kedgeree, stuffed buckwheat pancakes and piperade, as well as more traditional options, all accompanied by home-made bread, croissants and preserves.

Recommended in the area

Symonds Yat; Goodrich Castle; Forest of Dean

Goodrich Castle, overlooking the River Wye

Portland House Guest House

★★★★ GA

Address: WHITCHURCH, Ross-on-Wye HR9 6DB
Tel: 01600 890757
Email: info@portlandguesthouse.co.uk
Website: www.portlandguesthouse.co.uk
Map ref: 2, SO51
Directions: Off A40 between Monmouth and Ross on Wye. Take turn for Whitchurch/Symonds Yat W
Rooms: 6 en suite, S £40–£55 D £59–£90
Parking: 6 **Notes:** ⊗ ⊗ ♦ **Closed:** 25–26 Dec & Jan

This impressive dwelling dates in part from the 17th century. The comfortable bedrooms, including a large family suite, a ground-floor accessibility bedroom, and a four-poster suite, all have many thoughtful extras. Guests can make use of the Boot Room, the laundry, the terrace garden area and the attractive lounge. Breakfast, cooked on the Aga, includes local ingredients, home-made bread and home-made preserves and is served around the shared dining table, or at a separate table in the elegant dining room. With prior arrangement, evening meals can be provided.

Recommended in the area

Forest of Dean; Ross-on-Wye; Tintern Abbey

HERTFORDSHIRE

Hatfield House

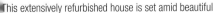

Farmhouse B&B

★★★★★ BB

Address: Hawkins Grange Farm, Hawkins Hall Lane,
DATCHWORTH, Knebworth SG3 6TF
Tel/Fax: 01438 813369
Email: mail@hawkinsgrangefarm.com
Website: www.hawkinsgrangefarm.com
Map ref: 3, TL21
Directions: A1(M) junct 7 onto A602 (Hertford). From Bragbury End onto Bragbury Ln, 2m on left after phone box
Rooms: 3 (2 en suite), S £35–£45 D £70 **Parking:** 8 **Notes:** ⊘ on premises ⊗ on premises ⋔

This extensively refurbished house is set amid beautiful countryside, yet is within easy reach of Hertford, Stevenage and Welwyn Garden City. The tastefully designed bedrooms are comfortably furnished and come with an abundance of thoughtful accessories. All have good views over the open countryside. Jane's locally sourced breakfasts offer Full English, vegetarian (and vegan) or continental choices, including 'Braughing' sausages and Datchworth honey.

Recommended in the area

Hertford; Datchworth Museum; Welwyn

Rushen

★★★★★ BB

Address: Mount Pleasant, HERTFORD HEATH
SG13 7QY
Tel: 01992 581254
Fax: 01992 534737
Email: wilsonamwell@btinternet.com
Map ref: 3, TL31
Directions: From A10 exit at Hertford slip road, 1st left onto B1502. 1st right at top of lane, bear left at village green. Rushen on left at end of green

Rooms: 2 (1 en suite), S £35–£40 D £60–£70 **Parking:** 3 **Notes:** ⊘ ⊗⋔ **Closed:** 22 Dec–3 Jan

Rushen is a well-presented detached house with one twin and one double room – both comfortable and well appointed, with a range of thoughtful extras such as TV/DVD, hairdryer, wireless internet connection, dressing gowns and slippers and well-stocked tea and coffee-making facilities, including mineral water and chocolates. Breakfast offers a good range of choices, based on local and organic produce when possible.

Recommended in the area

Hertford Castle; Henry Moore Foundation; Forge Museum and Victorian Cottage Garden

ISLE OF WIGHT

The Needles

Blandings

★★★★ BB

Address: Horringford, ARRETON,
Nr Newport PO30 3AP

Tel: 01983 865720

Fax: 01983 862099

Email: robin.oulton@horringford.com

Website: www.horringford.com/bedandbreakfast.htm

Map ref: 3, SZ58

Directions: S through Arreton (B3056), 300yds on left signed Horringford Gardens. Take U turn to left, then turn right. Blandings on left

Rooms: 1 en suite, D £60 Parking: 3 Notes: ⊘ on premises ⅍ allowed in bedrooms ⅟

Set within a small group of farm buildings, Blandings has a delightful rural setting with pleasant views of the downs. On warm sunny days its wooden sun deck is a good place to enjoy breakfast or relax with an evening sundowner. The cycle route from Cowes to Sandown (A23) runs past the front gate and cycles and equipment are available for hire in the village and can be delivered ready for use.

Recommended in the area

Osborne House; beaches at Sandown, Shanklin and Ryde; Bembridge; Newport

Chale Bay Farm

★★★★★ GA

Address: Military Road, CHALE PO38 2JF

Tel: 01983 730950

Fax: 01983 730395

Email: info@chalebayfarm.co.uk

Website: www.chalebayfarm.co.uk

Map ref: 3, SZ47

Directions: In village on A3055, nr St Andrew's Church

Rooms: 8 en suite Parking: 50 Notes: ⊗ in bedrooms ⅟

Situated on National Trust coastline with uninterrupted views of the Needles and Tennyson Downs, Chale Bay Farm is a tranquil place to unwind. The spacious bedrooms are all on the ground floor, around a courtyard with a floodlit Japanese-style water garden. The rooms are all en suite with king-size beds, and equipped to a high standard including tea and coffee facilities and hairdryers, several have their own private patio. Before setting off to explore the island, enjoy a hearty home-cooked breakfast, served at individual tables dressed with fresh flowers in the pleasant dining room.

Recommended in the area

Blackgang Chine; Freshwater Bay; Dinosaur Farm

The Needles, Headon Warren

Braunstone House

★★★★ ⇔ GA

Address: 33 Lugley Street, NEWPORT PO30 5ET
Tel: 01983 822994
Fax: 01983 526300
Email: lugleys@uwclub.net
Website: www.isleofwight.com
Map ref: 2, SZ58
Directions: Just off Newport High Street
Rooms: 5 (4 en suite), S £65–£80 D £85–£95
Notes: ⊗ in bedrooms ⊗ in bedrooms ♦♦

The renovation of this Grade II listed building, just a stone's throw from Newport town centre, has carefully retained its original Georgian charm. The dedicated staff do an excellent job, and the elegant, good-size bedrooms have individual character and are equipped with many extras. The building houses a popular brasserie, Lugley's, where flagstone floors and a modern aspect set the scene for a choice of tasty, well-prepared meals – there's a bar lounge where you can sit while you make your choice. In summer, meals can be served in the sheltered gardens.

Recommended in the area

Carisbrooke Castle; Robin Hill; Osborne House

The Enchanted Manor

★ ★ ★ ★ ★ GA

Address: Sandrock Road, NITON
PO38 2NG
Tel: 01983 730215
Email: info@enchantedmanor.co.uk
Website: www.enchantedmanor.co.uk
Map ref: 3, SZ57
Directions: Niton is west of Ventnor on the A0355.
In the town, follow the high street to Sandrock Road
Rooms: 7 en suite **Parking:** 15 **Notes:** ⊘ on
premises ⊗ in bedrooms 🐾

The Enchanted Manor is a delightful, friendly establishment providing top-class facilities but without the formal atmosphere of some larger hotels. Enviably set within walking distance of the sea, this unique B&B was inspired by the artist Josephine Wall, whose paintings adorn the manor along with crystal chandeliers and sumptuous furnishings. Above all, the ambience is tranquil and very relaxing, thanks in part to the stunning surroundings, overlooking the coastline at the most southern point of the island. All of the suites here are beautifully appointed, and most feature ornate four-posters and have their own lounge and dining area, with thoughtful extras such as LCD TV, DVD, fridge/minibar and gourmet food basket provided. The en suite bathrooms boast clawfoot baths, jet-spray showers, fluffy robes and luxury toiletries. Outside, the private gardens and enchanting woodlands are the perfect place to enjoy the special fairy grand high teas or you can swim in the large open-air pool. On balmy evenings, guests can watch the stars from the spa while sipping champagne. Owner Maggie provides a delicious array of gourmet breakfasts prepared from local produce in the Badger Watch dining room, and a variety of health and beauty treatments are available in the Zodiac suite.

Recommended in the area

Haven St Steam Railway; Brading Experience; Ventnor Botanic Gardens

The Lawns

★★★★ GA

Address: 72 Broadway,
SANDOWN PO36 9AA
Tel: 01983 402549
Email: lawnshotel@aol.com
Website: www.lawnshotelisleofwight.co.uk
Map ref: 3, SZ58
Directions: On A3055 N of town centre
Rooms: 13 en suite Parking: 15
Notes: ⊗ on premises ⊗ on premises ♦♦

A warm welcome always awaits you at the Lawns, which has been lovingly upgraded by owners Nick and Stella to provide every home comfort. The hotel, built in 1865 and offering ample parking, stands in its own southwest-facing gardens. Situated in the pleasing area of Sandown, it is just a short walk away from a blue-flag beach, public transport and the town centre, with its restaurants and shops, and is an ideal base from which to explore the rest of the island. Other local attractions on offer include the pier, go-karting, crazy golf and the Tiger and Big Cat Sanctuary, as well as many opportunities to take part in watersports. The hotel has a comfortable lounge, with freeview television and a selection of games available, as well as a bar. Evening meals, available by arrangement, and breakfast are served in the bright dining room. Service is friendly and attentive, and the bedrooms, three of which are on the ground floor and one of which has a four-poster bed, are comfortably equipped with colour television and hospitality trays. The Lawns is a very family-friendly establishment and has a wide range of equipment for babies and small children available. In addition to cots and highchairs there are sterilisers, baby monitors and disposable bibs, making a weekend or holiday with small children so much easier.

Recommended in the area

Isle of Wight Zoo; Dinosaur Isle; Sandown Pier

Carisbrooke Castle

The Belmont

★★★★ GA

Address: 8 Queens Road, SHANKLIN PO37 6AN
Tel: 01983 867875
Email: enquiries@belmont-iow.co.uk
Website: www.belmont-iow.co.uk
Map ref: 3, SZ58
Directions: From Sandown (on A3055), half left at
fiveways lights signed Ventnor. Hotel 400 mtrs on
right, opp St Saviour's church
Rooms: 13 en suite, S £31–£61 D £54–£84
Parking: 9 **Notes:** ⊗ on premises ⊗ on premises ⅙ under 5yrs **Closed:** Nov–Feb

This imposing Victorian residence offers friendly personal service and a relaxing atmosphere. The
secluded garden is an attractive suntrap with a swimming pool heated in summer. Bedrooms mostly face
the sea or the garden and are well appointed, some having king-size or four-poster beds. Full English,
continental or vegetarian breakfasts are served in the elegant dining room overlooking the garden and an
evening bar opens onto the colonial-style veranda. Car ferry-inclusive breaks can be arranged.

Recommended in the area

Shanklin old village; Osborne House; The Needles

Foxhills

★★★★★ GA

Address: 30 Victoria Avenue,
SHANKLIN PO37 6LS
Tel: 01983 862329
Fax: 01983 866666
Email: info@foxhillsofshanklin.co.uk
Website: www.foxhillsofshanklin.co.uk
Map ref: 3, SZ58
Directions: A3020 from Shanklin centre towards
Newport, Foxhills 450yds on left
Rooms: 8 en suite, S £59–£108 D £88–£118 **Parking:** 13
Notes: ⊘ on premises ⊗ on premises ⚸ under 14yrs
Closed: 3–31 Jan

Every effort is made to pamper guests at this superbly maintained establishment. It is set in beautiful gardens just a short walk from Shanklin town and Old Village with its multitude of restaurants and pubs, the Chine and the downs. Hospitality is exemplary, and you are welcomed with tea and chocolates on arrival. There are high levels of comfort in the en suite bedrooms, with DVD/CD players (plus comprehensive library of DVDs), direct-dial telephones, hairdryers and refreshment trays all provided. Wi-fi is also available. For that special occasion the four-poster Osborne suite has a touch of modernised Victorian luxury. Bathrooms are beautifully fitted with quality units, and furnished with luxury towels, dressing gowns and toiletries. The large whirlpool spa is free and available for private sessions. Health and beauty treatments are relaxing options, or else take a drink or afternoon tea in front of the log fire. Comprehensive room packs are supplied with routes for local walks, bike rides and car tours.

Recommended in the area

Shanklin Chine; Carisbrooke Castle; Osborne House; Bembridge Down

The Grange

★★★★ GA

Address: 9 Eastcliff Road,
SHANKLIN PO37 6AA
Tel: 01983 867644
Fax: 01983 865537
Email: jenni@thegrangebythesea.com
Website: www.thegrangebythesea.com
Map ref: 3, SZ58
Directions: Off A3055 High St
Rooms: 17 (14 en suite), S £69–£77 D £88–£104
Parking: 8 **Notes:** ⊘ on premises ⊗ in bedrooms ♿

Nestled in the heart of Shanklin's Old Village, and only moments from its long, sandy beach, The Grange is the perfect retreat from the hectic pace of modern life. It enjoys a tranquil yet convenient setting and its atmosphere is friendly and relaxed. Built in the 1820s and recently renovated throughout, The Grange has original features such as the ornate, carved fireplace in the lounge which is now complemented by a collection of paintings and sculptures ranging in style from bold and striking to classic and elegant. The beautifully presented bedrooms are decorated in natural tones that mirror the surrounding environment and newly fitted power showers and complementary luxury toiletries ensure a great start to each day. In addition, there are a wide range of inspirational courses and activities available including yoga, massage and beauty treatments, coastline walks, creative writing and art. The Grange meets high standards of cuisine, using the freshest ingredients, local and organic where possible. Breakfast and morning coffee can be taken outside in the garden in fine weather.

Recommended in the area

Shanklin Chine; Tiger Sanctuary in Sandown; Brading Roman Villa

Compton Bay

Hayes Barton

★★★★ ⇔ GA

Address: 7 Highfield Road, SHANKLIN PO37 6PP
Tel: 01983 867747
Email: williams.2000@virgin.net
Website: www.hayesbarton.co.uk
Map ref: 3, SZ58
Directions: A3055 onto A3020 Victoria Av, 3rd left
Rooms: 9 en suite, S £50–£55 D £100–£110
Parking: 8 **Notes:** ⊗ in bedrooms ⋔ allowed in
bedrooms ⋔ **Closed:** Nov–Mar

Hayes Barton has the relaxed atmosphere of a family home in a quiet area of Shanklin, with the Old
Village, beach and promenade all nearby. The well-equipped bedrooms come with colour TV and tea
and coffee-making facilities. There is also a restful lounge, with TV and DVD player, and a cosy licensed
bar. Guests are also invited to make use of the secluded garden, which is a sun trap in summer.
Generous breakfasts and good, home-cooked evening meals, served from a daily-changing menu
based on freshly prepared seasonal produce, are recommended.
Recommended in the area
Brading Roman Villa; Donkey Sanctuary; Botanic Gardens; Amazon World

Leeds Castle

Bay Tree Broadstairs

★★★★ GA

Address: 12 Eastern Esplanade, BROADSTAIRS CT10 1DR
Tel: 01843 862502
Fax: 01843 860589
Map ref: 4, TR36
Directions: A255 onto Rectory Rd & Eastern Esplanade
Rooms: 10 en suite, S £40–£65 D £80–£90 **Parking:** 11
Notes: ⊗ on premises ⊗ on premises ✟under 10yrs
Closed: Xmas & New Year

This family-run establishment is situated on an elevated position
overlooking East Cliff, with panoramic views over the English
Channel, yet is close to the town centre with all its amenities.
Inside, the attractive en suite bedrooms, one of which is on the ground floor, are well equipped with
colour TV, hairdryer and tea and coffee-making facilities, and some have their own balcony with a sea
view. There is a comfortable lounge bar, and a good breakfast and dinner menu is offered in the dining
room. Car parking is available.

Recommended in the area
Dickens House Museum; Viking Bay; Deal

Chislet Court Farm

★★★★ FH

Address: Chislet, CANTERBURY CT3 4DU
Tel: 01227 860309
Fax: 01227 860444
Email: kathy@chisletcourtfarm.com
Website: www.chisletcourtfarm.com
Map ref: 4, TR15
Directions: Off A28 in Upstreet, farm on right 100yds
past church
Rooms: 2 en suite, S £45–£50 D £70–£75

Parking: 4 **Notes:** ⊗ on premises ⊗ on premises ✟ under 12yrs **Closed:** Xmas

Chislet Court is an 800-acre arable farm, with an 18th-century farmhouse, set in mature gardens
overlooking the village church and surrounding countryside. There are two spacious double bedrooms,
each with modern bath and shower rooms, and tea and coffee facilities. You are welcome to relax
in the garden and in the conservatory dining room where breakfast is served. There is a good choice of
pubs and restaurants in the area for lunch and dinner.

Recommended in the area
Canterbury Cathedral; Sandwich; Howletts Zoo Park

anterbury

Magnolia House

★★★★★ GA

ddress:	36 St Dunstan's Terrace, CANTERBURY CT2 8AX
el/Fax:	01227 765121
mail:	info@magnoliahousecanterbury.co.uk
ebsite:	www.magnoliahousecanterbury.co.uk
ap ref:	4, TR15

irections: A2 E onto A2050 for city centre, 1st rdbt ft signed University of Kent. St Dunstan's Terrace rd right

ooms: 7 en suite, S £55–£65 D £95–£145 **Parking:** 5 **Notes:** ⊗ ⊗ ⊮ under 12yrs

his attractive Georgian house stands in a quiet residential street just a short walk from the city centre. he property is beautifully maintained and exudes hospitality. Bedrooms are equipped with plenty of seful features, including a fridge, and guests are provided with their own key. A cosy lounge looks cross the front garden, while the dining room looks onto the walled garden at the rear. Delicious vening meals are served by arrangement, and in the morning breakfast offers plenty of choice.

ecommended in the area

anterbury Cathedral; St Augustine's Abbey; Canterbury Tales Museum

Yorke Lodge

★★★★★ GA

Address: 50 London Road, CANTERBURY CT2 8LF
Tel: 01227 451243
Fax: 01227 462006
Email: enquiries@yorkelodge.com
Website: www.yorkelodge.com
Map ref: 4, TR15
Directions: 750yds NW of city centre
Rooms: 8 en suite, S £50–£65 D £90–£115
Parking: 5 **Notes:** ⊘ on premises 🐾 allowed on premises 👫

In a leafy street in north Canterbury, this Victorian town house is a 10-minute walk from the city centre, with all its historic and cultural attractions. It is also just 5 minutes from Canterbury West station, making it perfectly feasible to arrive by public transport. However, there is parking here, and it's just a 15-minute drive to the Kent coast. Decked on the outside with colourful window boxes and canopies, the interior also exudes a sense of style and elegance, with light, contemporary furniture and restful coordinating fabrics. Bedrooms are individually styled – twin-bedded, double-bedded and triple rooms are available – and the superior rooms have queen-sized four-poster beds. All rooms have colour TV, a radio/alarm, a hairdryer and tea- and coffee-making facilities. There are several areas where guests can relax: a light and cosy conservatory; a sunny terrace of wooden decking overlooking the garden; and the library, with a large selection of books and several board games to suit adults or children. The spacious dining room is the setting for breakfast, which might be a traditional English breakfast or a lighter selection of cereals, yoghurts, fruits and seasonal compotes. It also houses the family's interesting collections of toys, household items, tobacco memorabilia and royal family mementoes.

Recommended in the area

Canterbury Cathedral; North Downs Way; Howletts Wild Animal Park, Bekesbourne

Waterside Guest House

★★★ GA

Address: 15 Hythe Road, DYMCHURCH, Romney Marsh TN29 0LN
Tel: 01303 872253
Fax: 01303 872253
Email: info@watersideguesthouse.co.uk
Website: www.watersideguesthouse.co.uk
Map ref: 4, TR12
Directions: M20 junct 11 onto A259 follow signs for the then Dymchurch, 0.5m past village sign

Rooms: 5 (5 en suite), S D £55–£60 **Parking:** 7 **Notes:** ⊘ on premises ⊗ on premises ♿

This charming house stands on the banks of a quiet stretch of water, beyond which are the marshes. A choice of en suite single, twin, double or family accommodation is available. Each room is attractively decorated and includes TV, clock radio and many other extras. Guests can relax in the oak-beamed bar. Meals are served in the dining room or on the waterside terrace, and include English breakfast (or a lighter alternative), afternoon tea, and dinner from a varied menu of Kentish fare.

Recommended in the area

Romney, Hythe and Dymchurch Railway; Port Lympne Animal Park; Dover Castle and the White Cliffs

Court Lodge B&B

★★★ GA

Address: Court Lodge, Church Road, Oare, FAVERSHAM ME13 0QB
Tel/Fax: 01795 591543
Email: d.wheeldon@btconnect.com
Website: www.faversham.org/courtlodge
Map ref: 4, TR06
Directions: A2 onto B2045, left onto The Street, right onto Church Road, 0.25m on left

Rooms: 2 (1 en suite), D £60 **Parking:** 10 **Notes:** ⊘ on premises ⊗ in bedrooms ♿ **Closed:** Dec–Jan

This sympathetically restored 16th-century listed farmhouse stands in 1.5 acres of gardens amid arable farmland – the perfect place to relax. The spacious rooms have private bathrooms, TV, and tea- and coffee-making facilities. Breakfast is served in the farmhouse kitchen, using the best of local produce including fish and home-made preserves. Court Lodge is ideal for those visiting Oare Creek or walking the Saxon Shore Way. Several pubs and restaurants are only a short distance away.

Recommended in the area

Faversham; Canterbury; Whitstable

The Relish

★★★★★ GA

Address: 4 Augusta Gardens, FOLKESTONE CT20 2RR
Tel: 01303 850952
Fax: 01303 850958
Email: reservations@hotelrelish.co.uk
Website: www.hotelrelish.co.uk
Map ref: 4, TR23
Directions: Off A2033 Sandgate Rd
Rooms: 10 en suite, S £65 D £90–£140 **Parking:** 2 **Notes:** ⊘ on premises ⊗ in bedrooms ♦♦ **Closed:** 22 Dec–2 Jan

You will get a warm welcome from Sarah and Chris at this stylish Victorian property overlooking Augusta Gardens in the fashionable West End of town. On arrival you will be greeted with a complimentary glass of wine or beer and fresh coffee, tea and home-made cakes are available throughout your stay. The bedrooms feature lovely coordinated fabrics, great showers and all have DVD players. Public rooms include a modern lounge-dining room and a terrace where breakfast is served during summer.

Recommended in the area

Dover Castle; Romney, Hythe and Dymchurch Railway; Canterbury

Seabrook House

★★★★ GA

Address: 81 Seabrook Road, HYTHE CT21 5QW
Tel: 01303 269282
Fax: 01303 237822
Email: seabrookhouse@hotmail.co.uk
Website: www.seabrook-house.co.uk
Map ref: 4, TR13
Directions: 0.9m E of Hythe on A259
Rooms: 13 en suite, S £35–£40 D £60–£65
Parking: 13 **Notes:** ⊘ ⊗ ♦♦

This striking Victorian property, easily recognised by the heavily timber-framed frontage and pretty gardens, is conveniently located for the M20 and Eurotunnel. Many of the art-deco style bedrooms have lovely sea views. These spacious en suite rooms, with their attractive decor and furnishings, also have hospitality trays, TV and hairdryers. A memorable full English breakfast sets you up for the ferries from Folkestone or Dover or for sightseeing in the local area, and there are plenty of comfortable places for relaxation, including a sunny conservatory and an elegant lounge.

Recommended in the area

Romney, Hythe and Dymchurch Railway; Dover Castle; Port Lympne Animal Park; Royal Military Canal

Langley Oast

★★★★ GA

Address: Langley Park, Langley,
MAIDSTONE ME17 3NQ
Tel: 01622 863523
Fax: 01622 863523
Email: margaret@langleyoast.freeserve.co.uk
Map ref: 4, TQ75
Directions: 2.5m SE of Maidstone off A274. After Parkwood Business Estate lane signed Maidstone Golf Centre

Rooms: 3 (2 en suite), S £35–£55 D £55–£95 **Parking:** 5 **Notes:** ⊘ ⊗ ♥♥ **Closed:** Xmas

This is an authentic Kentish oasthouse, built in 1873 and originally used for drying hops used in the making of local beer. The interior has been the subject of a tasteful conversion, with exposed brick, clean white walls and period furniture, and the distinctive shape of the oast towers adds extra interest to the two 24-ft diameter "roundel" bedrooms, which include sofas and en suite bathrooms, one of which has a Jacuzzi bath. Breakfasts are served in an elegant dining room around a single table.

Recommended in the area

Leeds Castle; Sissinghurst Castle Gardens; Canterbury

Merzie Meadows

★★★★★ BB

Address: Hunton Road, MARDEN TN12 9SL
Tel/Fax: 01622 820500
Email: pamela@merziemeadows.co.uk
Website: www.merziemeadows.co.uk
Map ref: 4, TQ74
Directions: A229 onto B2079 for Marden, 1st right onto Underlyn Ln, 2.5m large Chainhurst sign, right onto drive

Rooms: 2 en suite, S £75 D £80–£90 **Parking:** 4
Notes: ⊘ ⊗ ♥♥ under 15yrs **Closed:** mid Dec–mid Feb

Merzie Meadows is set in 20 acres in the Kent countryside and the grounds are made up of conservation areas for wildlife, woodland, and an environment for waterfowl. The generously proportioned bedrooms are housed in two wings. The ground-floor location makes for easy access, and one room is a suite with its own terrace. Rooms are carefully decorated and furnished. The breakfast room has superb garden views.

Recommended in the area

Sissinghurst Castle Garden (NT); Leeds Castle; The Hop Farm Country Park, Yalding Organic Gardens

Danehurst House

★★★★★ GA

Address: 41 Lower Green Road, Rusthall,
ROYAL TUNBRIDGE WELLS TN4 8TW
Tel: 01892 527739
Fax: 01892 514804
Email: info@danehurst.net
Website: www.danehurst.net
Map ref: 4, TQ53
Directions: 1.5m W of Tunbridge Wells in Rusthall.
Off A264 onto Coach Rd & Lower Green Rd

Rooms: 4 en suite Parking: 6 Notes: ⊗ on premises ⊗ on premises ⋔ under 8yrs
Closed: Xmas

Angela and Michael Godbold's spacious Victorian home stands just west of the historic spa town of Tunbridge Wells. There is a baby grand piano in the drawing room, and the Victorian-style conservatory is a delightful setting for breakfast, whether full English, fish, cold meats or continental. The four cosy bedrooms are en suite, and have a wealth of thoughtful extras and notably comfortable beds. No pets.

Recommended in the area

Groombridge Place; Hever Castle; Chartwell (NT)

Prospect House B&B

★★★★ GA

Address: Long Barn Road, Weald, SEVENOAKS TN14 6NJ
Tel: 01732 461900
Email: rgmannering@hotmail.com
Website: www.prospecthouse.info
Map ref: 4, TQ55
Directions: M25 junct 5, then 3rd exit on A21 signed Weald, 4th exit on rdbt signed Weald. Follow Morleys Rd to Long Barn Rd
Rooms: 2 en suite, S £45 D £55–£60 Parking: 10
Notes: ⊗ on premises ⊗ in bedrooms ⋔

This charming property set in the Weald countryside consists of a purpose-built guest wing with a private entrance that houses two fresh, bright bedrooms and a shared lounge/TV area. Both rooms are on the ground floor and have fine views of the tranquil garden. Hospitality is as abundant as the bountiful breakfast that includes local produce and home-grown tomatoes, when possible, as well as owner Jan's home-made preserves, all served up in the country breakfast room. Continental breakfast and lighter options are available.

Recommended in the area

Knole (NT); Chartwell (NT); Penshurst Castle, Ightham Mote (NT); Hever Castle (NT)

LANCASHIRE

Blackpool Pleasure Beach

Whitestake Farm

★★★★★ BB

Address: Pope Ln, Whitestake, PRESTON PR4 4JR
Tel: 01772 619392
Fax: 01772 611146
Email: enquiries@gardenofedenspa.co.uk
Map ref: 6, SD52
Directions: M6 junct 29, A582 Lytham St Annes
Penwortham Way, left onto Chain House Lane, right
onto Pope Lane, on right is B&B sgn
Rooms: 2 en suite, D £120 **Parking:** 6 **Notes:** ⊗ on
premises ⊗ in bedrooms ♦♦

This attractive white farmhouse is peacefully located just minutes from Preston and is within easy
reach of Southport and Lytham. Inside, the beautifully appointed bedrooms and en suite bathrooms
are spacious and thoughtfully equipped, and there is a guest lounge for relaxing. Carefully prepared,
substantial breakfasts are taken around a huge table in the elegant dining room. Guests can also make
use of the indoor swimming pool and two treatment rooms for added luxury.

Recommended in the area

The National Football Museum; Beacon Fell Country Park; The Ribble Steam Museum

The Bower

★★★★★ BB

Address: YEALAND CONYERS LA5 9SF
Tel/Fax: 01524 734585
Email: info@thebower.co.uk
Website: www.thebower.co.uk
Map ref: 6, SD57
Directions: M6 junct 35, A6 towards Milnthorpe
for 0.75m, under narrow bridge, take next left onto
Snape Ln & bear left at end
Rooms: 2 (1 en suite), S £47 D £74–£84 **Parking:** 6
Notes: ⊗ on premises ⊗ on premises ♦♦ under 12yrs

The Bower, run by affable hosts Michael and Sally-Ann, is in a beautiful village setting with views
of Ingleborough and surrounding hills just 10 minutes from the M6. This modernised property retains
many original features and provides stylish accommodation in spacious bedrooms and opulent public
rooms. There are two double rooms, one en suite and with an additional single bed, and the other
with a private bathroom.

Recommended in the area

Leighton Hall; RSPB Reserve, Leighton Moss; Sizergh Castle (NT)

Town Hall Square, Leicester

Great Central Railway, Loughborough

The Swan Inn

★★★★ INN

Address: 10 Loughborough Road,
MOUNTSORREL LE12 7AT
Tel: 0116 230 2340
Fax: 0116 237 6115
Email: office@swaninn.eu
Website: www.the-swan-inn.eu
Map ref: 3, SK51
Directions: In village centre
Rooms: 1 en suite, S £72–£120 D £72–£120
Parking: 12 Notes: ⊘ on premises ⊗ in bedrooms ♦♦:

This is a traditional seventeenth-century inn, a Grade II listed building located on the banks of the River
Soar. The accommodation consists of one luxury suite with everything you could want – a large en suite
bedroom, a fully equipped office with PC and wi-fi, an en suite bathroom with shower and antique roll-
top cast-iron bath, a fitted kitchen and a private lounge. Meals are served inside or, weather permitting,
in the secluded riverside garden. A continental breakfast is served in the suite.

Recommended in the area

Beacon Hill Country Park; Charnwood Museum; Great Central Railway

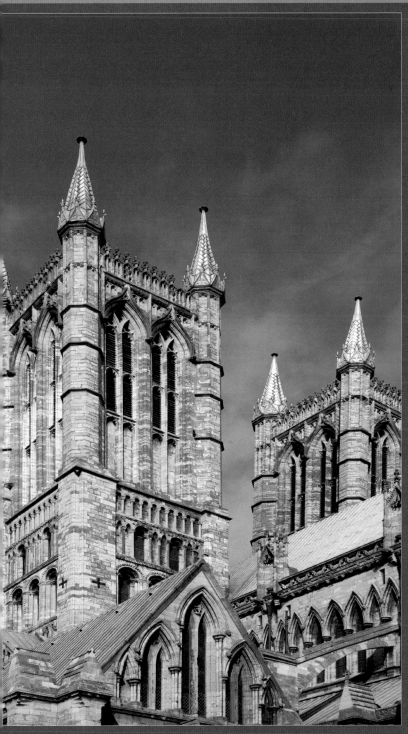

Lincoln Cathedral

Lincoln

Wesley Guest House

★★★★ GA

Address: 16 Queen Street, EPWORTH DN9 1HG
Tel: 01427 874512
Fax: 01427 874592
Email: enquiries@wesleyguesthouse.com
Website: www.wesleyguesthouse.com
Map ref: 8, SE70
Directions: In town centre, 200yds off Market Place
Rooms: 4 en suite, S £40–£60 D £60–£90
Parking: 4 Notes: ⊘ ⊗ ♦♦

A pleasurable stay is a certainty at this friendly and well-maintained detached house in the market town of Epworth. Epworth is the birthplace of John Wesley, founder of Methodism, and places associated with Wesley are all within walking distance. The good-size bedrooms, decorated in soft pastels, have mini-fridges, fresh flowers and complimentary toiletries. Cheerful tablecloths and lovely views over the large garden enhance the pristine breakfast room. Unwind with a game on the full-size snooker table or try one of the leisure options nearby, such as golf and fishing.

Recommended in the area

Normanby Hall and Park; Sandtoft Museum; John Wesley Museum; St Andrew's Church, Epworth

Church Farm B&B

★★★★ BB

Address:	High Street, FILLINGHAM,
	Gainsborough DN21 5BS
Tel:	01427 668279
Email:	enquiries@churchfarm-fillingham.co.uk
Website:	www.churchfarm-fillingham.co.uk
Map ref:	8, SK98
Directions:	Off B1398 into village, 1st house on right
Rooms:	3 (1 en suite), S £38 D £55–£60
Parking:	6 Notes: ⊘ on premises ⊗ on premises

🚼 under 5yrs Closed: 24 Dec–1 Jan

Church Farm lies on the edge of the small, peaceful stone village of Fillingham, which nestles at the base of the Lincolnshire Scarp, the limestone edge that slices through the country and extends down to the Cotswolds. Relax and unwind in this large 19th-century stone farmhouse set in secluded mature gardens overlooking farmland. The traditional bedrooms decorated in various styles offer one en suite twin, and a double and a single that share a bathroom. Plush sofas and chairs and an open fire in the lounge make for a relaxed atmosphere. The English breakfast includes cereals, porridge, yoghurts and fresh fruit to start, followed by local bacon and sausages, free-range eggs cooked to your liking and fresh mushrooms and tomatoes, plus a choice of breads and a selection of preserves. Special dietary needs can be catered for and packed lunches can be provided if advance notice is given. Host Kathleen Needham is very proud (and rightly so) of her housekeeping and warm hospitality – if you arrive before 5pm you are greeted with complimentary tea and home-made cake. For the keen angler, there is a large, privately owned lake in the village offering fishing with a daily permit (£10) open to Church Farm's guests.

Recommended in the area

Lincoln's cathedral, castle and museums; RAF Scampton; antiques at Neward Swinderby and Hemswell

The Brownlow Arms

★★★★★ ⊚ INN

Address: High Road, HOUGH-ON-THE-HILL,
Grantham NG32 2AZ
Tel: 01400 250234
Fax: 01400 271193
Email: paulandlorraine@thebrownlowarms.com
Website: www.thebrownlowarms.com
Map ref: 8, SK94
Directions: North of Grantham on the Manthorpe Rd
Rooms: 4 en suite, S £65–£96 **Parking:** 20
Notes: ⊘ in bedrooms ⊗ in bedrooms 🚸 under 14yrs **Closed:** 25–27 Dec & 31 Dec–20 Jan

The Brownlow Arms is a 17th-century country inn that enjoys a peaceful location in the heart of this picturesque stone village, located between Newark and Grantham. Once owned by Lord Brownlow, today it offers peace and relaxation alongside the twin delights of exceptional modern comforts and good old-fashioned country hospitality. The establishment is tastefully decorated throughout, and all of its comfortable double bedrooms are en suite; extras such as LCD flatscreen TVs, DVD players and DVDs, power/drench showers, and hairdryers make them particularly well equipped. The friendly bar here serves prize-winning ales from a hand pump, while the elegant restaurant offers a setting and atmosphere reminiscent of an intimate country house. Chef Paul Vidic works with premium produce to produce imaginative dishes from a menu that has both traditional and modern influences – examples include house potted brown shrimps with avruga caviar, tiger prawns in tempura batter, braised blade of beef with horseradish mash, and caramelised passion fruit crème brulée– all supported by an interesting wine list. Guests may also make use of the luxurious lounge, a landscaped terrace in summer, or they can sit back and relax next an open log fire in winter.
Recommended
Belton House; Lincoln Castle; Lincoln Cathedral

Bail House & Mews

★★★★★ GA

Address: Bailgate,
LINCOLN LN1 3AP
Tel: 01522 541000
Fax: 01522 521829
Email: info@bailhouse.co.uk
Website: www.bailhouse.co.uk
Map ref: 8, SK94
Directions: 100yds N of cathedral
Rooms: 10 en suite, S £69.50–£109.50
D £89–£175 Parking: 16 Notes: ⊘ ⊗ ♦♦

Bail House commands a prime position on the Bailgate in the historic cathedral quarter of the city of Lincoln, just 230 yards from the cathedral and castle. This outwardly Georgian house encapsulates remains of a 14th-century hall, including part of the beamed roof and exposed stone walls. The building has evolved over the years into a carefully restored guesthouse with spacious, interesting bedrooms which are comfortably furnished with antique and reproduction pieces and equipped with the most up-to-date facilities. Each room has a view of the castle, cathedral spires or the Bailgate. Colour televisions, telephones and hostess trays are provided in all rooms. For that special occasion there is a luxurious double room with a vaulted ceiling and exposed brickwork, a large plasma screen TV, and a separate bath and shower en suite, while another double room has an ornately carved four-poster bed, a feature fireplace and a comfy sofa. Guests can relax in the lounge which has a flat screen TV and DVD player, and make use of the breakfast room which doubles as a quiet reading room during the day and also has a computer with wireless Internet access. Breakfast is taken around a large polished

table, and offers a choice of full continental or traditional English, with plenty of tea, coffee, orange juice and toast. Evening meals are not available but there are many good restaurants all, within a few minutes' walking distance of the hotel, and the proprietors are happy to make a booking for you. There are extensive enclosed gardens, with a heated outdoor swimming pool (seasonal), barbeque and patio area, and to the rear is a secure car park. A number of activites can be arranged from the hotel including local walks, fishing trips, golf, shooting and horse riding. High-quality self-catering cottages are available in the grounds of Bail House.

Recommended in the area

Lincoln Castle; Lincoln Cathedral; Lincolnshire Wolds; Museum of Lincolnshire Life; The Usher Gallery; The Collection

Carholme Guest House

★★★★ GH

Address: 175 Carholme Road,
LINCOLN LN1 1RU
Tel: 01522 531059
Email: enquiries@carholmeguesthouse.com
Website: www.carholmeguesthouse.com
Map ref: 8, SK97
Directions: From A1 take A57. From A46 take A57,
0.5m on left after racecourse
Rooms: 5 (4 en suite), S £30–£35 D £50–£55
Parking: 5 **Notes:** ⊗ on premises ⊗ on premises ♦♦
Closed: 23 Dec–2 Jan

Carholme is a family-owned establishment offering a friendly and relaxed atmosphere in a clean and comfortable Edwardian house. It is well located, within walking distance of the centre of Lincoln, with all its parks, historical sites and shopping facilities, and the owners are happy to advise on the best places to visit. The house itself has been carefully renovated to blend original features with modern home comforts, and most of the bedrooms have en suite facilities; a ground-floor family room is also available. Guests here are provided with a range of thoughtful extras such as colour TV, tea and coffee-making facilities and radio alarm clock. Hairdryers can be provided on request, and a laundry/ironing facility is available for a small charge. Guests are welcome to relax in the large, comfortable TV lounge, and a selection of toys and games is available to keep children busy. Traditional English breakfasts are served using fresh local produce such as Lincolnshire sausages and free-range eggs, or a selection of lighter options may be taken if preferred. Vegetarians and anyone with special dietary requirements can also be catered for, and there's even a special breakfast menu for children. Parking is available.

Recommended in the area

Brayford Marina; Lincoln Cathedral; Bailgate

The Old Bakery

★★★ ◎◎ RR

Address: 26/28 Burton Road, LINCOLN LN1 3LB
Tel: 01522 576057
Email: enquiries@theold-bakery.co.uk
Website: www.theold-bakery.co.uk
Map ref: 8, SK97
Directions: Exit A46 at Lincoln North follow signs for cathedral. 3rd exit at 1st rdbt, 1st exit at next rdbt. Located between Museum of Lincolnshire Life and Lawns Visitor centre
Rooms: 4 (2 en suite), S £48–£53 D £53–£63
Notes: ⊘ on premises ⊗ in bedrooms ♨

Situated close to the castle in the Uphill area at the top of the town, this converted bakery is close to Lincoln Cathedral and the castle. It was originally built in 1837 and operated as a bakery until 1954. In 1994 the property was restored and many of the original bakery features remain. Today it offers well-equipped bedrooms and a delightful and informal dining operation. The pretty bedrooms come with en suite or private facilities, and all benefit from digital colour TV with freeview, broadband wireless internet access, radio alarm clock, hairdryer and tea and coffee-making facilities. Ironing facilities are available on request. The restaurant here is popular, and the characterful dining room at the Old Bakery has been created in the location of the original ovens. A superb room has recently been created and described as a 'Garden under Glass' which extends the restaurant from 45 to 85 covers and is fully climate controlled for all year use. The cooking is Modern British with an Italian accent and has a dedication toward the use of local produce – the Old Bakery even has its own garden allotment that provides many of the vegetables served in the restaurant. Expect good friendly service from a dedicated staff at all times.

Recommended in the area

Lincoln Cathedral; Viking Way walking route; The Museum of Lincolnshire Life

Black Swan Guest House

★★★★ GA

Address: 21 High Street, MARTON,
Gainsborough DN21 5AH
Tel: 01427 718878
Email: info@blackswanguesthouse.co.uk
Website: www.blackswanguesthouse.co.uk
Map ref: 8, SK88
Directions: On A156 in village centre
Rooms: 10 en suite, S £45–£55 D £68–£78
Twin £68 **Parking:** 10 **Notes:** ⊗ on premises 🐾
allowed on premises ♦♦ Wi-fi available

Located in the village centre, the 18th-century Black Swan offers good hospitality and comfortable bedrooms with modern facilities. A four-poster bedroom is also available. The guest house caters to business travellers, tourists and local families, who return frequently for the home-from-home comforts. Generous, tasty breakfasts are served in the dining room and a comfortable lounge is available. An added bonus is transport to and from nearby pubs and restaurants.
Recommended in the area
Lincoln Cathedral; Lincoln Castle; Lincoln Showground; Museum of Lincolnshire Life

La Casita

★★★★★ BB

Address: Frith House, Main Street,
NORMANTON, Grantham NG32 3BH
Tel/Fax: 01400 250302
Email: jackiegonzalez@btinternet.com
Website: www.lacasitabandb.co.uk
Map ref: 8, SK94
Directions: In village centre on A607
Rooms: 1 en suite, S £95 D £125 **Parking:** 3
Notes: ⊗ on premises ⊗ in bedrooms ♦♦

Set independently in the grounds of the owners, this converted stable offers considerable luxury. The suite provides a rural retreat and complete privacy in sumptuous, spacious open-plan accommodation with its own entrance and terrace. There is a living room with kitchen area and log fire and the slate-tiled bathroom is pure 'state of the art' complete with luxury toiletries and bathrobes. Extras include two flat-screen TVs, DVD, CD, and broadband internet. Breakfast is served in the elegant dining-room of the main house. An ideal place for a romantic getaway, family break and business travellers.
Recommended in the area
Lincoln; Nottingham; Grantham

LONDON

The London Eye and Big Ben

MIC Conferences and Accommodation

★★★★ ⇌ GA

Address: 81–103 Euston Street,
LONDON NW1 2EZ
Tel: 020 7380 0001
Fax: 020 7387 5300
Email: sales@micentre.com
Website: www.micentre.com
Map ref: 3, TQ38

Directions: Euston Rd left at lights onto Melton St, 1st left onto Euston St, MIC 100yds on left
Rooms: 28 en suite, S £87–£150 D £87–£150 Notes: ⊘ on premises ⊗ on premises ♦♦

The top floor of the MIC building was completely overhauled in 2004 and has been designed to offer the highest standards and value for money. The hotel is staffed around the clock, thus ensuring a safe environment. The stylish, air-conditioned bedrooms are en suite and come with LCD televisions and radios, room safes, a desk space with Internet access, complimentary hospitality trays and mineral water. The spacious and airy Atrium Bar and Restaurant is perfect for an informal meeting, drink or meal. For breakfast, a traditional English buffet features eight hot items with eggs cooked to order, pancakes and waffles served with maple syprup or sauces, fruit juices, a good selection of cereals, a fruit and yoghurt bar, plus assorted teas and fresh coffee. The centre also offers a range of meeting rooms and private dining rooms for special events, which can be catered for. There are special weekend discount rates. The hotel is located in a quiet street close to Euston Station which has a mainline station, an underground and local bus connections.

Recommended in the area

West End theatres; The BA London Eye; Madame Tussauds

The Windermere

★★★ GA

Address: 142/144 Warwick Way, Victoria,
LONDON SW1V 4JE
Tel: 020 7834 5163
Fax: 020 7630 8831
Email: reservations@windermere-hotel.co.uk
Website: www.windermere-hotel.co.uk
Map ref: 3, TQ38
Directions: On B324 off Buckingham Palace Rd, at junct Alderney St
Rooms: 20 en suite, S £89 D £114–£139 **Notes:** ⊘ on premises ⊗ on premises ♦♦

Individual care and attention is paramount at The Windermere, which retains its charm and character while successfully combining tradition with modern living. The individually styled bedrooms are well equipped and for the business executive there are ISDN 2 facilities for video conferencing. The Pimlico licensed restaurant (open to non-residents) offers a hearty cooked breakfast and delicious evening meals. It is in a central location close to the capital's many attractions and Victoria Station.

Recommended in the area

Buckingham Palace; Houses of Parliament; Tate Britain

The Mayflower

★★★★ GH

Address: 26–28 Trebovir Road, LONDON SW5 9NJ
Tel: 020 7370 0991
Fax: 020 7370 0994
Email: info@mayflower-group.co.uk
Website: www.mayflowerhotel.co.uk
Map ref: 3, TQ38
Directions: Left from Earls Court tube station & 1st left into Trebovir Rd, premises on left
Rooms: 47 en suite, S £69–£79 D £85–£185 **Parking:** 4
Notes: ⊘ on premises ⊗ on premises ♦♦

Hospitality and service are the keywords here at this smart guest house not far from Earls Court and Olympia, conveniently located and perfect for a visit to London. Each of the individually designed bedrooms have a marbled walk-in bath or shower room, as well as satellite TV and refreshment trays. Public areas include a stylish lounge and breakfast is served in the bright and equally stylish dining room.

Recommended in the area

Kensington Palace; Harrods; Madame Tussauds; Victoria & Albert Museum

Hart House

★★★★ GA

Address: 51 Gloucester Place,
          LONDON W1U 8JF
Tel: 020 7935 2288
Fax: 020 7935 8516
Email: reservations@harthouse.co.uk
Website: www.harthouse.co.uk
Map ref: 3, TQ38
Directions: Off Oxford St behind Selfridges, near Baker St or
Marble Arch tube stations
Rooms: 15 en suite, S £75–£85 D £105–£125
Notes: ⊘ on premises ⊗ on premises ♦♦

This delightful, well-cared for property occupies a Georgian terrace just off Oxford Street. Much of its original elegance and grand ambience survive from the late 18th century, when during the French Revolution it was home to members of the French aristocracy. Hart House has been carefully restored so that modern comforts abound, and the en suite bedrooms have been refurbished to a high standard with quality furnishings and smart bathrooms. The rooms are each equipped with a desk or writing table, relaxing seating, direct-dial telephone with modem point, a multi-channel television, individually controlled heating and a hospitality tray. There is a choice of single, double, twin and family rooms. A tasty traditional English breakfast is served in the cottage-style dining room. Andrew Bowden, whose family has owned and run Hart House for many years, is a charming and helpful host who is justly proud of his reputation for providing a comfortable and hospitable atmosphere. Hart House is well placed for both business and leisure travellers visiting London and is within easy walking distance of public transport and London's major tourist attractions.

Recommended in the area

Madame Tussauds; Oxford Street; West End theatres

The Victoria and Albert Museum, South Kensington

The Royal Albert Hall, South Kensington

The New Linden

★★★★ GH

Address: 59 Leinster Square, Notting Hill, LONDON W2 4PS
Tel: 020 7221 4321
Fax: 020 7727 3156
Email: newlindenhotel@mayflower-group.co.uk
Website: www.newlinden.co.uk
Map ref: 3, TQ38
Directions: Off A402, Bayswater Rd
Rooms: 52 en suite, S £79–£110 D £85–£145
Notes: ⊘ on premises ⊗ on premises ♦♦

The friendly and newly refurbished New Linden has a good location north of Kensington Gardens and just a short walk from Portobello Road market. Its stylish en suite bedrooms are richly furnished and equipped with flatscreen TV with satellite and cable channels, CD player, Wi-fi connection, iron, hairdryer, tea and coffee-making facilities and safe as standard. A lift, 24-hour reception and laundry and concierge services are all provided, and a continental breakfast is served in the dining room.

Recommended in the area

Hyde Park; Kensington Palace Gardens; Victoria & Albert Museum

Blickling Hall

Bon Vista

★★★★ GH

Address: 12 Alfred Road,
CROMER NR27 9AN
Tel: 01263 511818
Email: jim@bonvista-cromer.co.uk
Website: www.bonvista-cromer.co.uk
Map ref: 4, TG24
Directions: From pier onto A148 Copast Rd, 400yds
left onto Alfred Rd
Rooms: 5 en suite, D £54–£68 Parking: 2
Notes: ⊘ on premises ⊗ in bedrooms ⋔

One might consider this the epitome of the traditional seaside guest house, a sturdy, three-storey Victorian home, peacefully set in a residential area near the town and beach, which, along with its neighbours, sums up much of the character of this charming east-coast resort. Jim and Margaret have renovated the house to a very high standard, while retaining many of its 100-year-old features and have dedicated more than a decade to endowing it with a warm and friendly atmosphere. The first-floor lounge, with its original fireplace and big bay window, makes the most of the sea views and is a cosy place to relax in the evening. The dining room is on the ground floor and it's here that the traditional English breakfasts can be enjoyed, bathed in the light of the morning sun. The five bedrooms, each with an en suite bathroom, are very prettily decorated with cottagey wallpapers and colour-coordinated fabrics. Some still have their original fireplaces, and the climb up to the front room on the top floor is rewarded with a sea view. The other top-floor bedroom can accommodate a family, with bunk beds for the children. Each room has a TV, and Sky channels are available in the lounge. Another plus point here is the off-street parking, but it is limited so early arrival is recommended.

Recommended in the area

Cromer Pier Pavilion Theatre; North Norfolk Railway; Sheringham Park (NT).

ncleborough House

★★★★ BB

ddress: Lower Common, East Runton,
CROMER NR27 9PG

el: 01263 515939

ax: 01263 510022

mail: enquiries@incleboroughhouse.co.uk

ebsite: www.incleboroughhouse.co.uk

ap ref: 4, TG24

rections: On A149 turn left onto Felbrigg road,
0mtrs on left

ooms: 3 en suite, S £105–£112.5 D £140–£150 **Parking:** 7

otes: ⊗ on premises 🐕 allowed in ground floor bedroom only 🚸 under 14yrs

uests at this award-winning B&B can look forward to tea and home-made cake on arrival, and indeed very afternoon, at this large 17th-century property, situated on the heritage North Norfolk Coast and ose to the beach. A Grade II listed building built in 1687, it has been lovingly restored by the current wners. The attractively decorated bedrooms, one of which is on the ground floor and has a National ccessible Scheme rating, are carefully furnished throughout with lovely coordinated fabrics, huge beds d fine garden or common views. All have a wealth of useful extras, such as a comfortable sitting ea, small fridge, LCD TV with freeview, DVD, CD and radio, as well as broadband internet access. The acious public areas include a luxurious drawing room with plush leather sofas and an open fireplace. eakfast made from local produce is freshly cooked on the Aga and served at individual tables in e large open-plan conservatory, which has a lush indoor tropical garden. For special occasions, a ampagne breakfast can be served in guests' own rooms. Evening meals can be prepared with prior tice from October to June, and the owners are happy to advise on nearby eating places.

ecommended in the area

omer and Sheringham beaches; Blakeney Point; North Norfolk Steam Railway

Shrublands Farm

★★★★ FH

Address: Church Street, Northrepps,
CROMER NR27 0AA
Tel: 01263 579297
Fax: 01263 579297
Email: youngman@farming.co.uk
Website: www.broadland.com/shrublands
Map ref: 4, TG24
Directions: Off A149 to Northrepps, through village,
past Foundry Arms, cream house 50yds on left
Rooms: 3 (1 en suite), S £40–£42 D £60–£64 Parking: 5 Notes: ⊘ ⊗ ⛄under 12yrs

Shrublands is a working farm set in mature gardens amid 300 acres of arable farmland, an ideal base
for exploring the coast and countryside of rural north Norfolk. Traditional hospitality is a distinguishing
feature at the 18th-century farmhouse, with good cooking using home-grown and fresh local produce
Breakfast is served at a large table in the dining room, and there is also a cosy lounge, with a log fire,
books and a television. The bedrooms have TVs, radio alarms and tea and coffee facilities. No pets.
Recommended in the area

Blickling Hall and Felbrigg Hall (NT); Sandy beaches at Cromer and Overstrand; Blakeney Point

The White Cottage

★★★★ BB

Address: 9 Cliff Drive, CROMER NR27 0AW
Tel: 01263 512728
Email: jboocock@whitecottagecromer.freeserve.
co.uk
Website: www.whitecottagecromer.co.uk
Map ref: 4, TG24
Directions: Off A149 Norwich Rd onto Overstrand
Rd, 2nd right
Rooms: 3 en suite, D £35–£45 Parking: 3
Notes: ⊘ on premises ⊗ on premises ⛄ under 18yrs Closed: Xmas

This immaculate detached house, situated on the cliff path at Cromer, offers a high standard
of comfort and attentive service. The spacious bedrooms are individually decorated and equipped with
every home comfort including tea and coffee trays, electric blankets and micro fridges. The delicious
breakfast, using local produce, and home-made bread and preserves, is served in an elegant dining
room, on the terrace in summer, or in the cosy breakfast room in winter. Packed lunches to order.
Recommended in the area

Felbrigg Hall (NT); Norfolk Shire Horse Centre; Cley bird reserves

Whitehouse Farm

★★★★★ GA

Address: Knapton, NORTH WALSHAM NR28 0RX
Tel: 01263 721344
Email: info@whitehousefarmnorfolk.co.uk
Website: www.whitehousefarmnorfolk.co.uk
Map ref: 4, TG23
Directions: Follow the A49 south of Cromer
Rooms: 3 en suite, S £50 D £60–£70 **Parking:** 8
Notes: ⊘ ⊗ in bedrooms ⛛ under 12yrs

Enjoy a true taste of country living at this delightful Grade II listed 18th-century flint cottage, which is in close proximity to the miles of sandy beaches that make up Norfolk's Heritage Coastline. At Whitehouse Farm caring hosts, Graham and Catherine Moorhouse, offer a very warm welcome. The property is surrounded by open farmland and has been carefully restored to ensure the modern decor blends beautifully with the historic character and period features of the farmhouse. The three large, very tastefully decorated bedrooms have luxury en suite bathrooms and are equipped with many thoughtful touches including tea- and coffee-making facilties and colour television. The tranquil Pulford Room has a four-poster bed and far-reaching views across the fields, while the Orton Room, also with a four-poster bed, looks out onto the farm – there is an additional single bedroom in this suite that can be used to provide twin accommodation if preferred. A traditional full English breakfast that features home-made and local produce is served in the smart dining room and guests have the use of a lounge which is decorated in warm peach shades and has plush sofas and a cosy log fire. Set in the peaceful mature gardens are two charming self-catering cottages which are suitable for families. There is ample off-road parking at Whitehouse Farm. No children under 12 years in the bed and breakfast accommodation.

Recommended in the area

Sandringham; Blickling Hall and Felbrigg Hall (NT); Norfolk Broads

Old Thorn Barn

★★★★ GA

Address: Corporation Farm, Wymondham Road,
          Hethel, NORWICH NR14 8EU
Tel: 01953 607785
Fax: 01953 601909
Email: enquires@oldthornbarn.co.uk
Website: www.oldthornbarn.co.uk
Map ref: 4, TG20
Directions: 6m SW of Norwich. Follow signs for Lotus
Cars from A11 or B1113, on Wymondham Rd
Rooms: 7 en suite, S £33–£37 D £52–£56 Parking: 14 Notes: ⊘ on premises ⊗ on premises ♦♦

Reconstruction of a group of derelict buildings has resulted in this delightful conversion. The substantial 17th-century barns and stables feature a stylish open-plan dining room, where you can linger over breakfast around individual oak tables. At the other end of the room there is a cosy lounge area with a wood-burning stove. Antique pine furniture and smart en suites are a feature of the spacious bedrooms which have tea and coffee trays, trouser presses and hairdryers.

Recommended in the area

Fairhaven Woodland and Water Garden; Pettitts Animal Adventure Park; Wolterton Park

At Knollside

★★★★ BB

Address: 43 Cliff Road, SHERINGHAM NR26 8BJ
Tel/Fax: 01263 823320
Email: millar@knollside.free-online.co.uk
Website: www.broadland.com/knollsidelodge.html
Map ref: 4, TG14
Directions: 250yds E of town centre. A1082 to High
St, onto Wyndham St & Cliff Rd
Rooms: 3 en suite, S D Parking: 3 Notes: ⊘ on
premises ⊗ on premises ♦♦under 2yrs

You're welcomed with a glass of sherry and fresh fruit in your room at this guest house a short walk along the promenade from the centre of Sheringham. The bedrooms offer twin, king size and super king beds, or a carved four-poster, enhanced with crisp white linen. Easy chairs and tea and coffee facilities, trouser press, hair dryer and television are provided for extra comfort. Each bathroom is crammed with thoughtful toiletries such as hair spray, mousse, hand cream, shower gel, shampoo and cotton wool. Some rooms have sea views. Start the day with the impressive full English breakfast.

Recommended in the area

Felbrigg Hall (NT); North Norfolk Heritage Coast – Blakeney; Holkam Hall

Fairlawns

★★★★★ GH

Address: 26 Hooks Hill Rd, SHERINGHAM NR26 8NL
Tel: 01263 824717
Email: info@fairlawns-sheringham.co.uk
Website: www.fairlawns-sheringham.com
Map ref: 4, TG14
Directions: Sheringham is on A148 from Kings Lynn and signposted from the A140 (from Norwich)
Rooms: 5 en suite, S £60 D £80–£90 **Notes:** ⊘ on premises ⊗ on premises ⚫

Set in tranquil grounds, in which guests can relax and have a drink or play croquet, Fairlawns has been lovingly renovated to provide tasteful and well-equipped bedrooms, each with its own luxury en suite bathroom, fluffy towels and bathrobes, as well as LCD television with DVD player, internet connection, hairdryer and well-stocked beverage tray. The stylish public areas include a comfortable and spacious lounge with a fully licensed bar, games and books, and a conservatory dining room, serving locally sourced produce.

Recommended in the area

North Norfolk Railway; Muckleburgh Collection; Sheringham Golf Club

Holly Lodge

★★★★★ ⊜ BB

Address: The Street, THURSFORD NR21 0AS
Tel/Fax: 01328 878465
Email: info@hollylodgeguesthouse.co.uk
Website: www.hollylodgeguesthouse.co.uk
Map ref: 4, TF93
Directions: Off A148 into Thursford village
Rooms: 3 en suite, S £60–£100 D £80–£120
Parking: 6 **Notes:** ⊘ on premises ⊗ on premises ⚫ under 14yrs **Closed:** Jan

This 18th-century property is situated in a picturesque location surrounded by open farmland. The lovely landscaped gardens include a large sundeck, which overlooks the lake and water gardens, providing a great place to relax. The lodge and its guest cottages have been transformed into a splendid guest house, with stylish ground-floor bedrooms that are individually decorated and beautifully furnished. En suite bathrooms, televisions and lots of thoughtful extras make for a pleasant stay. The attractive public areas are full of character, with flagstone floors, oak beams and open fireplaces.

Recommended in the area

North Norfolk Coast; Thursford Museum; Walsingham

Tresham Lodge, Rushton

Hunt House Quarters

★ ★ ★ 🛏 GA

Address: Main Road, KILSBY,
Rugby CV23 8XR
Tel: 01788 823282
Email: luluharris@hunthouse.fsbusiness.co.uk
Website: www.hunthousekilsby.com
Map ref: 3, SP57
Directions: On B3048 in village
Rooms: 4 en suite, S £59.95–£75 D £75–£85
Parking: 8 Notes: ⊗ ⊗ in bedrooms ♦♦

Hunt House Quarters in Kilsby is set in a beautiful peaceful courtyard and forms one part of a magnificently restored 1656 thatched hunting lodge and covered stables. Steeped in history, the lodge was originally used for deer hunting. The property is ideally placed as a touring base for visiting Stratford-upon-Avon, the Cotswolds and Warwick. Nearby there are stately homes, castles and gardens to visit as well as opportunities for some excellent walking. The spacious en suite bedrooms have their own character and are named the Manger, the Smithy, the Saddlery and the Tack Room. Set around a large courtyard, they retain features such as oak beams and old glass but are furnished in a modern, contemporary style. All rooms are equipped to a high standard and have Internet broadband connection, colour TV, tea- and coffee-making facilities and hairdryer. Breakfast is served in the restaurant where guests are offered the choice of full English, continental or vegetarian breakfast. All breakfasts are freshly cooked and prepared to order at times convenient to the guests. For other meals, there are two village pubs serving food seven days per week, and a selection of Indian, Chinese, Italian, Mexican, English, and Thai restaurants only 5–10 minutes away. The gardens surrounding Hunt House Quarters are a peaceful haven in which to relax and take a stroll.

Recommended in the area

Rugby School; Crick Boat Show; National Exhibition Centre

Bridge Cottage Bed & Breakfast

★★★★ BB

Address: Oundle Rd, Woodnewton,
OUNDLE PE8 5EG
Tel: 01780 470779
Email: judycolebrook@btinternet.com
Website: www.bridgecottage.net
Map ref: 3, TL08
Directions: 4m N of Oundle by bridge in Woodnewton
Rooms: 3 (2 en suite), S £35–£55 D £50–£80
Parking: 3 **Notes:** ⊗ 🐾 allowed in bedrooms ♦♦

Bridge Cottage enjoys a delightful and peaceful location on the periphery of the village of Woodnewton and bordered by open countryside. This friendly and relaxing B&B offers real home-from-home comforts and tastefully appointed accommodation, with broadband wireless internet connection available in every room. This, along with the tasty, freshly cooked Northamptonshire breakfast made from local ingredients, ensures that guests return time and again. Breakfast is taken in the open-plan kitchen, which overlooks the lovely gardens.

Recommended in the area

Burghley House; Peterborough Cathedral; Fotheringhay village

The Courtyard

★★★★★ GA

Address: Rutland Lodge, West Street,
STANWICK NN9 6QY
Tel: 01933 622233
Fax: 01933 622276
Email: bookings@thecourtyard.me.uk
Website: www.thecourtyard.me.uk
Map ref: 3, SP97
Directions: A45 rdbt to Stanwick, from Stanwick rdbt entrance just on the right
Rooms: 12 en suite, S £55 D £69 **Parking:** 12 **Notes:** ⊗ on premises ⊗ on premises ♦♦

Comfort and luxury abound at this attractive house, where the hospitality is unforgettable. The house stands in delightful large gardens on the edge of Stanwick village. The bedrooms have either garden or country views, are stylish and modern, and all come equipped with internet access, satellite televisions, and tea and coffee facilities. Business meeting rooms are available. Fully licensed, the Courtyard specialises in weddings and has a permanent marquee in the garden.

Recommended in the area

Rockingham Castle; Oundle; Santa Pod

Cragside House

Bondgate House

★★★★ GH

Address: 20 Bondgate Without,
ALNWICK NE66 1PN
Tel: 01665 602025
Email: enquiries@bondgatehouse.co.uk
Website: www.bondgatehouse.co.uk
Map ref: 10, NU11
Directions: A1 onto B6346 into town centre, past war memorial Rooms: 6 en suite, D £75–£85
Parking: 8 Notes: ⊘ ⊗ ⅰ⅟ Closed: Xmas

Experience relaxed hospitality of the highest standards in an elegant Grade II listed Georgian town house; with comfortable, restful en-suite bedrooms, private car park and a delightful herb garden and patio. The lounge has a splendid selection of local literature, books and walks. With a private car park which abuts the Alnwick Garden, it is an easy stroll to visit the Garden, castle, town, restaurants and shops. Alnwick is an ideal centre for visiting or touring both inland and coastal Northumberland. Anne also offers local herb walks in Spring and Summer, as well as tours of her herb garden.

Recommended in the area

Alnwick Castle & Gardens; Lindisfarne; Northumberland National Park

Market Cross Guest House

★★★★★ ≘ GA

Address: 1 Church Street, BELFORD NE70 7LS
Tel: 01668 213013
Email: info@marketcross.net
Website: www.marketcross.net
Map ref: 10, NU13
Directions: Off A1 into village, opp church
Rooms: 3 en suite, S £40–£60 D £70–£90
Parking: 3 Notes: ⊘ ⅰ ⅰ⅟

Set in the heart of the charming village of Belford, just off the Great North Road, this Grade II listed building is well placed for visiting the Northumbrian coast. The traditional northern hospitality here is matched by the high quality of the accommodation, with bedrooms that are large enough to include easy chairs and sofas. Each has a flat screen TV and a wealth of extras including a fridge with fresh milk for the complimentary beverages, fruit, and fresh flowers. The breakfasts, which may include kedgeree, smoked salmon scrambled eggs, pancakes and griddle scones, have an AA Award for their quality and range. Many ingredients are sourced locally and there are also vegetarian options.

Recommended in the area

Lindisfarne (Holy Island); Alnwick Castle and gardens; the Farne Islands; Northumberland National Park

Ivy Cottage

★★★★★ GA

Address: 1 Croft Gardens, Crookham,
CORNHILL-ON-TWEED TD12 4ST
Tel/Fax: 01890 820667
Email: ajoh540455@aol.com
Website: www.ivycottagecrookham.co.uk
Map ref: 10, NT83
Directions: 4m E of Cornhill. Off A697 onto B6353
to Crookham village
Rooms: 2, S £44 D £66–£74 **Parking:** 2
Notes: ⊘ on premises ⊗ on premises 🐾 under 5yrs

This pristine stone-built modern cottage is testament to the many years spent in the hospitality industry by owners Alan and Doreen Johnson, and guests soon feel the benefit of their experience and dedication. Set in delightful gardens, the summerhouse provides a welcome spot in which to take tea on fine afternoons. Inside, everything is bright and spotless, and the two spacious bedrooms offer a choice of furnishings – the downstairs room is smart and modern while the room upstairs is beautifully done out in antique pine. With fresh flowers, crisp embroidered bedding, home-baked biscuits and tea-making facilities, they are immediately welcoming and relaxing. Each room has its own private bathroom with a deep tub, Crabtree & Evelyn toiletries, huge terry towels and bathrobes. Breakfasts, served in the formal dining room or in the farmhouse-style kitchen, with its Aga cooking range, are sumptuous. Whichever room is used, the feast always includes local free-range eggs, organic produce where possible, home-made preserves, freshly squeezed orange juice and home-baked bread made from stone-ground flour from nearby Heatherslaw Mill. Ivy Cottage is perfectly located for exploring the Northumberland coast and the Cheviot Hills.

Recommended in the area

Holy Island; Alnwick Castle and Gardens; Flodden Battlefield

Pheasant Inn

★★★★ INN

Address: Stannersburn, FALSTONE NE48 1DD
Tel: 01434 240382
Fax: 01434 240382
Email: enquiries@thepheasantinn.com
Website: www.thepheasantinn.com
Map ref: 6, NY78
Directions: 1m S of Falstone. Off B6320 to Kielder Water, via Bellingham or via Hexham A69 onto B6320 via Wall-Wark-Bellingham
Rooms: 8 en suite, S £50–£55 D £80–£85 Parking: 40 Notes: ⊗ in bedrooms ⚲ allowed in bedrooms ⏹ Closed: Xmas

Set close by the magnificent Kielder Water, this classic country inn, built in 1624, has exposed stone walls, original beams, low ceilings, open fires and a display of old farm implements in the bar. Run by the welcoming Kershaw family since 1985, the inn was originally a farmhouse and has been refurbished to a very high standard. The bright, modern en suite bedrooms, some with their own entrances, are all contained in stone buildings adjoining the inn and are set round a pretty courtyard. All the rooms, including one family room, are spotless, well equipped, and have tea and coffee facilities, hairdryer, colour TV and radio alarm clock; all enjoy delightful country views. Delicious home-cooked breakfasts and evening meals are served in the bar or in the attractive dining room, or may be taken in the pretty garden courtyard if the weather permits. Irene and her son Robin are responsible for the traditional home cooking using local produce and featuring delights such as game pie and roast Northumbrian lamb, as well as imaginative vegetarian choices. Drying and laundry facilities are available and, for energetic guests, cycle hire can be arranged.

Recommended in the area

Hadrian's Wall; Kielder Water Reservoir (sports facilities); Cragside House (NT)

Hadrian's Wall

Brookside Villa

★ ★ ★ ★   🛏 BB

Address: GILSLAND CA8 7DA
Tel: 016977 47300
Email: brooksidevilla@hotmail.co.uk
Website: www.brooksidevilla.com
Map ref: 6, NY66
Directions: A69, take Gilsland exit, continue for 2m left onto B6318, Brookside Villa 100yds on left
Rooms: 2 en suite, S £40–£50 D £60–£70
Parking: 2 **Notes:** ⊗ 🐾 allowed in bedrooms ♦♦

This lovely Victorian villa sits on the Northumberland-Cumbria border at the edge of the magnificent Northumberland National Park, in the heart of 'Hadrian's Wall Country'. The stylish bedrooms have contemporary en suites; there are tremendous views from the lounge-dining room; and polished wood floors gleam throughout. Arrive home from your day out to browse the collection of books and CDs; relax on the terrace soothed by the sound of the brook; or curl up on a sofa by the log fire. Brookside Villa is licensed and offers evening meals for guests.

Recommended in the area
Northumberland National Park; Carlisle; Hadrian's Wall

Bush Nook

★★★★ GH

Address: Upper Denton, GILSLAND,
Nr Haltwhistle CA8 7AF
Tel/Fax: 016977 47194
Email: info@bushnook.co.uk
Website: www.bushnook.co.uk
Map ref: 6, NY66
Directions: Halfway between Brampton and
Haltwhistle, off A69 signed Spadeadam, Birdoswald,
Bush Nook
Rooms: 6 en suite, S £35–£40 D £68–£80 Parking: 6 Notes: ⊘ on premises ⊗ on premises ♦♦
Closed: Xmas & New Year

Set in wonderful open countryside, Bush Nook overlooks Birdoswald Roman Fort on Hadrian's Wall
and is close to the dramatic centre section of the Roman frontier. Like most properties in the area, it
was built using stones 'borrowed' from the nearby Hadrian's Wall fortifications. Today this converted
farmhouse offers comfortable accommodation in which to rest, relax and recuperate after exploring the
area. The comfortable bedrooms, all of which are at first-floor level, are split between the main house
and the barn, and most have open-beam lofted ceilings and many original features; each offers a good
view of the surrounding countryside. The many thoughtful little extras, such as 'just in case' toiletries
and hand-made chocolates, help make your stay as comfortable as possible. Dinners are made as far
as possible using fresh seasonal and local produce, and breakfast choices include full English, smoked
haddock or kipper, or a continental breakfast, often served with home-made bread and preserves.
As well as the spacious dining room, other guest areas include the cosy lounge and the impressive
conservatory, which leads out to a large, well-maintained garden.

Recommended in the area

Lanercost Priory; Birdoswald Roman Fort; Hadrian's Wall

dolanda Roman fort, near Bardon Mill

allum Lodge

★★★ GH

dress:	Military Road, Twice Brewed, HALTWHISTLE NE47 7AN
:	01434 344248
x:	01434 344488
ail:	stay@vallum-lodge.co.uk
bsite:	www.vallum-lodge.co.uk
p ref:	6, NY76
ections:	On B6318, 400yds W of Once Brewed ional Park visitors centre

oms: 6 en suite, S £45–£56 D £66 **Parking:** 15 **Notes:** ⊗ ⊗ ♦ **Closed:** Nov–Feb

s licensed roadside guest house provides a home from home in the heart of the Northumberland ional Park. It is perfectly placed for walking and cycling in this unspoiled part of England. The rbished bedrooms are all on the ground floor and feature hospitality trays and complimentary etries. Laundry and drying facilities are also available. Breakfast is served in the smart dining room there is a cosy lounge with a television and a selection of books and games.

commended in the area

drian's Wall; Vindolanda; Housesteads; Roman Army Museum; the Pennine Way

Peth Head Cottage

★★★★ BB

Address: Juniper, HEXHAM NE47 0LA
Tel: 01434 673286
Fax: 01434 673038
Email: peth_head@btopenworld.com
Website: www.peth-head-cottage.co.uk
Map ref: 6, NY96
Directions: B6306 S from Hexham, 200yds fork right, next left. Continue 3.5m, house 400yds on right after Juniper sign
Rooms: 2 en suite, S £27 D £54 Parking: 2 Notes: ⊗ on premises ⊗ on premises ⋔

This lovingly maintained rose-covered cottage dates back to 1825 and is popular for its warm welcome, idyllic setting, and home comforts. Tea and hand-made biscuits are offered on arrival, and the delicious home cooking is enjoyed at breakfast too, along with freshly baked bread and delicious homemade preserves. The inviting sandstone cottage is set in peaceful, well-kept gardens. There are two bright, south-facing bedrooms, both overlooking the gard with shower rooms en suite, a hairdryer, colour TV, radio alarm and hospitality trays. The relaxing lounge is heavily beamed and furnished with comfortable chairs. Peth Head Cottage is ideallly situate for visiting Durham and Newcastle as well as nearby Roman sites, and there are plenty of opportunit for walking and cycling in the area. A wide range of tourist information and maps are on hand for visitors to browse through and plan the day. The owner, Joan Liddle, is an excellent host who knows how to ensure her guests have an enjoyable stay. There is private off-road parking. Sorry, no pets ca be accommodated.

Recommended in the area

Beamish Open Air Museum; Hadrian's Wall; the Northumberland coast; Durham Cathedral; Finchale Priory; Lanercost Priory

wick Gardens

The Old Manse

★★★★ GA

dress: New Road, Chatton, WOOLER NE66 5PU
l: 01668 215343
nail: chattonbb@aol.com
ebsite: www.oldmansechatton.co.uk
ap ref: 10, NT92
rections: 4m E of Wooler. On B6348 in Chatton
ooms: 3 en suite, S £35–£60 D £70–£80
rking: 4 **Notes:** ⊗ ⊗ in bedrooms ✸ under 13yrs

ilt in 1875 and commanding excellent views over the open countryside, this imposing former manse
nds on the edge of the pretty village of Chatton between the Cheviot Hills and the scenic North
rthumberland Heritage Coast. You approach the house by a sweeping gravel drive bordered with
vns and conifers. You can explore the extensive gardens, which include a wildlife pond. The Rosedale
ite is an elegant four-poster room with a Victorian-style bathroom en suite; Buccleuch
s a sitting room and private patio. All rooms are well appointed, spacious and luxurious. Enjoy
me-made cakes and biscuits and hearty breakfasts in the elegant conservatory-dining room.
ecommended in the area
wick Garden; Chillingham Castle and wild cattle; Bamburgh Castle

The Bridge of Sighs, Oxford

The Boar's Head

★★★★ ◉◉ INN

ddress: Church Street, ARDINGTON,
Wantage OX12 8QA
el/Fax: 01235 833254
mail: info@boarsheadardington.co.uk
Vebsite: www.boarsheadardington.co.uk
Iap ref: 3, SU48
irections: In village next to church
ooms: 3 en suite, S £75–£95 D £85–£130
arking: 20 **Notes:** ⊘ in bedrooms ⊗ ♦♦

ocated in the downland village of Ardington, this inn combines a village pub, a first-class restaurant
nd stylish accommodation. The village is part of the Lockinge Estate, a great base for walking and
ycling, and only a half-hour drive from Oxford. Great care has gone into creating a stylish bedrooms,
while retaining many original features. One room has a luxurious bathroom, another has an adjoining
itting room. Food is a passion, with ingredients fresh, local and seasonal whenever possible. Fish is a
articular speciality. Excellent wines and good local ales.

Recommended in the area

)xford colleges; Vale of the White Horse; Blenheim Palace

Jpham House Bed & Breakfast

★★★★ BB

ddress: The Lanes, BAMPTON OX18 2JG
el/Fax: 01993 852703
mail: encompass5@aol.com
Iap ref: 3, SU48
irections: A4095 between Faringdon and
•rize Norton
ooms: 2 (1 en suite), S D £65–£75 **Parking:** 2
lotes: ⊘ on premises ⊗ on premises ♦♦ under 10
losed: 25–26 Dec and New Year

delightful stone-built house in a traditional country style, Upham House provides well-appointed
nd tastefully decorated accommodation, with a welcoming atmosphere; quality linen and towels,
omfortable beds, fresh flowers and local produce whenever possible. Situated in part of the
onservation Area of Bampton, with no passing traffic, yet only five minutes' walk from the village
entre, it also benefits from being just a short drive from the River Thames and Kelmscott Manor
home of William Morris. Bampton is just eight miles from Burford, 'the gateway to the Cotswolds'.

Recommended in the area

otswold Wildlife Park; Woodstock Palace; Blenheim Palace

Blenheim Palace, Woodstock

Mill House Country Guest House

★★★★ GA

Address: North Newington Rd, BANBURY OX15 6AA
Tel: 01295 730212
Email: lamadonett@aol.com
Website: www.themillhousebanbury.com
Map ref: 3, SP44
Directions: M40 junct 11, signs to Banbury Cross, onto B4035 (Shipston-on-Stour), 2m right for Newington
Rooms: 7 en suite, S £69–£79 D £89–£109
Parking: 20 **Notes:** ⊘ on premises ⊗ ♚ **Closed:** 2wks at Xmas

The former miller's house, surrounded by rolling countryside, offers luxurious accommodation in three rooms in the house and four refurbished self-contained cottages in the courtyard. Most of the en suite rooms have DVD players and/or digital TV. All have telephones and tea and coffee equipment. The cottages are available on a self-catering or bed and breakfast basis, and have a separate lounge or lounge-kitchen. There is a charming lounge bar in the main house.

Recommended in the area

Blenheim Palace; Straftord-upon-Avon; The Cotswolds

The Angel at Burford

★ ★ ★ ◎◎ RR

dress: 14 Witney Street, BURFORD OX18 4SN
l: 01993 822714
x: 01993 822069
ail: paul@theangelatburford.co.uk
bsite: www.theangelatburford.co.uk
p ref: 3, SP21
ections: Off A40 at Burford rdbt, down hill, 1st
nt onto Swan Ln, 1st left to Pytts Ln, left at end
to Witney St

oms: 3 en suite, S £70–£85 D £93–£110 **Notes:** ⊘ on premises 🐾 allowed in bedrooms 👶
der 9yrs

st 100 yards from Burford's bustling high street, the Angel is a haven of tranquillity and comfort. Built
1652, this cosy restaurant with rooms is packed with original features. Old oak beams adorn the
lings, and in the winter months flickering log fires reflect on the gleaming copper and brass, while
the summer you can relax in the peaceful courtyard or in the walled garden. The bedrooms are all
 suite, individually decorated for comfort and style, and have everything that you need to make you
 comfortable and at home. In the residents' lounge you will find information on local attractions,
 literature to help you plan long or short walks In the candlelit restaurant the menus reflect all that
 good about the local Cotswold produce, with an imaginative range of seasonal dishes, incorporating
 me from local estates, great fish dishes, and stunning desserts, all created using the freshest and
 st ingredients available. In the bar you'll find well-kept Hook Norton Ales, and arguably the finest bar
 unter in Burford, made from the increasingly rare Burr Elm. You may also find some locals, enjoying a
 t or two of Cotswold hospitality!

 commended in the area

 aftford-upon-Avon; The Cotswolds; Bicester Shopping Village

Burford House

★★★★★ GA

Address: 99 High Street,
BURFORD OX18 4QA
Tel: 01993 823151
Fax: 01993 823240
Email: stay@burfordhouse.co.uk
Website: www.burfordhouse.co.uk
Map ref: 3, SP21
Directions: Off A40 into town centre
Rooms: 8 en suite, S £95–£125 D £145–£160
Notes: ⊘ in bedrooms ⊗ on premises ♦♦

Set in the heart of historic and picturesque Burford, a famous Cotswolds market town with its range of specialist shops, this house, a 17th-century landmark on the High Street, is a haven for travellers. Marked by a half-timbered and stone exterior, it is quite simply a beautiful home in a beautiful location. The charming en suite bedrooms, including one family room and some with four-poster beds, are individually decorated and furnished to a very high standard and come with a host of homely extras – too many to mention, but including Witney blankets, fine bedlinen, flatscreen satellite TV/DVD, bathrobes, books and complimentary mineral water. Wireless internet connection is available in all rooms. Guests are welcome to use the two comfortable lounges, each with huge squashy sofas; one cosy with a log fire for chillier days, the other bright and sunny, with doors opening out to the courtyard. Superb breakfasts, morning coffees, light lunches and afternoon teas are made from local produce and served in the elegant dining room, and the well-stocked 'honour' bar contains a fine array of malt whiskies and cognacs, as well as home-made damson gin. Outside, the wisteria-clad courtyard garden is an oasis of peace and calm.

Recommended in the area

Historic Burford; Cotswold Wildlife Park; Bicester Shopping Village; Daylesford Organic Farmshop

Chowle Farmhouse B&B

★★★ FH

Address: Great Coxwell, FARINGDON SN7 7SR
Tel: 01367 241688
Email: info@chowlefarmhouse.co.uk
Website: www.chowlefarmhouse.co.uk
Map ref: 3, SU29
Directions: From Faringdon rdbt on A420, 2m west on right. From Watchfield rdbt 1.5m east on left
Rooms: 4 en suite **Parking:** 10 **Notes:** ⊗ on premises 🐾 allowed in bedrooms 🕴

This delightful, friendly establishment makes an ideal base for visiting the Thames Valley and surrounding area. The bedrooms and large en suite bathrooms in this modern farmhouse are all very well equipped, with flatscreen TV, hairdryer, fresh flowers, complimentary soft drinks, bath and/or power shower and good toiletries. One room has its own balcony, overlooking the outdoor pool. Downstairs is the charming and airy breakfast room, where breakfasts are prepared to order from fresh, local ingredients, including home-produced eggs, family-reared bacon and local honey.

Recommended in the area
Market town of Faringdon; Blenheim Palace

The Tollgate Inn & Restaurant

★★★ ⌫ INN

Address: Church Street, KINGHAM OX7 6YA
Tel: 01608 658389
Email: info@thetollgate.com
Website: www.thetollgate.com
Map ref: 3, SP22
Directions: Turn off B4450 (towards Chipping Norton)
Rooms: 9 en suite, S £60 D £90–£100 **Parking:** 12
Notes: ⊗ in bedrooms 🕴

Nestling in an idyllic village of stone cotswold cottages, this 17th-century farmhouse blends in perfectly with its surroundings, and makes a good base from which to explore the beautiful countryside. The building is fronted by a stone terrace and outside seating. Step inside and The Tollgate Inn and Restaurant creates an informal yet stylish atmosphere with flagstone floors, beamed ceilings, huge inglenook fireplaces and friendly faces. The inn has been lovingly restored to provide nine en suite bedrooms, each with an individual identity. Some of the finest food in the area, well-kept beers and good wines await you at The Tollgate Inn's restaurant.

Recommended in the area
Blenheim Palace; Batsford Park Arboretum; Oxford

Brasenose College, Oxford University

Byways

★★★★ BB

Address: Old London Road, MILTON COMMON, Thame OX9 2JR

Tel: 01844 279386

Email: byways.mott@tiscali.co.uk

Website: www.bywaysbedandbreakfast.co.uk

Map ref: 3, SP60

Directions: Off Junction 7 and 8a of the M40

Rooms: 3 (2 en suite), S £35–£40 D £60–£65

Parking: 3 **Notes:** ⊗ ⊗ in bedrooms 🐾 under 7yrs

Situated in 3 acres of English country garden, yet just a few minutes from the M40, Byways is a TV-free establishment with the emphasis on providing a peaceful and relaxing stay away from it all. The bedrooms here, all at ground level, are comfortable and tastefully decorated, with extras such as robe radios and English lavender products supplied. Breakfast makes use of organic and local produce where possible, and includes Byways' own freshly laid eggs, home-made bread and preserves made from home-grown fruit. Guests are encouraged to enjoy the large garden.

Recommended

Waterperry Gardens; Le Manoir aux Quat'Saisons; The Swan Antique Centre

lemere Country Park

The Laurels

★★★★ GH

Address: Broadoak, Six Ashes,
BRIDGNORTH WV15 6EQ
Tel: 01384 221546
Email: george.broadoak75@btinternet.com
Website: www.thelaurelsbandb.co.uk
Map ref: 2, SO79
Directions: On right 5m from Bridgnorth travelling towards Stourbridge on the A458
Rooms: 6 (5 en suite) Parking: 6 Notes: ⊘ on premises ⊗ on premises ♥♥ Closed: Xmas & New Year

At the end of a long day exploring the Shropshire countryside, this immaculate Victorian house located in a lovely hamlet is a lovely spot to unwind. Bedrooms are furnished to a good homely standard, and are equipped with tea and coffee facilities and hairdryers, and some have bathrooms en suite. Three rooms are in a converted stable block. Breakfast is served in the conservatory-dining room, there is a lounge and heated indoor swimming pool, a patio and manicured gardens.

Recommended in the area

Ironbridge; Black Country Museum; Redhouse Cone

Belvedere Guest House

★★★★ GH

Address: Burway Rd, CHURCH STRETTON SY6 6DP
Tel: 01694 722232
Email: info@belvedereguesthouse.co.uk
Website: www.belvedereguesthouse.co.uk
Map ref: 2, SO49
Directions: Off A49 into town centre, over x-rds onto Burway Rd
Rooms: 7 en suite D £62 Parking: 9 Notes: ⊘ ♞ ♥♥

This impressive, well-proportioned Edwardian house entices guests with its relaxed atmosphere and range of homely bedrooms, including a family room. All of the rooms, complemented by modern bathrooms, are equipped with practical extras such as hairdryer, shaver point and tea and coffee-making facilities. Ground-floor areas include a cottage-style dining room overlooking the pretty garden where a full English breakfast is served, a television lounge and a large reading room, with an extensive selection of books. Packed lunches can be provided by prior arrangement, and secure parking for cars and cycles is available.

Recommended in the area

Stokesey Castle; Cardingmill Valley (NT); Ludlow Castle

The Orchards

★★★★ BB

dress: Eaton Road, Ticklerton, CHURCH
STRETTON SY6 7DQ

l: 01694 722268

nail: lnutting@btinternet.com

ebsite: www.theorchardsticklerton.com

ap ref: 2, SO49

rections: 2m SE of Church Stretton. Off B4371 to
:klerton village

oms: 3 (2 en suite) **Parking:** 6 **Notes:** ⊘ on
emises ⊗ in bedrooms ⊁ under 3yrs

s modern house, set in more than 4 acres of grounds, gardens and, of course, an orchard, offers high
ndards of comfort throughout. The bedrooms are thoughtfully equipped with hairdryers, tea- and coffee-
aking facilities, TV, armchairs and radio alarms, (an iron and ironing board are available on request) and each
s a private bathroom, all but one of them en suite. Ann and Lloyd Nutting, the owners, not only maintain the
ality but also provide the exceptionally warm and welcoming atmosphere.

commended in the area

ng Mynd and the Carding Mill Valley; Shropshire Hills Discovery Centre; Ironbridge Gorge museums

The Crown Inn

★★★ INN

dress: Hopton Wafers, CLEOBURY MORTIMER
DY14 0NB

l: 01299 270372

nail: desk@crownathopton.co.uk

ebsite: www.crownathopton.co.uk

ap ref: 2, SO67

rections: In village on A4117 2m W of Cleobury
ortimer

oms: 18, S £59.5–£69.5 D £95–£115 **Parking:**
Notes: ⊘ in bedrooms ⊁ ⊁

rrounded by farmland, wooded valleys and tumbling streams, this 16th-century coaching inn
fers fine hospitality. The bedrooms vary: you can choose between the original, oak-beamed rooms
the inn, self-contained cottage-style rooms, and luxurious new rooms. Each is decorated in cottage
le, with quality fabrics. Cosy sofas in the public areas are inviting, and there is a choice of dining
oms. The menus feature modern cuisine, which is imaginatively prepared using fresh local produce.

commended in the area

dlow; Severn Valley Railway; Bridgnorth; Wyre Forest

Saracens at Hadnall

★★★★ ◉ RR

Address: Shrewsbury Road, HADNALL SY4 4AG
Tel/Fax: 01939 210877
Email: reception@saracensathadnall.co.uk
Website: www.saracensathadnall.co.uk
Map ref: 6, SJ52
Directions: M54 onto A5, at junct of A5/A49 take A49 towards Whitchurch. Follow A49 until Hadnall, diagonal from church
Rooms: 5 en suite, S £45 D £60–£75 **Parking:** 20
Notes: ⊘ on premises ⊗ in bedrooms ♦♦

This 18th-century Grade II listed coaching inn offers a warm welcome, excellent food and wine and comfortable accommodation. Each room offers Egyptian cotton bed linen, goose-down duvets and pillows, and all have been designed to be comfortable and cosy. There are many original features, including a 35-foot glass-topped well and beautiful parquet flooring. Wake up to a full English breakfast with Gloucester Old Spot sausages and free-range eggs from the owners' family farm.
Recommended in the area
Shrewsbury; Telford; Grosvenor Park Minature Railway

Broseley House

★★★★ GH

Address: 1 The Square, Broseley,
IRONBRIDGE TF12 5EW
Tel/Fax: 01952 882043
Email: info@broseleyhouse.co.uk
Website: www.broseleyhouse.co.uk
Map ref: 2, SJ60
Directions: 1m S of Ironbridge in Broseley centre
Rooms: 6 en suite, S £40–£50 D £60–£80
Notes: ⊘ on premises ⊗ in bedrooms ♦♦ under 5yrs

This impressive and lovingly restored Georgian house prides itself on being 'the friendly place to stay'. offers high-quality decor and soft furnishings throughout, and the thoughtfully and individually furnishe en suite bedrooms, one of which is a family room, all come with homely extras such as colour TV with DVD/CD/video, with a free borrowing library, hairdryer, radio alarm, bathrobes and beverage tray. Self-catering accommodation is also available. Comprehensive breakfasts, ranging from full English to lighter alternatives, are freshly cooked from local produce and served in the elegant dining room.
Recommended in the area
Benthall Hall; Blists Hill Victorian Town; Buildwas Abbey

The Library House

★★★★ GA

Address: 11 Severn Bank, IRONBRIDGE,
Telford TF8 7AN
Tel: 01952 432299
Fax: 01952 433967
Email: info@libraryhouse.com
Website: www.libraryhouse.com
Map ref: 2, SJ60
Directions: 50yds from Iron Bridge
Rooms: 4 (4 en suite), S £60–£75 D £70–£85
Notes: ⊗ on premises ⊗ in bedrooms 🕯 under 10yrs

Located just 60 yards from the famous Iron Bridge, this Grade II listed Georgian building is tucked away in a peaceful thoroughfare yet close to good pubs and restaurants. Hanging baskets and window boxes enhance the creeper-covered walls of the former library, and in the spring and summer the gardens are immaculate. All of the bedrooms have a television with DVD, a small DVD library, and a hospitality tray. Excellent breakfasts are served in the pine-furnished dining room.

Recommended in the area

Ironbridge World Heritage Site; Telford International Exhibition Centre; Blists Hill Victorian Town

Woodlands Farm Guest House

★★★ BB

Address: Beech Road, IRONBRIDGE TF8 7PA
Tel/Fax: 01952 432741
Email: woodlandsfarm@ironbridge68.fsnet.co.uk
Website: www.woodlandsfarmguesthouse.co.uk
Map ref: 2, SJ60
Directions: Off B4373 rdbt in Ironbridge onto Church
Hill & Beech Rd, house on private lane 0.5m on right
Rooms: 5 en suite, S £35–£70 D £60–£70
Parking: 8 **Notes:** ⊗ 🐾 🐕 🕯 under 5 yrs
Closed: 24 Dec–1 Jan

This green oasis, set in two acres of garden features a host of comforts and well-equipped suites. The three ground floor rooms have garden facing lounges and upstairs studio bedrooms also provide comfortable seating arrangements. Most suites have refrigerators and a generous selection of toiletries and refreshments are supplied. The grounds are open to guests and include pleasant seating areas and a car park. A comprehensive breakfast is served in the cheerful, welcoming dining room.

Recommended in the area

Ironbridge Gorge Museums; Portmeirion; Cadbury's World

Top Farm House

★★★★ GH

Address: KNOCKIN SY10 8HN
Tel: 01691 682582
Fax: 01691 682070
Email: p.a.m@knockin.freeserve.co.uk
Website: www.topfarmknockin.co.uk
Map ref: 5, SJ32
Directions: Off B4396 in village centre
Rooms: 3 en suite, S £35–£40 D £65–£75
Parking: 6 Notes: ⊗ in dining room ┮ allowed on
premises ⁑

Set in pretty gardens and retaining many original features, including exposed beams and open log
fires, Top Farm House combines traditional hospitality with elegant surroundings. The bedrooms are
equipped with many thoughtful extras. There is a relaxing beamed drawing room with a grand piano,
and imaginative and comprehensive breakfasts are served in the spacious period dining room which
overlooks the garden. The village of Knockin is one of the prettiest in this part of Shropshire.
Recommended in the area
Shrewsbury; Powis Castle (NT); Llanthaedr Waterfall

Bromley Court B&B

★★★★ BB

Address: Lower Broad Street, LUDLOW SY8 1PH
Tel: 01584 876996
Fax: 01584 873666
Email: phil@ludlowhotels.com
Website: www.ludlowhotels.com
Map ref: 2, SO57
Directions: Off B4361 at bridge into town centre
Rooms: 3 en suite, S £90–£115 D £100–£120
Notes: ⊗ on premises ┮ allowed in bedrooms ⁑

Located close to the river and attractions of the historic town, these three tiny Tudor cottages have ea
been converted into a private suite, complete with exposed oak beams, inglenook fireplaces
(in two cottages) and a stylish decorative theme. Each suite has a sitting room and bathroom en suite
antique bed with quality furnishings, many thoughtful extras and access to a lovely courtyard garden.
A continental breakfast is offered in the comfort of the suites (or the garden in warm weather), or
a full English breakfast is available at the nearby Bull Hotel.
Recommended in the area
Ludlow town, castle and church; woodland and riverside walks; Shropshire Hills Discovery Centre

esay Castle, near Ludlow

live Bar Restaurant with Rooms

★ ★ ★ ★   ◉◉ RR

ess: Bromfield, LUDLOW SY8 2JR
01584 856565

il: info@theclive.co.uk

site: www.theclive.co.uk

ref: 2, SO57

ctions: 2m N of Ludlow on A49 in village

ns: 15 en suite, S £60–£85 D £85–£110

ing: 100 Notes: ⊘ ⊗ ♦♦ Closed: 25–26 Dec

lish makeover of a former farmhouse has given The Clive a smart contemporary look. This
known restaurant has an emphasis on the use of fresh produce ranging from local meats,
ked products and vegetables to Cornish fish. Special dietary requirements can be catered for on
est. The spacious en suite bedrooms have been refurbished to provide well-equipped modern
mmodation. All rooms have colour TV, radio, telephone and wi-fi internet connection and facilities
aking tea and coffee; some rooms have easy access for guests with mobility problems. Paul and
ara Brooks and their team offer a sincere welcome and a warm atmosphere throughout.

ommended in the area

esay Castle, Craven Arms; Ludlow Food Hall; Ludlow Race Course and Golf Club; Offa's Dyke

De Grey's of Ludlow

★★★★★ GH

Address: 5–6 Broad Street, LUDLOW SY8 1NG
Tel: 01584 872764
Fax: 01584 879764
Email: degreys@btopenworld.com
Website: www.degreys.co.uk
Map ref: 2, SO57
Directions: Off A49, in town centre, 50yds beyond the clock tower
Rooms: 9 en suite, S £60–£120 D £80–£180
Notes: ⊗ on premises ⊗ in bedrooms ♿ Closed: 26 Dec & 1 Jan

This 16th-century timber-framed property houses De Grey's Tea Rooms, a well-known establishme in Ludlow town centre. It now also provides high-quality accommodation with luxurious modern facilities. All of the individually decorated and spacious bedrooms – including two suites and one ro on the ground floor – have been carefully renovated, the design of each governed by the labyrinth c historic timbers that comprise this Tudor building. Sporting evocative names such as The Buttercro Valentines View, Castle View and Market View, all the rooms have en suite facilities, and some feature stunning bathrooms with roll-top baths and large, powerful showers; one even has his and hers bathrooms separated by a 4 foot beam. Furnishings are tasteful, with lots of lush fabrics used throughout and four-poster beds in some rooms. Combined with the latest in entertainment technol this creates a successful fusion of past and present, and guests are encouraged to return to their rooms, unwind and relax with a bottle of wine. Breakfast, taken in the adjacent tearoom/restaurant bakery shop, includes award-winning breads and pastries freshly made on the premises, and is ser by smartly dressed waitresses, helping make a stay at De Grey's even more memorable.
Recommended
Ludlow Castle; Long Mynd; Cardin Mill Valley

Crown Country Inn

★★★ ◉◉ INN

Address: MUNSLOW, Craven Arms SY7 9ET
Tel: 01584 841205
Fax: 01584 841255
Email: info@crowncountryinn.co.uk
Website: www.crowncountryinn.co.uk
Map ref: 2, SO58
Directions: Off B4368 into village
Rooms: 3 en suite, S £50 D £70–£75 **Parking:** 20
Notes: ⊘ on premises ⊗ on premises ♦♦
Closed: 25 Dec

The historic character of this impressive Tudor inn is retained in the massive oak beams, flagstone floors and a large inglenook fireplace in the main bar area. The bedrooms, in a converted stable block at the rear, have sitting areas, hospitality trays, fresh fruit and mineral water. Traditional ales and food prepared from local produce are served in the bar and restaurant, and the day begins with a substantial English breakfast.

Recommended in the area

Ironbridge World Heritage Site; Shropshire Hills Discovery Centre; Ludlow Castle

Fieldside Guest House

★★★ GH

Address: 38 London Road, SHREWSBURY SY2 6NX
Tel: 01743 353143
Fax: 01743 354687
Email: info@fieldsideguesthouse@btinternet.com
Website: www.fieldsideguesthouse.co.uk
Map ref: 2, SJ41
Directions: A5 onto A5064, premises 1m on left
Rooms: 4 en suite, S £45 D £65
Parking: 8 **Notes:** ⊘ on premises ⊗ on premises ♦ under 10yrs

Fieldside, which dates back to 1835, is just 1 mile from the centre of Shewsbury and a 5-minute walk from Shrewsbury Abbey. This delightful house is attractively furnished and decorated and offers both single and double/twin rooms, all en suite. The bedrooms feature period-style furniture and are equipped with tea and coffee facilities. Breakfast is served at individual tables in the spacious dining room. Traditional English or vegetarian or lighter options are available. There is ample private parking.

Recommended in the area

Shrewsbury Castle and Abbey; Attingham Park (NT); Ironbridge Gorge and museums

Tudor House

★★★★ 🛏 GH

Address: 2 Fish Street,
SHREWSBURY SY1 1UR
Tel: 01743 351735
Email: enquiry@tudorhouseshrewsbury.co.uk
Website: www.tudorhouseshrewsbury.co.uk
Map ref: 2, SJ41
Directions: Enter town over English Bridge, ascend Wyle Cop,
50yds 1st right
Rooms: 3 (2 en suite)
Notes: ⊗ on premises ⊗ on premises ⭑ under 11yrs

Located in the beautiful medieval town centre of Shrewsbury, on
a quiet street, this fine Grade II listed 15th-century house makes an ideal base for visiting the town
with its many attractions and excellent shopping. This is a family-run establishment with the emphasis
on a relaxed atmosphere, and guests are well looked after, whether staying for business or pleasure;
much attention is paid to detail throughout. Inside, the house retains a wealth of historical features,
such as the original oak beams and fireplaces, enhanced by the tasteful decor and furnishings. The
attractively decorated and cosy bedrooms – all with en suite or private facilities – are filled with
thoughtful extras such as wall-mounted LCD TV and crisp white sheets, so that guests can retire to
their rooms and relax after exploring all that Shrewsbury has to offer. Broadband wireless internet
connection is available for an additional charge. The hearty full English breakfast served in the dining
room features local organic produce where possible, and special dietary needs will be catered for
where possible. Parking is available at a secure car park nearby, for a small charge.

Recommended in the area

Attingham Park; Wroxeter Roman Vineyard; Ironbridge

Soulton Hall

★★★★ ⌂ GA

Address:	Soulton, WEM SY4 5RS
Tel:	01939 232786
Fax:	01939 234097
Email:	enquiries@soultonhall.co.uk
Website:	www.soultonhall.co.uk
Map ref:	6, SJ52

Directions: A49 between Shrewsbury & Whitchurch turn onto B5065 towards Wem. Soulton Hall 2m NE of Wem on B5065

Rooms: 7 en suite, S £55–£73 **Parking:** 52 **Notes:** ⊘ on premises ⌖ allowed on premises ⛊

The Ashton family can trace their tenure of this impressive hall back to the sixteenth century, and much evidence of the building's age remains. The family and their staff offer excellent levels of personal service where the care of guests is of the utmost importance. The welcoming entrance lounge leads into the well-stocked bar on one side and an elegant dining room on the other. Here a good range of freshly prepared dishes, using fresh local produce wherever possible, are served in a friendly and relaxed formal setting. After the meal, coffee and liqueurs are served in the lounge hall in front of a blazing log fire in season. The house has central heating as well as log fires. The bedrooms in the hall reflect the character of the house with mullioned windows and exposed timbers; one room also has wood panelling. The converted carriage house across the garden offers ground-floor accommodation in two spacious double rooms each with spa baths. Standing in its own grounds beyond the walled garden, Cedar Lodge provides a choice of a peaceful four-poster suite or more modest family accommodation. Soulton Hall stands in 500 acres of open farmland, parkland and ancient oak woodland and you are welcome to explore the grounds.

Recommended in the area

Chester; Ironbridge; Shrewsbury

SOMERSET

Sunset over the Quantocks

Apsley House

★★★★ BB

ddress: Newbridge Hill, BATH BA1 3PT
el: 01225 336966
ax: 01225 425462
mail: info@apsley-house.co.uk
ebsite: www.apsley-house.co.uk
ap ref: 2, ST76
irections: 1.2m W of city centre on A431
ooms: 11 en suite, S £55–£120 D £70–£165
arking: 12 **Notes:** ⊘ on premises ⊗ on premises
Closed: 3 days at Xmas

uilt by the Duke of Wellington in 1830, this country house in the city, owned by Nick and Claire Potts, fers a gracious taste of Georgian Bath at its finest. Here guests can really soak up the atmosphere Britain's only World Heritage City. The location of Apsley House, in a peaceful residential area about mile from the city centre, ensures a truly relaxing stay, and this is enhanced by the presence of a arming and secluded rear garden, to which two of the bedrooms have direct access. The on-site arking and walking distance into the heart of the Bath are also great benefits in a city that can at nes seem besieged by traffic. Public rooms include a large drawing room with bar and a light and egant dining room, where the outstanding, freshly cooked breakfasts are served. All of the bedrooms ave en suite bathrooms, complete with Molton Brown toiletries, and each is individually decorated d furnished. The beds are either super-king size or four-posters, and other in-room facilities include itscreen TVs, Freeview, hospitality trays, direct-dial telephones and wireless Internet access. Apsley ouse is an aristocrat among bed and breakfast establishments and, maintained to the highest andards, is, in fact, fit for a duke.

ecommended in the area

oman Baths and Pump Room and the many museums in Bath; Longleat; Cheddar Gorge

Gough's Cave, Cheddar Gorge

Aquae Sulis

★★★★ GA

Address: 174/176 Newbridge Road, BATH BA1 3LE
Tel: 01225 420061
Fax: 01225 446077
Email: enquiries@aquaesulishotel.co.uk
Website: www.aquaesulishotel.co.uk
Map ref: 2, ST76
Directions: On A4 1.28m W of city centre, on A4 (Upper Bristol Rd)
Rooms: 14 (12 en suite), S £59–£75 D £65–£110
Parking: 12 **Notes:** ⊘ on premises ✸ allowed on premises ♦♦ **Closed:** 25–26 Dec

Situated within easy reach of the city, yet away from the crowds, this non-smoking Edwardian house offers a warm and genuine welcome. The good size en suite rooms are equipped with beverage trays, hairdryers, Sky TV, radio alarms and wi-fi access. There is a lounge with a small but well-stocked bar and a separate lounge with computer and patio garden for warm summer evenings. Traditional English or Continental breakfast is served in the dining room and snacks are available in the evening.
Recommended in the area
Roman Baths; Longleat; Cheddar Gorge and Caves

The Ayrlington

★ ★ ★ ★ ★ GA

Address: 24/25 Pulteney Road, BATH BA2 4EZ

Tel: 01225 425495

Fax: 01225 469029

Email: mail@ayrlington.com

Website: www.ayrlington.com

Map ref: 2, ST76

Directions: A4 onto A36, pass Holburne Museum, premises 200yds on right

Rooms: 14 en suite, S £75–£175 D £100–£175

Parking: 14 **Notes:** ⊘ on premises ⊗ on premises 🚼 under 14 yrs **Closed:** 22 Dec–5 Jan

Built of golden Bath stone, this impressive Grade II listed Victorian house is full of splendour and set right in the heart of Bath. Owners Simon and Mee-Ling Roper fuse western and eastern themes to stunning effect throughout. Asian antiques, artworks and fine fabrics sit comfortably alongside classical fireplaces, drapes and seating. All of the spacious bedrooms are furnished and decorated to individual themes, including a Chinese room, an Empire room, and the Pulteney room which has a four-poster bed. Other facilties include hospitality trays, direct-dial telephones, in-room safes, ironing facilities, TV and radio, and free wireless broadband access (a laptop is available for guests' use). Bathrooms are equipped with quality fixtures and fittings, and luxurious towels and toiletries, and some have a spa bath. While you enjoy your freshly cooked breakfast you can also enjoy superb views over the Oriental style walled gardens to Bath and the medieval abbey. There is also a bar and a welcoming lounge. This hotel offers a tranquil atmosphere and has ample secure parking. Simon and Mee-Ling also own the Lopburi Art & Antiques gallery, which is within walking distance. Bath's magnificent historic sites and many excellent restaurants are also close by.

Recommended in the area

Bath Abbey; Thermal Bath Spa; Museum of East Asian Art

The Bailbrook Lodge

★★★★ GH

Address: 35/37 London Road West, BATH BA1 7HZ
Tel: 01225 859090
Fax: 01225 852299
Email: hotel@bailbrooklodge.co.uk
Website: www.bailbrooklodge.co.uk
Map ref: 2, ST76
Directions: M4 junct 18, A46 S to A4 junct, left signed Batheaston, Lodge on left
Rooms: 15 (14 en suite), S £55 D £70–£135
Parking: 15 Notes: ⊗ on premises ⊗ on premises ♦♦

Lovely manicured lawns and gardens surround this stately Georgian country house just 1.5 miles from the city centre. The rooms retain their period charm and are well equipped. Five of the rooms have four-poster beds and additional facilities, including dressing gowns and cotton slippers. A bar and lounge overlook the patio and garden, and in the dining room the breakfast menu has an English flavour. The owners will be glad to recommend a restaurant nearby for dinner.

Recommended in the area

Roman Baths; Bath Abbey; Thermae Spa

The Bath House

★★★★ GA

Address: 40 Crescent Gardens, BATH BA1 2NB
Tel: 01179 374495
Fax: 01179 374921
Email: info@thebathhouse.org
Website: www.thebathhouse.org
Map ref: 2, ST76
Directions: 100yds from Queen Sq on A431
Rooms: 4 (4 en suite), S £65–£85 D £75–£105
Parking: 4 Notes: ⊗ ⊗ ♦♦ under 8yrs

Recently refurbished to a high standard, this accommodation is stylish and just a few minutes' level walk from the Georgian city of Bath. The en suite bedrooms are attractive, spacious, light and airy and equipped with modern accessories, including flatscreen television with freeview, hairdryer and wireless internet connection. Breakfast is made from fresh and where possible organic ingredients and served in the privacy of guests' bedrooms – a full-height dining table in each room ensures that the range of tasty options can be enjoyed to the full. Limited car-parking space is available.

Recommended in the area

Bath Abbey; The Pump Rooms; Thermae Bath Spa

The Roman Baths, Bath

Brocks Guest House

★★★★ GA

Address: 32 Brock Street, BATH BA1 2LN
Tel: 01225 338374
Fax: 01225 338425
Email: brocks@brocksguesthouse.co.uk
Website: www.brocksguesthouse.co.uk
Map ref: 2, ST76
Directions: Just off A4 between Circus & Royal Crescent
Rooms: 6 en suite, S £65–£70 D £79–£99 **Parking:** 2
Notes: ⊘ ⊗ ♦♦ **Closed:** 24 Dec–1 Jan

For an authentic taste of Georgian Bath, there are few places to surpass Brocks, which enjoys a superb location, between the Royal Crescent and The Circus. The accommodation, in rooms that retain all the elegance of that bygone age, is supremely comfortable and all the expected conveniences are there. The service and atmosphere is pleasantly informal and the hosts will help guests plan their sightseeing trips to make the most of their time here.

Recommended in the area

Royal Crescent; Prior Park; Thermae Bath Spa

Cheriton House

★★★★★ GA

Address: 9 Upper Oldfield Park, BATH BA2 3JX
Tel: 01225 429862
Fax: 01225 428403
Email: info@cheritonhouse.co.uk
Website: www.cheritonhouse.co.uk
Map ref: 2, ST76
Directions: A36 onto A367 Wells Rd, 1st right
Rooms: 11 en suite Parking: 11 Notes: ⊘ on
premises ⊗ on premises ⚹ under 12yrs

This grand Victorian house has panoramic views over Bath and is only a short walk from the city centre
Expect a friendly welcome from proprietors Iris and John who work hard to achieve a
relaxed atmosphere at Cheriton House. The carefully restored en suite bedrooms are all charmingly
individual and are furnished with a mix of antiques and modern furniture, and include a two-bedroom
suite in a converted coach house. All rooms have colour TV and a well-stocked hospitality tray. Wireless
internet access is also available for guests' use. A substantial breakfast is served in the
large conservatory-breakfast room overlooking beautifully manicured and secluded gardens which
are ablaze with colour during the summer months. The morning gets off to a good start with an
excellent buffet of cereals, fruits and juices with a traditional full English breakfast to follow. Special
dietary requirements can be catered for. Plan your day in the comfortable lounge, where you can
browse the ample supply of brochures and guide books and discover all that the city and the
surrounding area has to offer. Dinner is not available but Bath has many excellent restaurants and
Iris and John are happy to make recommendations to help you with your choice. Cheriton House
is a non-smoking establishment.

Recommended in the area

The Abbey and the many museum in Bath; Cheddar Gorge; Wells; Longleat

Chestnuts House

★★★★ GA

Address: 16 Henrietta Road, BATH BA2 6LY
Tel: 01225 334279
Fax: 01225 312236
Email: reservations@chestnutshouse.co.uk
Website: www.chestnutshouse.co.uk
Map ref: 2, ST76
Directions: M4, junct 18 onto A46, then A4 to Bath
Rooms: 5 en suite, S £60–£85 D £65–£95
Parking: 5 Notes: ⊘ ⊗ in bedrooms ♦♦

Chestnuts House, a fine Edwardian house with an enclosed garden, is ideally situated off the main road and adjacent to Henrietta Park, but is within a few minutes' level stroll of the city centre with its many attractions. Built from natural Bath stone, it offers fresh, airy accommodation. The bedrooms feature stylish contemporary furnishings and decor, and some have kingsize and wrought-iron beds. All offer colour TV, broadband wireless internet connection, hairdryer and refreshment tray; one has its own private patio area. Breakfast features an extensive buffet and daily specials, and there is a cosy lounge.

Recommended in the area

Bath's Roman Baths; Royal Crescent; Thermae Bath Spa

Dorian House

★★★★★ GA

Address: 1 Upper Oldfield Park, BATH BA2 3JX
Tel: 01225 426336
Fax: 01225 444699
Email: info@dorianhouse.co.uk
Website: www.dorianhouse.co.uk
Map ref: 2, ST76
Directions: A36 onto A367 Wells Rd, right onto
Upper Oldfield Park, 3rd building on left
Rooms: 11 en suite, S £55–£89 D £60–£160
Parking: 11 Notes: ⊘ on premises ⊗ in bedrooms ♦♦

Extensively refurbished in 2007, Dorian House is a fully restored Victorian town house with stunning views over the city. The period charm of the en suite bedrooms is enhanced by luxurious fabrics and furnishings, including Egyptian cotton sheets, large flat-screen TVs, and the award-winning breakfasts and lovely gardens. Several bedrooms have fine oak four-poster beds and all the rooms are named after famous musical figures, including Jacqueline du Pre, the owner's cello teacher.

Recommended in the area

Roman Baths and abbey; Royal Crescent and The Circus; Stourhead (NT)

Grove Lodge

★★★★ GA

Address: 11 Lambridge, BATH BA1 6BJ
Tel: 01225 310860
Email: stay@grovelodgebath.co.uk
Website: www.grovelodgebath.co.uk
Map ref: 2, ST76
Directions: 0.6m NE of city centre. Off A4, 400yds
W from junct A46
Rooms: 5 (4 en suite), S £48–£58 D £69–£83
Notes: ⊗ on premises ⊗ on premises ⊀under
6yrs Closed: Xmas, New Year & January

Owners Isobel Miles and her husband Peter Richards have refurbished their Grade II listed Georgian home to highlight the period features. Bedrooms are spacious with original marble or stone fireplaces. Furnishings blend modern and antique styles, and all rooms have large bathrooms. Each room has a radio-alarm clock, hairdryer, king-size bed and a courtesy tray. Healthy breakfasts are served in the sunny dining room; vegetarian and gluten-free diets are catered for with prior notice.

Recommended in the area

Georgian Bath; Roman Baths; Bath Abbey

Haydon House

★★★★★ GH

Address: 9 Bloomfield Park, BATH BA2 2BY
Tel: 01225 444919
Email: stay@haydonhouse.co.uk
Website: www.haydonhouse.co.uk
Map ref: 2, ST76
Directions: A36 onto A367 Wells Rd, right onto
Bloomfield Rd, 2nd right
Rooms: 5 (5 en suite), S £65–£95 D £77–£160
Parking: 1 Notes: ⊗ on premises ⊀⊀

This small, charming establishment contains a wealth of original Edwardian features and offers excellent standards of comfort and hospitality. Its spacious bedrooms, including a family room, are decorated with Laura Ashley fabrics, and all come with en suite facilities and extras such as a generous hospitality tray; the four-poster or canopied rooms all enjoy good views. Breakfast here is excellent, with freshly prepared meals of the highest quality served in the elegant dining room overlooking the colourful terraced gardens. Chocolates, flowers or champagne can all be provided for special occasions.

Recommended in the area

Longleat; Stonehenge; Cheddar Gorge

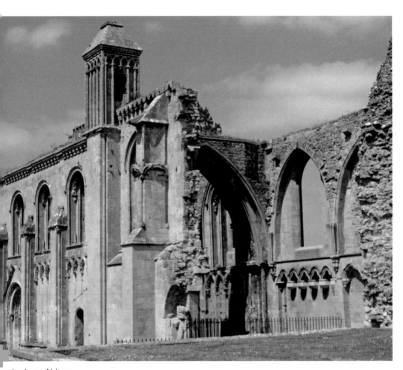

Glastonbury Abbey

The Kennard

★★★ GA

Address: 11 Henrietta Street, BATH BA2 6LL
Tel: 01225 310472
Fax: 01225 460054
Email: reception@kennard.co.uk
Website: www.kennard.co.uk
Map ref: 2, ST76
Directions: A4 onto A36 Bathwick St, 2nd right onto Henrietta Rd & Henrietta St
Rooms: 12 (10 en suite), S £58–£89 D £98–£130
Notes: ⊘ on premises ⊗ in bedrooms ⼈ under 8yrs **Closed:** 2 wks Xmas

This Georgian town house – now restored as a charming small hotel with its own special character. Was built as a lodging house in 1794. Situated just off the famous Great Pulteney Street, it is only five minutes from the Abbey, the Roman Baths, the new spa complex and the railway station. All of the bedrooms are thoughtfully and individually furnished, most are en suite, and some are located at ground-floor level. Breakfast includes a cold buffet as well as a selection of hot items.

Recommended in the area

Stonehenge; Castle Combe; Wells

The Villa Magdala

★★★★★ GA

Address: Henrietta Road, BATH BA2 6LX
Tel: 01225 466329
Fax: 01225 483207
Email: office@villamagdala.co.uk
Website: www.villamagdala.co.uk
Map ref: 2, ST76
Directions: A4 onto A36 Bathwick St, 2nd right
Rooms: 17 en suite, S £75–£95 D £98–£170
Parking: 17 **Notes:** ⊘ on premises ⊗ on premises
🚫under 7yrs

Ideally located for visiting Bath, this stylish Victorian town house built in 1868 was named after the Battle of Maqdala fought the same year – Field Marshall Lord Robert Napier, who commanded the campaign, lived nearby, hence the name. Originally built as two family homes, it has since become a delightful single building. It is just a short walk away from the city's attractions, yet offers a haven of peace and tranquillity overlooking Henrietta Park, one of Bath's most beautiful green spaces. Today the cast-iron balustrade to the main stairway and the elegant hallway indicate the style and grandeur of the families who lived here in the past. There are pleasant views from the attractively furnished and spacious en suite bedrooms, all of which are well equipped, with colour TV, radio and refreshment tray all standard. Four-poster, superior and family rooms are all available here. Guests are welcome to rel. in the charming and comfortable lounge, which is packed with useful information, including details of good local restaurants, while full English breakfast is served in the sunny dining room looking out onto the park opposite. Villa Magdala also provides wireless internet connection and sought-after private parking within the grounds.

Recommended in the area

The Cotswolds; Salisbury and Wells cathedrals; Stonehenge

Clanville Manor

★★★ FH

dress: CASTLE CARY BA7 7PJ
: 01963 350124
x: 01963 350719
ail: info@clanvillemanor.co.uk
bsite: www.clanvillemanor.co.uk
p ref: 2, ST63
ections: A371 onto B3153, 0.75m entrance to
nville Manor via white gate & cattle grid under bridge
oms: 4 en suite, S £30–£37.50 D £60–£75
king: 6 **Notes:** ⊘ on premises ⊗ on premises ∗ under 10yrs
sed: 21 Dec–2 Jan

It in 1743 from local honey-coloured Cary stone, Clanville Manor has been owned by the Snook
hily since 1898 and still functions as a beef-rearing farm. On hot summer days guests can enjoy
heated outdoor swimming pool, relax in the walled garden or take a walk along the banks of
River Brue. In summer there are often newborn calves and chicks. Guests enter the farmhouse
the flagstone entrance hall and climb a polished oak staircase up to the individually decorated
drooms, which retain much original character and offer fine views. The rooms, including one with
olid oak four-poster, each have flatscreen TV, hairdryer and complimentary tea and coffee. Hearty
akfasts made mainly from local produce are served in the elegant dining room overlooking the pond
d driveway. Fresh, golden-yolked eggs come from the farm's own hens, honey comes from Chris
ight's bees, and the Aga is called into play to cook the full English breakfast – lighter alternatives are
o on the menu. In the evenings, you can dine at one of several excellent local restaurants and pubs,
unwind in the spacious drawing room. Assistance dogs only are allowed.

commended in the area
stonbury; Stourhead (NT); Wells Cathedral; Cheddar Gorge and Wookey Hole Caves; Glastonbury Tor

Batts Farm

★★★★★ ≜ FH

Address: Nyland, CHEDDAR BS27 3UD
Tel: 01934 741469
Email: clare@batts-farm.co.uk
Website: www.batts-farm.co.uk
Map ref: 2, ST45
Directions: A371 from Cheddar towards Wells,
2m right towards Nyland, Batts Farm 1m on left
Rooms: 4 en suite, D £75–£95 **Parking:** 8
Notes: ⊗ on premises ⊗ in bedrooms 👶 under
12yrs

Batts Farm overlooks open farmland and moors at the foot of the Mendip Hills. The 200-year-old property, built of local Draycott stone, is full of character and owners Clare and John Pike make you feel at home. Clare's home-made biscuits and cakes are just part of the warm welcome here. The la bedrooms, all located on the first floor, are decorated and furnished to a high standard and include especially comfortable beds. One splendid room, with views to the Mendips, has a king-size antique four-poster bed with light drapes, a large bath and a double shower cubicle. Original sash windows, tiled floors and Victorian fireplaces have been retained throughout the farmhouse. Guests can relax ir the lounge or retreat to the walled garden with its summerhouse which is furnished with comfy sofas for a drink or a cream tea or just relax and read a book. Otherwise sit in the romantic formal garden and watch the birds in the water feature. Breakfast in the bright dining room, where guests sit around one large table, is a wide choice with home-made bread and local preserves. There are excellent wal in the area to help you work off all the delicious food and there are flat, quiet lanes for cycling – stora is available if you want to bring your own bike. There is plenty of parking on the gravel drive.

Recommended in the area

Cheddar Caves and Gorge; Wookey Hole Caves; Wells

or Farm

★★★ GA

dress: Nyland, CHEDDAR BS27 3UD

: 01934 743710

x: 01934 743710

ail: info@torfarm.co.uk

bsite: www.torfarm.co.uk

p ref: 2, ST45

ections: A371 from Cheddar towards Wells,
r 2m turn right towards Nyland. Tor Farm 1.5m
right

oms: 8 en suite, D £65–£95 Parking: 12 Notes: ⊘ in bedrooms ⊗ on premises ♦♦

cked away in the glorious Somerset countryside, and close to the Mendip Hills and Somerset Levels,
r Farm is an ideal base for walkers and anyone interested in exploring the local area. A real rural
ll, it offers attractive, contemporary accommodation and provides guests with many welcome extras,
luding its own outdoor heated swimming pool situated in a south-facing walled garden. The smartly
nished en suite bedrooms, including several on the ground floor, all have wonderful views of the
ture gardens and surrounding area, and most boast their own private terrace or balcony with French
rs. They also benefit from crisp cotton bedlinen and beverage-making facilities, and one room has
ur-poster bed. For special occasions, a range of thoughtful extras can be provided in the room with
r notice, including flowers, champagne and strawberries dipped in chocolate. Hearty breakfasts are
de using local produce where possible, including fresh eggs from Tor Farm's own hens, along with
m-cured bacon and sausages, porridge and kippers. Guests are welcome to relax in the cosy lounge,
d to make use of the complimentary film library, or to enjoy barbecues in the garden during summer
nths. Off-road parking is available.

commended in the area

ngleat; Cheddar Gorge; Bath; Stonehenge; Glastonbury

Wells Cathedral

Tarr Farm Inn

★★★★★ ⊛ INN

Address: Tarr Steps, Exmoor National Park,
DULVERTON TA22 9PY
Tel: 01643 851507
Fax: 01643 851111
Email: enquiries@tarrfarm.co.uk
Website: www.tarrfarm.co.uk
Map ref: 2, SS92
Directions: 4m NW of Dulverton. Off B3223 signed
Tarr Steps, signs to Tarr Farm Inn
Rooms: 9 en suite, S £90 D £150 **Parking:** 10 **Notes:** ⊗ in bedrooms 🐾 🐕 under 14yrs

Tarr Farm dates from the 16th century and nestles just above Tarr Steps and the River Barle. The new bedrooms with en suite bathrooms display careful attention to detail with thick fluffy bathrobes, fridge organic toiletries and much more. When it comes to food you will not be disappointed with wonderful cream teas, scrumptious breakfasts and delicious dinners with ingredients sourced from Devon and Somerset farms and suppliers. The farm is set in beautiful countryside ideal for walkers.

Recommended in the area

Exmoor National Park; South West Coast Path; Dunster Castle (NT)

Freedom Cottage

★★★ BB

Address: Cumhill, PILTON BA4 4BG
Tel: 01749 890188
Fax: 01749 890188
Email: freedomcottage@aol.com
Website: www.freedomcottage.com
Map ref: 2, ST64
Directions: On A361 SW of Shepton Mallet
Rooms: 2 en suite, S £45 (2 nights or more only) D from £60
Parking: 9 Notes: ⊘ on premises ⊗ in bedrooms ⊶ under 2yrs Closed: mid Dec–13 Jan

Set in the conservation area of Pilton, this lovely cottage provides an ideal base for exploring the Somerset countryside. The cottage is smart, light and airy and the individually styled bedrooms are both en-suite. An open plan mezzanine area adds to the charm of this peaceful haven. Local produce is used to make breakfast, which is served in the dining room where there are wonderful views of the surrounding countryside.

Recommended in the area

Wells; Glastonbury Tor; Bath and West Showground

Cannards Grave Farmhouse

★★★ GA

Address: Cannards Grave,
SHEPTON MALLET BA4 4LY
Tel: 01749 347091
Fax: 01749 347091
Email: sue@cannardsgravefarmhouse.co.uk
Website: www.cannardsgravefarmhouse.co.uk
Map ref: 2, ST64
Directions: On A37 between Shepton Mallet & The Bath & West Showground, 100yds from Highwayman pub towards showground on left
Rooms: 4 en suite, S £40–£50 D £55–£65 Parking: 6 Notes: ⊘ ⊗ ⊶ under 5yrs

Warming host Sue Crockett offers quality accommodation at this welcoming 17th-century farmhouse. The bedrooms are delightful and have thoughtful touches such as hospitality trays, mineral water, biscuits and mints. One room has a four-poster bed and a fridge with fresh milk. Delicious breakfasts are served in the garden conservatory and there is a comfortable lounge to relax in.

Recommended in the area

Bath and West Showground; Historic Wells; Glastonbury Tor; City of Bath

Greyhound Inn

★★★★ 🍺 INN

Address: STAPLE FITZPAINE,
Taunton TA3 5SP
Tel: 01823 480227
Fax: 01823 481117
Email: thegreyhound-inn@btconnect.com
Website: www.greyhoundinn.biz
Map ref: 2, ST21
Directions: Off A358 into village
Rooms: 4 en suite, S £55 D £80 **Parking:** 60
Notes: 🚭 in bedrooms ⊗ on premises 👶 under 12yrs

The creeper-clad Greyhound Inn is set in an Area of Outstanding Natural Beauty; it is a picturesque village inn tucked away in the village of Staple Fitzpaine. It makes an ideal base for touring the local countryside, yet being close to the M5 it is also a good choice for business travellers. Inside it has great atmosphere and character, and has been extended over the years to provide a series of rambling connecting rooms with a rustic mix of flagstone floors, old timbers, natural stone walls and open fires. The delightful en suite bedrooms are spacious, comfortable and well equipped, with many extras such as colour TV, direct-dial telephone, trouser-press, hairdryer and hospitality tray, as well as a good supply of toiletries, coming as standard. Wireless internet connection is also available. In the candlelit restaurant, an imaginative choice of freshly prepared seasonal dishes using locally sourced ingredients is featured on the ever-changing blackboard menu, complemented by a good choice of wines, and the hearty full English breakfasts are definitely worth getting up for. Award-winning, properly kept ales can be enjoyed in the locals' bar, with its barrel stools and wood-burning stove. Parking is available for guests.

Recommended in the area

Taunton; Blackdown Hills; Longleat

Cutsey House

★★★★ GA

Address: Cutsey, Trull, TAUNTON TA3 7NY
Tel: 01823 421705
Email: cutseyhouse@btconnect.com
Website: www.cutseyhouse.co.uk
Map ref: 2, ST22
Directions: M5 junct 26, into West Buckland, right at
T-junct, 2nd left, next right
Rooms: 3 en suite, S £35–£40 D £60–£70
Parking: 11 **Notes:** ⊘ ⊗ ⋔ **Closed:** Xmas–Etr

This Victorian house is set in over 20 acres of gardens and grounds, with parts of the building dating back to the 15th and 16th century, including a Tudor staircase. Inside, careful renovation has resulted in an elegant and traditional establishment. The comfortable, spacious bedrooms have glorious views of the countryside towards the Blackdown Hills. Public rooms are well proportioned and comfortable and include the library, main dining room, billiards room and parlour room (which doubles as the 'daily' dining room). Dinner is available by arrangement and guests can enjoy their drinks in the library.

Recommended in the area

Blackdown Hills (Area of Oustanding Natural Beauty); Barrow Mump (NT); Somerset County Museum

Lower Farm

★★★★ FH

Address: Thornfalcon, TAUNTON TA3 5NR
Tel: 01823 443549
Email: doreen@titman.eclipse.co.uk
Website: www.somersite.co.uk
Map ref: 2, ST22
Directions: M5 junct 25, 2m SE on A358, left opp
Nags Head pub, farm signed 1m on left
Rooms: 11 (8 en suite), S £45 D £65–£70 **Parking:** 10
Notes: ⊘ on premises ⊗ on premises ⋔ under 5yrs

This charming thatched 15th-century longhouse is full of character. Lovely gardens and open farmland surround this pretty property, where beamed ceilings and inglenook fireplaces testify to its age. The bedrooms include some in a converted granary, and all are either en suite or have private facilities. All rooms have high standards of furnishings – some are ideal for families. A hearty breakfast is cooked on the Aga and served in the farmhouse kitchen, using quality local bacon and sausages, and free-range eggs from proprietor Doreen Titman's own hens.

Recommended in the area

Hestercombe Gardens; Willow and Wetlands Visitors Centre; Quantock Hills

Crown & Victoria

★★★★ INN

Address: Farm Street, TINTINHULL,
Yeovil BA22 8PZ
Tel: 01935 823341
Fax: 01935 825786
Email: info@thecrownandvictoria.co.uk
Website: www.thecrownandvictoria.co.uk
Map ref: 2, ST41
Directions: Off A303, signs for Tintinhull Gardens
Rooms: 5 en suite Parking: 60 Notes: ⊘ in
bedrooms ⊗ on premises ♦♦

The Crown and Victoria country inn stands in the heart of the pretty village of Tintinhull. In days gone by, as well as being the village pub the inn was also a private school – lessons took place where the existing bar is situated. Today, above the new restaurant, the unfussy bedrooms are light and airy and very well equipped with hairdryers, TVs with DVD players, tea and coffee facilities, and wireless broadband Internet access. The staff ensure you are well cared for. The contemporary bar and restaurant offers a successful combination of traditional pub atmosphere and quality dining. Carefully presented dishes are available for lunch and dinner under the direction of head chef, London-trained Stephen Yates. The menu ranges from traditional English dishes such as steak and ale pie to the more elaborate pan-roasted breast of duck on a bed of spinach with a potato rösti, plum and port jus. The extensive wine list includes ten fine house wines and there is a choice of local real ales. When the weather is kind, guests can relax in the garden with a drink or a light meal or enjoy a candlelit dinner in the conservatory with lovely garden views.

Recommended in the area

Tintinhull House Garden (NT); Montacute House (NT); Barrington Court (NT); Yeovil;
Fleet Air Arm Museum, Yeovilton

Double-Gate Farm

★ ★ ★ FH

dress: Godney, WELLS BA5 1RX

: 01458 832217

x: 01458 835612

ail: doublegatefarm@aol.com

bsite: www.doublegatefarm.com

p ref: 2, ST54

ections: A39 from Wells towards Glastonbury, at
sham right signed Godney/Polsham, 2m to x-rds,
tinue to farmhouse on left after inn

oms: 6 en suite, S £50–£55 D £65–£70 **Parking:** 20 **Notes:** ⊘ on premises ⊗ on premises 🚻

sed: 21 Dec–4 Jan

pecial welcome awaits you not just from the owners, but from Jasper and Paddy, the very friendly
rievers at this fine stone farmhouse situated on the banks of the River Sheppey on the Somerset
els, which has good views of Glastonbury Tor and the Mendip Hills. Cycle trips can be taken from
farmhouse on quiet roads to the Levels, which abound with birds and wildlife. Guests can play
le-tennis or snooker (on a full-size table) in the games room, or watch their own DVDs in the well-
uipped bedrooms, all of which are en suite and offer hairdryers, complimentary tea and coffee, and
eview television. There is free internet access in the guest lounge. Double-Gate Farm is well known
its beautiful summer flower garden, home-grown tomatoes and fruit and its delicious breakfasts,
ich are served at two refectory tables in the dining room, or on the patio in summer. Choose from a
ection of fruit, cereals, juice, yoghurt, compote and local cheeses, as well as full English breakfasts
d mouth-watering American pancakes with fresh fruit and maple syrup – all accompanied by
icious home-made bread. Other meals may be taken at local inns, including the pub next door.

commended in the area

lls (England's smallest city); Glastonbury; Cheddar Gorge

Collett Park, Shepton Mallet

Camellia Lodge

★★★★ GH

Address: 76 Walliscote Road,
WESTON-SUPER-MARE BS23 1ED
Tel/Fax: 01934 613534
Email: dachefs@aol.com
Website: www.camellialodge.net
Map ref: 2, ST36 **Directions:** 200yds from seafront
Rooms: 5 en suite, S £27.5–£30 D £55–£65
Notes: ⊗ on premises 🐾 allowed on premises ♦♦

With the mile-long promenade and pier right on the doorstep, Camellia Lodge is a great choice for a seaside break. The proprietors create a warm atmosphere that makes you want to return again and again – they are so pleased to have you stay they will even collect you from the train or bus stations. Inside their three-storey Victorian home you will find immaculate bedrooms well equipped for a long or short stay. Most are a good size and have all bathrooms en suite. Breakfast is a wide choice using local produce and excellent home-cooked evening meals are available by prior arrangement. Both are served the dining room.

Recommended in the area

Weston Golf Club; Sea Life Centre; Cheddar Gorge

Rookery Manor

★★★ GA

Address: Edingworth Road, Edingworth,
WESTON-SUPER-MARE BS24 0JB
Tel: 01934 750200
Fax: 01934 750014
Email: enquiries@rookery-manor.co.uk
Website: www.rookery-manor.co.uk
Map ref: 2, ST36
Directions: M5 junct 22, A370 towards Weston, 2m
right to Rookery Manor

Rooms: 22 en suite, S £50–£65 D £75–£95 **Parking:** 460 **Notes:** ⊗ ♠ ♦♦

Rookery Manor, a 16th-century manor house best known for its extensive wedding and conference facilities, is situated in its own delightful gardens and grounds, with water features, a lake, a waterfall, fragrant flowerbeds, sculptures and covered walkways all combining to form a picturesque and tranquil setting. Yet it is within easy reach of the M5 and all the resort attractions of Weston-Super-Mare. Most of the bedrooms are situated in the converted barns and coach house adjacent to the manor house – many have individual features such as circular windows and wooden beams. The wide choice of individually decorated en suite rooms includes well-thought-out family rooms and two luxurious suites; the latter have four-poster beds. All of the rooms are modern and bright and have their own access to the garden; thoughtful extras include kingsize beds, TV, telephone, hairdryer and tea and coffee-making facilities. A residents' lounge with sumptuous leather couches and two fireplaces is available, and a varied menu, making use of local and organic produce and accompanied by a comprehensive wine list, is offered in Truffles Restaurant. Other facilities include a tennis court and a games room.

Recommended in the area

Cheddar; Weston-Super-Mare; Glastonbury; Thermal Bath Spa

The Tarr Steps, Exmoor National Park

North Wheddon Farm

★★★★ 🏠 🍽 FH

Address: WHEDDON CROSS TA24 7EX
Tel: 01643 841791
Email: northwheddonfarm@aol.com
Website: www.go-exmoor.co.uk
Map ref: 2, SS93
Directions: 500yds S of village x-rds on A396. Pass Moorland Hall on left, driveway next right
Rooms: 3 (2 en suite), S £27.50–£35 D £55–£70
Parking: 5 **Notes:** ⊗ 🐾 👫

North Wheddon Farm is a delightfully friendly and comfortable environment with great views. It is set within a private estate of 17 acres and includes a paddock and duck pond, as well as a pleasant garden. Dinners and breakfasts here are memorable and feature local and the farm's own fresh produce on the interesting menus. The bedrooms are all individually decorated and thoughtfully equipped with extras such as TV/DVD and tea and coffee-making facilities, and the beds are most comfortable – one room features a four-poster.

Recommended in the area

Minehead; Exmoor; Dunster

Karslake House

★★★★ @ GH

Address: Halse Lane, WINSFORD,
Exmoor National Park TA24 7JE
Tel: 01643 851242
Email: enquiries@karslakehouse.co.uk
Website: www.karslakehouse.co.uk
Map ref: 2, SS93
Directions: In village centre, past the pub and up the hill
Rooms: 6 (5 en suite), S £55–£75 D £80–£115
Parking: 15 **Notes:** ⊘ on premises 🐾 allowed on premises 👶 under 12yrs **Closed:** Feb & Mar

This small country house is very much a family home where guests are made to feel like old friends. Original beams and fireplaces feature and quality is evident in the furnishings throughout the house. The bedrooms are attractively decorated and thoughtfully equipped – one has a four-poster bed. Food is a highlight, and interesting menus, home-baked bread, and home-made preserves are offered in the spacious restaurant. Riding, fishing and shooting can be arranged. Dogs are welcome.

Recommended in the area

Tarr Steps (medieval clapper bridge); Holnicote Estate (NT); Minehead

Mow Cop Castle folly (NT)

Coppers End

★★★★ GA

Address: Walsall Road, Muckley Corner,
LICHFIELD WS14 0BG
Tel: 01543 372910
Fax: 01543 360423
Email: info@coppersendguesthouse.co.uk
Website: www.coppersendguesthouse.com
Map ref: 3, SK10
Directions: A5 onto A461 N for 100yds
Rooms: 6 (4 en suite), S £35–£43 D £52–£64
Parking: 9 **Notes:** ⊘ on premises ⊗ in bedrooms ♦♦ **Closed:** Xmas & New Year

This family-run establishment provides well-appointed modern bedrooms: two are on the ground floor for easy access. All rooms have vanity units, tea- and coffee-making facilities, TV, Wi-fi, hairdryers, a safe and cooling fans. The spacious lounge with a TV is just the place to unwind before bedtime. A full English breakfast, accompanied by a selection of fruit and cereals, is served in the modern conservatory dining room which overlooks a patio and pretty walled garden. Special diets can be catered for.

Recommended in the area

Lichfield Cathedral; Cannock Chase Country Park; Shugborough Estate

The Crewe and Harpur Arms

★★★★ RR

Address: Market Square,
LONGNOR, Buxton SK17 0NS
Tel: 01298 83205
Fax: 01298 83689
Email: enquiries@creweandharpur.co.uk
Website: www.creweandharpur.co.uk
Map ref: 7, SK06
Directions: In village centre on B5053
Rooms: 11 (8 en suite) **Parking:** 100 **Notes:** ⊘ on premises ⊗ on premises ♦♦

Situated in the heart of the Peak District high on the Staffordshire moors, this Georgian pub has been stylishly renovated, maintaining original features and ambience. The en suite bedrooms have luxury Italian-style bathrooms with under-floor heating and heated towel rails. All rooms have flat screen TVs with digital Sky, and tea and coffee facilities. Real ales are served in the oak-panelled bar and meals can be taken in the separate dining room. There are three self-catering cottages in the courtyard.

Recommended in the area

Buxton; Haddon Hall; Peak Rail

llam Hall (NT), Peak District National Park

The Beehive Guest House

★★★★ GH

Address: Churnet View Road, OAKAMOOR ST10 3AE
Tel: 01538 702420
Email: thebeehiveoakamoor@btinternet.com
Website: www.thebeehiveguesthouse.co.uk
Map ref: 7, SK04
Directions: Off B5417 in village N onto Eaves Ln, sharp left onto Churnet View Rd
Rooms: 5 en suite, S £35–£54 D £52–£56
Parking: 6 **Notes:** ⊘ on premises ⊗ on premises ⋔

This spacious detached house offers a choice of thoughtfully equipped and comfortable bedrooms, one of which is a triple. All of the rooms, which benefit from central heating, colour TV, hairdryer and tea and coffee-making facilities, are en suite and come with four-poster beds, making this an ideal place for a romantic break or just a stress-free trip away from it all. The family-run Beehive also offers guests a comfortable lounge/dining room, where substantial and individually prepared breakfasts are served, and where dinner can be taken by prior arrangement. Private parking is available.

Recommended in the area

Peak District National Park; Stoke-on-Trent potteries; Chatsworth House

The Laurels Guest House

★★★ GH

Address: Star Bank, OAKAMOOR
ST10 3BN
Tel: 01538 702629
Fax: 01538 702796
Email: bbthelaurels@aol.com
Website: www.thelaurels.co.uk
Map ref: 7, SK04
Directions: On B5147 from Cheadle, 250yds on
right past Cricketers Arms public house in Oakamoor.
Also, west of Stoke-on-Trent, close to A52.
Rooms: 9 en suite, S £35–£50 D £50–£60 Parking: 9
Notes: ⊘ in bedrooms ⊗ in bedrooms ♿

On the edge of Oakamoor village in the Staffordshire Moorlands, this friendly guest house is ideally located for families wishing to visit Alton Towers or intent on touring rural Staffordshire and the Potteries. The pretty and comfortable en suite bedrooms, including a choice of adaptable family rooms, one room on the ground floor and two with four-poster beds, come equipped with homely extras such as colour TV and tea and coffee-making facilities. Guests can relax in the licensed residents' bar, which has a pool table, or enjoy dinner or a hearty breakfast in the restaurant, with its views of the large patio area. When weather allows, guests may choose to eat on the patio. Otherwise, there are a number of restaurants and pubs catering to a wide range of tastes within a few miles of the Laurels, and the owners are happy to advise on these. There is also a galleried seating area offering fine woodland views and a well-stocked magazine rack within the house. Family room rates are also available.

Recommended in the area

Alton Towers Theme Park; Peak District National Park; Gladstone Pottery Museum

Colton House

★★★★★ GH

Address: Colton, RUGELEY WS15 3LL
Tel/Fax: 01889 578580
Email: mail@coltonhouse.com
Website: www.coltonhouse.com
Map ref: 3, SK01
Directions: 1.5m N of Rugeley. Off B5013 into
Colton, 0.25m on right
Rooms: 4 en suite, S £42–£70 D £58–£90
Parking: 15 Notes: ⊘ ⊗ ⚲ under 12yrs

In a pretty, peaceful village, with two pubs and a church, this superbly restored luxurious Georgian home has views across the 1.5 acre garden to Cannock Chase. Sit on the south-facing patio, enjoy the sun and have a drink before a dinner made with home-grown organic vegetables. The individually designed bedrooms provide a choice, from a four poster, a 6' x 7' bed and round 5' Jacuzzi, to those with beamed ceilings and superb views. Enjoy the fluffy Egyptian cotton towels, power showers and P and Gay's dedication to ensuring you have an enjoyable stay.

Recommended in the area

The Potteries; Cannock Chase; Shugborough Estate (NT)

Haywood Park Farm

★★★★ FH

Address: Shugborough, STAFFORD ST17 0XA
Tel/Fax 01889 882736
Email: haywood.parkfarm@btopenworld.com
Website: www.haywoodparkfarm.co.uk
Map ref: 7, SJ92
Directions: 4m SE of Stafford off A513. Brown signs
to Shugborough, on right 400yds past Hall
Rooms: 2 en suite, S £65–£70 D £70–£75 Parking:
4 Notes: ⊘ on premises ⊗ on premises ⚲ under
14 yrs

The attractive farmhouse stands on a 120-acre arable and sheep farm on Cannock Chase, part of the Shugborough Estate. The large, attractively furnished bedrooms have a host of extras such as fresh flowers, fruit, tea facilities and shortbread. Large fluffy towels are provided in the luxury bathrooms. Breakfast, using local produce, is served in the lounge-dining room. The area is a paradise for walker and cyclists. Fishing is offered in the lake, which is well stocked with carp and other coarse fish.

Recommended in the area

Shugborough Estate (NT); Wedgewood Museum; Alton Towers; Trentham Gardens

annock Chase

Harlaston Post Office

★★★ GH

ddress:	Main Rd, Harlaston, TAMWORTH B79 9JU
el:	01827 383324
ax:	01827 383746
nail:	info@harlastonpostoffice.co.uk
ebsite:	www.harlastonpostoffice.co.uk
ap ref:	3, SK20
irections:	4.5m N, off A513 into Harlaston village
ooms:	4 en suite, S £30–£32 D £50–£55

arking: 5 Notes: ⊘ on premises ⊗ on premises ♦♦

he Post Office is a row of traditional cottages that has been renovated to create a desirable guest
ouse. Still incorporating a Post Office and stores, it stands opposite the church in an idyllic village,
ith pretty gardens behind. The bedrooms have been individually decorated and furnished, and have
omfy beds, bathrooms and hospitality trays, and plenty of thoughtful extras. Other considerate touches
re the guest kitchen, laundry and lounge, ideal for families with young children. Joyce Rowe
a delightful host, and her hearty cooked breakfasts have to be experienced.

ecommended in the area

rayton Manor Theme Park; Lichfield Cathedral; National Memorial Arboretum, Alrewas

SUFFOLK

River Blyth, Blythburgh

The Toll House

★★★★ GH

Address: 50 Victoria Road, ALDEBURGH IP15 5EJ
Tel: 01728 453239
Email: tollhouse@fsmail.net
Website: www.tollhouse.travelbugged.com
Map ref: 4, TM45
Directions: B1094 into town until rdbt, B&B on right
Rooms: 7 en suite, S £60 D £70–£75 **Parking:** 6
Notes: ⊘ on premises ⊗ on premises ♦♦

Expect a warm welcome at this delightful Victorian brick house, situated just a short walk from the seafront and half a mile from the centre of Aldeburgh, with its associations with composer Benjamin Britten. This coastal area is a paradise for birdwatchers and walkers. Snape Maltings, 5 miles away, is a collection of traditional buildings nestling beside the River Alde with shops, galleries, restaurants and the world-class concert hall. The bedrooms at The Toll House – twins and doubles – all have bathrooms en suite, attractive co-ordinated fabrics and tea and coffee facilities. Breakfast is served at individual tables in the smart dining room that overlooks the pretty, secluded garden.

Recommended in the area

Minsmere Bird Sanctuary (RSPB); Concert Hall, Snape; Suffolk Heritage Coast

The Chantry

★★★★ GA

Address: 8 Sparhawk Street,
BURY ST EDMUNDS IP33 1RY
Tel: 01284 767427
Fax: 01284 760946
Email: chantryhotel1@aol.com
Website: www.chantryhotel.com
Map ref: 4, TL86
Directions: From cathedral S onto Crown St, left onto Sparhawk St
Rooms: 15 en suite, S £59–£79 D £89–£99 **Parking:** 16
Notes: ⊘ on premises ↝ allowed on premises ♦♦

A delightful Grade II buidling where parking for each room is provided via a 19th-century carriage access. Bedrooms are decorated in period style, and the spacious superior double rooms (all non-smoking) have antique beds. There is a cosy lounge bar, and breakfast and dinner are served in the restaurant. Dishes are home cooked and prepared from fresh ingredients.

Recommended in the area

Abbey Gardens and ruins; Theatre Royal (NT); Ickworth House, Park & Gardens (NT)

Ickworth House, Park & Gardens (NT), Horringer

Clarice House

★★★★★ ◎ GA

Address: Horringer Court, Horringer Road,
BURY ST EDMUNDS IP29 5PH
Tel: 01284 705550
Fax: 01284 716120
Email: bury@claricehouse.co.uk
Website: www.claricehouse.co.uk
Map ref: 4, TL86
Directions: 1m SW from town centre on A143 towards Horringer
Rooms: 13 en suite, S £55–£60 D £85–£100 **Parking:** 85
Notes: ⊘ on premises ⊗ on premises ⋇ under 5yrs
Closed: 24–26 Dec & 31 Dec–1 Jan

This large mansion is set in 20 acres of landscaped grounds just a short drive from Bury St Edmunds. The family-run residential spa, with superb leisure facilites, has spacious, well-equipped bedrooms. Public rooms include a smart lounge bar, an intimate restaurant offering quality food and a changing menu, a further lounge and a conservatory.

Recommended in the area

Bury St Edmunds; Abbey Gardens; Ickworth House, Park and Gardens (NT)

The Three Kings

★★★★ INN

Address: Hengrave Road, Fornham All Saints, BURY ST EDMUNDS IP28 6LA

Tel: 01284 766979

Email: thethreekings@keme.co.uk

Website: www.the-three-kings.com

Map ref: 4, TL86

Directions: A14 junct 42, B1106 to Fornham, left into B1101, establishment on left

Rooms: 9 en suite, S £62 D £65–£80 family room £145 **Parking:** 28 **Notes:** ⊗ in bedrooms ⊗ in bedrooms ♦♦

The Three Kings, a family-run establishment full of character and renowned for its friendliness, is a charming 17th-century coaching inn. Situated in the pretty village of Fornham All Saints, it is just 2 miles north-west of historic Bury St Edmunds, with its amenities. Countryside walks, golfing and trout fishing are all also on the doorstep. The smartly furnished bedrooms here, including two family rooms and some on the ground floor, have recently been refurbished and are situated in the new building across the courtyard from the main property, providing guests with privacy and the freedom to come and go as they please. All are thoughtfully equipped with a range of extras to ensure a comfortable stay, such as colour TV, mini-bar, hairdryer, work-desk, internet connection point, alarm clock, trouser-press and tea and coffee-making services. Public rooms feature a smart and jovial lounge bar, a relaxing conservatory and a comfortable restaurant, and guests can enjoy an extensive selection of traditional home-cooked meals, with signature dishes such as steak and ale pie and daily specials, including fresh local fish, as well as a Sunday roast carvery. Locally brewed cask ale and wines chosen from an extensive wine list complement the food.

Recommended in the area

Bury Cathedral; West Stow Country Park; Ickworth House, Park & Gardens (NT)

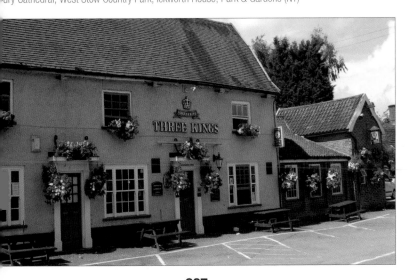

Lavenham Priory

★★★★★ BB

Address: Water Street, LAVENHAM,
Sudbury CO10 9RW
Tel: 01787 247404
Fax: 01787 248472
Email: mail@lavenhampriory.co.uk
Website: www.lavenhampriory.co.uk
Map ref: 4, TL94
Directions: A1141 to Lavenham, turn by side of
Swan onto Water St & R after 50yds onto private
drive **Rooms:** 6 en suite, S £75–£85 D £98–£165 **Parking:** 11 **Notes:** ⊘ on premises ⊗ on premises ⊷ under 10yrs **Closed:** 21 Dec–2 Jan

Gilli and Tim Pitt have created a sumptuous haven in the midst of historic Lavenham, one of England's prettiest medieval villages. The building dates back to the 15th century and retains many fine early features, including an oak Jacobean staircase, leading to beautiful bedrooms with crown posts, Elizabethan wall paintings and oak floors. Each room has a spectacular bed: a four poster, lit bateau (sleigh) bed, or domed canopy polonaise bed – some were made for the rooms by a Lavenham cabinetmaker. All are en suite, some with a slipper bath, and all have TV and tea and coffee facilities. The house stands in 3 acres of private grounds, all attractively landscaped and stocked with period herbs, plants and shrubs. Breakfast, taken in the Merchant's Room at an imposing polished table, is a choice of fruit compotes, yoghurts, orange juice, cereals, a traditional English breakfast, kippers, haddock, smoked salmon and scrambled eggs, and various breads, croissants, jams and preserves. The great hall with its Tudor inglenook fireplace and an adjoining lounge are lovely places to relax, and are well stocked with books and board games.

Recommended in the area

Lavenham Guildhall (NT); Sutton Hoo (NT); Kentwell Hall

·ield End

★★★ GH

dress: 1 Kings Road, LEISTON IP16 4DA

l: 01728 833527

x: 01728 833527

ail: herbert@herbertwood.wanadoo.co.uk

ebsite: www.fieldendbedandbreakfast.co.uk

ip ref: 4, TM46

ections: In town centre off B1122

oms: 5 (2 en suite), S £30–£35 D £60–£65

rking: 5 Notes: ⊗ ⊗ under 6mths

is large Edwardian house, south of Leiston town centre, has been refurbished to a high standard d is impeccably maintained by the present owners. The bedrooms, including a family room, feature -ordinated soft furnishings and many thoughtful touches. Breakfast, made from local produce where ssible, is chosen from a full menu and is served in the attractive dining room, which has a large sofa d a range of puzzles and games. It is directly below the family room and comes equipped with a baby onitor, making it ideal for parents of small children.

commended in the area

ffolk Coastal Walk; RSPB North Warren; Southwold

Somerton House

★★★ GA

dress: 7 Kirkley Cliff, LOWESTOFT NR33 0BY

l/Fax: 01502 565665

nail: pippin.somerton@btinternet.com

ebsite: www.hotelssuffolk.uk.com

ap ref: 4, TM59

rections: On the old A12, 100yds from aremont Pier

oms: 7 (5 en suite), S £35–£45 D £55–£60

tes: ⊗ on premises allowed on premises

osed: 25–26 Dec

ests visiting Somerton House are well placed to relax and unwind by the sea, for this Grade II listed ilding, designed by Sir Morton Peto. The house has managed to retain many of its original features er the years, and the bedrooms, also smartly furnished in a period style, have many thoughtful uches; some rooms have four-poster or half-tester beds. Breakfast and dinner, made from local oduce are served in the smart dining room, and guests have the use of a aviation-themed lounge.

commended in the area

lton Broad, gateway to the Broads National Park; Ness Point; Somerleyton Hall and Gardens

The White Hart Inn

★★★★ ◎◎ INN

Address: High St, NAYLAND, Colchester CO6 4JF
Tel: 01206 263382
Fax: 01206 263638
Email: nayhart@aol.com
Website: www.whitehart-nayland.co.uk
Map ref: 4, TL93
Directions: Off A134 into village centre
Rooms: 6 en suite, S £66–£109 D £86–£129
Parking: 6 Notes: ⊘ ⊗ ♥ Closed: 2 wks Jan

Relaxation and a warm welcome are guaranteed at this delightful 15th-century inn, located in a charming village in the heart of Constable Country. The spacious en suite bedrooms are individually decorated and carefully furnished, with lots of facilities, including wireless internet connection. Downstairs, the elegant restaurant, open for lunch and dinner as well as breakfast, retains the original overhanging beams and has an open fire. The varied menu offers seasonal, local produce – salmon is smoked on-site and herbs and walnuts grown in the garden. There is a garden terrace to the rear.

Recommended in the area

Colchester; Maldon; Frinton-on-Sea

Sandpit Farm

★★★★ BB

Address: Bruisyard, SAXMUNDHAM IP17 2EB
Tel: 01728 663445
Email: smarshall@aldevalleybreaks.co.uk
Website: www.aldevalleybreaks.co.uk
Map ref: 4, TM36
Directions: 4m W of Saxmundham. A1120 onto B1120, 1st left for Bruisyard, house 1.5m on left
Rooms: 2 en suite Parking: 4 Notes: ⊘ on premises ⊗ in bedrooms ♥ Closed: 24–26 Dec

This delightful Grade II listed farmhouse set in 20 acres of grounds, with the River Alde meandering along the boundary of the gardens, is well located for visiting the many places of interest in Suffolk. The en suite bedrooms have lots of thoughtful touches and enjoy lovely country views; one is located in its own wing of the house. There is also a cosy lounge for relaxing, as well as a secret garden, a wild-flower orchard and a hard tennis court. Breakfast features quality local and home-made produce as well as freshly laid free-range eggs.

Recommended in the area

Framlingham; Minsmere RSPB reserve; Sutton Hoo (NT)

SURREY

Hampton Court

Pembroke House

★★★★ GA

Address: Valley End Road, CHOBHAM GU24 8TB
Tel: 01276 857654
Fax: 01276 858445
Email: pembroke_house@btinternet.com
Map ref: 3, SU96
Directions: A30 onto B383 signed Chobham, 3m right onto Valley End Rd, 1m on left
Rooms: 4 (2 en suite), S £40–£50 D £80–£130
Parking: 10 Notes: ⊗ on premises 🐕 allowed on premises 👶 under 6yrs

Julia Holland takes great pleasure in treating guests as friends at spacious neo-Georgian home set amid rolling fields. The elegant public areas include an imposing entrance hall and a dining room with views over the surrounding countryside. The bedrooms are filled with thoughtful extras. Two single rooms share a bathroom, while the other rooms are en suite. There are many top-class golf clubs in the vicinity, as well as polo, horseracing and shooting. There is a tennis court in the attractive grounds.

Recommended in the area

Windsor Castle; Wisley RHS Gardens; shooting at Bisley

Bentley Mill

★★★★★ BB

Address: Bentley, FARNHAM GU10 5JD
Tel: 01420 23301
Fax: 01420 22538
Email: ann.bentleymill@supanet.com
Website: www.bentleymill.com
Map ref: 3, SU84
Directions: Off A31 Farnham-Alton road, opp Bull Inn, turn left onto Gravel Hill Rd
Rooms: 4 (2 en suite), D £95–£125 Parking: 6
Notes: ⊗ on premises ⊗ on premises 👶 under 8yrs

Ann and David do everything to ensure that you enjoy your stay at their country home, a former corn mill beside a river and set in 5 acres of beautifully tended grounds. The two main suites are in the former mill rooms where all the original beams survive. The rooms have superior quality featuring antiques, luxurious beds and deep sofas. A full breakfast is cooked on the Aga or choose seasonal fruit, croissants or bagels. The room service menu is available 7pm–9pm providing hot and cold snacks.

Recommended in the area

Jane Austen's House, Chawton; The Watercress Line, Alresford; Portsmouth Historic Dockyard

Wayfarer's Walk, Alresford

Asperion

★★★ GA

Address: 73 Farnham Road, GUILDFORD GU2 7PF
Tel: 01483 579299
Fax: 01483 457977
Email: enquiries@asperion.co.uk
Website: www.asperion.co.uk
Map ref: 3, SU94
Directions: From M25 jnct 10 take A3 into Guildford and follow signs to A31
Rooms: 15 (14 en suite), S £50–£65 D £75–£120
Parking: 11 **Notes:** ⊘ on premises ⊗ in bedrooms 👶 under 12yrs **Closed:** 22 Dec–6 Jan

The team of this stylish, contemporary accommodation care passionately about the environment, and this is evident in their use of organic, locally sourced and Fairtrade produce, green energy and sustainable work practices. Bedrooms are luxuriously decorated and feature extras, such as Egyptian cotton bedding, power showers, flatscreen TV and free internet access. The breakfasts feature organic breads, cereals and fresh fruit salads, smoked salmon, organic eggs and free-range bacon.

Recommended in the area

Loseley House; RHS Garden, Wisley; Clandon Park

The Seven Sisters cliffs

Brighton House

★★★★ GA

Address: 52 Regency Square,
BRIGHTON BN1 2FF
Tel: 01273 323282
Email: info@brighton-house.co.uk
Website: www.brighton-house.co.uk
Map ref: 3, TQ30
Directions: Opp West Pier
Rooms: 14 en suite **Notes:** ⊗ on premises ⊗ on premises
⋆ under 12yrs

This charming Regency town house is perfectly placed for shopping in The Lanes, all the town's attractions and the beach. Every smartly furnished bedroom has beds and linens of a high standard, TV, tea- and coffee-making facilities, hairdryers and fans for summer. The continental buffet-style breakfast provides a broad choice with produce locally sourced. Many ingredients are organic and the selection is impressive. There is a parking arrangement with the nearby car park.

Recommended in the area

Brighton Pavilion; Brighton seafront; South Downs

Five

★★★★ GA

Address: 5 New Steine, BRIGHTON BN2 1PB
Tel: 01273 686547
Fax: 01273 625613
Email: info@fivehotel.com
Website: www.fivehotel.com
Map ref: 3, TQ30
Directions: Along A259 heading E, 8th turning on left
Rooms: 10 (8 en suite), S £30–£60 D £60–£120
Notes: ⊗ on premises ⊗ in bedrooms ⋆⋆

Five, a period townhouse overlooking a classic Regency square, has far-reaching views and is only a few short steps to the beach, cafés, bars and restaurants of this lively seaside town's famous Lanes. The contemporary, versatile rooms are comfortable and well equipped, and each benefits from crisp white linen, luxurious duvet, TV (some have DVD), wi-fi and tea and coffee-making facilities. Some triple and family rooms are available. The copious breakfast, which includes organic bacon, eggs and mushrooms as well as fresh berries, is served in the spacious bay-fronted dining room.

Recommended in the area

Brighton Pier; Brighton Pavilion; shopping in The Lanes

George IV

★★★★ GA

Address: 34 Regency Square,
BRIGHTON BN1 2FJ
Tel: 01273 321196
Email: info@georgeivbrighton.co.uk
Website: www.georgeivbrighton.co.uk
Map ref: 3, TQ30
Directions: Opp West Pier, at top of square
Rooms: 8 en suite, S £45–£55 D £65–£130
Notes: ⊘ on premises ⊗ in bedrooms ♦♦
Closed: Xmas–mid Jan

Situated at the top of a prominent Regency square, George IV, a restored period townhouse, offers wonderful sea views. Some of the smartly furnished bedrooms have good views, and one has a balcony; all are beautifully decorated and very spacious. Optional continental breakfasts are served in the bedrooms, each with its own en suite bathroom and with a TV/DVD; a selection of films is available to borrow. There's a quirky touch in the 1950s jukebox at reception, and there's a lift to all floors.

Recommended in the area

Royal Pavilion; North Lanes; Brighton; Hove

The Kelvin Guest House

★★★★ GA

Address: 9 Madeira Place, Kemptown,
BRIGHTON BN2 1TN
Tel: 01273 603735
Email: enquiries@thekelvin.co.uk
Website: www.thekelvin.co.uk
Map ref: 3, TQ30
Directions: At Brighton Pier, turn left in Marine Drive. Madeira Place is 5th turning on left.
Rooms: 10 (7 en suite) Notes: ⊘ on premises ⊗ in bedrooms ♦♦ under 12yrs

Recently refurbished in an elegant, contemporary style, this Regency house offers a friendly and relaxed place to stay. The comfortable rooms are all stylishly decorated (with one on the ground floor) and each come with Italian-style shower room with power shower, LCD flatscreen freeview TV, dressing/work-station, refreshments and lush furnishings. Breakfast is served in the bright and cheery dining room, and hosts Paul and Shaun invite guests to make use of the attractive deck patio.

Recommended in the area

Brighton Royal Pavilion; The Lanes; Brighton Pier

The Camelot Lodge

★ ★ ★ GA

ddress: 35 Lewes Road, EASTBOURNE BN21 2BU
el: 01323 725207
ax: 01323 722799
mail: info@camelotlodgehotel.com
ebsite: www.camelotlodgehotel.com
ap ref: 4, TV69
rections: A22 onto A2021, premises 0.5m after hospital
the left
ooms: 8 en suite, S £35–£45 D £60–£80 **Parking:** 11
otes: ⊗ ⊗ ♦♦

is privately owned and family-run establishment maintains
e highest standards of comfort and cleanliness throughout. All of the tastefully decorated en suite
drooms, one of which is on the ground floor and some of which are family rooms, are double-
azed and have gas central heating, and all offer a range of facilities, including freeview TV/DVD
th CD player, hospitality tray, radio alarm clock and hairdryer. For guests who are hard of hearing,
portable 'T' induction loop is available on request. Drinks can be enjoyed at the bar in the spacious
nd attractive guest lounge, where a selection of books and games and even a piano are all available.
eakfast, served in the bright conservatory dining room, which overlooks the garden and fishpond, is
hearty affair with a cold buffet of cereal, fruit, yoghurt and juices, as well as porridge and full English
eakfast on offer; traditional English evening meals can also be ordered by prior arrangement. Guests
ave access to free wireless internet connection, as well as to private parking.

ecommended in the area

edoubt Fortress and Military Museum; Eastbourne Bandstand; Eastbourne Downland

The Gables

★★★★★ BB

Address: 21 Southfields Road,
EASTBOURNE BN21 1BU
Tel: 01323 644600
Email: info@gablesbandb.co.uk
Website: www.gablesbandb.co.uk
Map ref: 4, TV69
Directions: A2270 into town centre, 2nd exit at rdbt by station, bear right into Southfields Rd
Rooms: 3 (2 en suite), D £64–£72 Parking: 2
Notes: ⊗ on premises ⊗ in bedrooms 🚼 under 12yrs

The Gables is a splendid Edwardian property with an attractive garden, spacious accommodation and friendly hosts. The bedrooms offer en suite or private facilities, and are well-stocked with mineral water, colour TV, hairdryer and lots of information on the local area. The freshly cooked breakfasts are served in the elegant dining room and offer a range of choices. Free wireless internet connection is also available for guests. A short walk will take you to the station, town centre and pier.

Recommended in the area

Eastbourne beach; Brighton Pavilion; South Downs Way

The Manse B&B

★★★★★ BB

Address: 7 Dittons Road, EASTBOURNE BN21 1DW
Tel: 01323 737851
Email: anne@themansebandb.co.uk
Website: www.themansebandb.co.uk
Map ref: 4, TV69
Directions: A22 to town centre railway station, onto Old Orchard Rd, right onto Arlington Rd
Rooms: 3 en suite, S £42–£48 D £70–£80
Parking: 2 Notes: ⊗ ⊗ in bedrooms 🚼

This character home is in a quiet residential area only a 5-minute walk from the town centre. It was built as a Presbyterian manse in 1906 in the Arts and Crafts style and retains many original features such as oak panelling and stained-glass windows. The beautifully decorated en suite bedrooms are spacious and comfortable, and come with armchairs, radios, tea and coffee trays and hairdryers. Anne Walker's breakfasts are very good, using a range of quality produce. If the traditional English is too much then try the continental (smoked ham, cheese, tomato and olives) or vegetarian options.

Recommended in the area

South Downs and Beachy Head; Charleston Farmhouse (Bloomsbury group); Michelham Priory

Ocklynge Manor

★ ★ ★ ★ ★ GA

Address: Mill Road, EASTBOURNE BN21 2PG
Tel: 01323 734121
Email: ocklyngemanor@hotmail.com
Website: www.ocklyngemanor.co.uk
Map ref: 4, TV69
Directions: From Eastbourne Hospital follow town centre/seafront sign, 1st right onto Kings Av, Ocklynge Manor at top of road
Rooms: 3 (2 en suite), D £70–£80 **Parking:** 3
Notes: ⊘ on premises ⊗ on premises 🚸 under 12yrs

Instantly inviting, this 300-year-old house is set in extensive grounds and it's hard to imagine that you are just 10 minutes' walk from the centre of Eastbourne. The manor is on land that was previously occupied by a monastery, and this was also site of a 12th-century Commandery of the Knights of St John of Jerusalem. More recently, according to a blue plaque, the house was once the home of the renowned children's book illustrator Mabel Lucie Atwell. Today, David and Wendy Dugdill welcome guests to the manor, providing a charming personal touch to every aspect of the place. The bedrooms, all accessed via the main staircase, are spacious and sunny, with views across the garden from the large windows. The decor and furnishings are comfortable and elegant, and top quality Egyptian cotton bed linen and towels are provided. Fresh flowers, a TV, DVD, radio, hairdryers and plenty of lamps are among the extra touches that so enhance a stay here. The bathrooms are modern and luxurious, and two adjoining rooms can be used as a suite. The public rooms include a gracious drawing room with grand piano and the beautiful garden is a lovely place to stroll on a summer evening. A full English breakfast is served in the dining room.

Recommended in the area

South Downs Way; Beachy Head; Great Dixter; Bodiam Castle; Bateman's

Parkside House

★★★★ GA

Address: 59 Lower Park Road,
        HASTINGS & ST LEONARDS TN34 2LD
Tel: 01424 433096
Fax: 01424 421431
Email: bkentparksidehse@aol.com
Map ref: 4, TQ80
Directions: A2101 to town centre, right at rdbt,
1st right
Rooms: 5 (4 en suite), S £35–£45 D £55–£65
Notes: ⊗ on premises ⊗ on premises ♦♦

Parkside House is in a quiet conservation area opposite Alexandra Park, with its lakes, tennis courts
and bowling green, yet is only a 15-minute walk from the seafront. The rooms are stylishly furnished,
with many antique pieces, and generously equipped with video recorders, hairdryers, tongs, toiletries,
bathrobes, and beverage trays. A good choice of breakfast – English or continental – is served
at individual tables in the elegant dining room, and there is also an inviting lounge.
Recommended in the area
Battle Abbey; Bodiam Castle (NT); Michelham Priory

Stream House

★★★★★ GA

Address: Pett Level Road, Fairlight,
        HASTINGS & ST LEONARDS TN35 4ED
Tel: 01424 814916
Email: info@stream-house.co.uk
Website: www.stream-house.co.uk
Map ref: 4, TQ80
Directions: 4m NE of Hastings. Off A259 on
unclassified road between Fairlight & Cliff End
Rooms: 2 (1 en suite), S D £70–£85 Parking: 4
Notes: ⊗ on premises ⊗ on premises ♦♦ under 10yrs Closed: Dec–Feb

Lovingly renovated from three cottages, Stream House is situated in 3 acres of grounds within attracti
countryside, and is only a mile from the beach at Pett Level and cliff walks at Fairlight. The pretty
bedrooms, with quality furnishings, are well equipped with complimentary toiletries, hospitality tray, T
and good-sized baths and power showers. Breakfast is served in the lounge dining room, which has a
original inglenook fireplace; there are plenty of books and magazines to read.
Recommended in the area
Hastings Country Park; Rye; Great Dixter House and Gardens

The Blacksmiths Arms

★★★ ⊜ INN

Address: London Road, Offham, LEWES BN7 3QD
Tel: 01273 472971
Email: blacksmithsarms@tiscali.co.uk
Website: www.theblacksmithsarms-offham.co.uk
Map ref: 3, TQ41
Directions: 2m N of Lewes. On A275 in Offham
Rooms: 4 en suite, S £45–£75 D £65–£80
Parking: 22 **Notes:** ⊗ on premises ⊗ on premises. Guide
dogs only ⊀ under 5yrs

Situated just outside Lewes, this charming 18th-century inn is set amid beautiful surroundings in an Area of Outstanding Natural Beauty. Nestled beneath the Sussex Downs, this is a great location for touring the South coast. Each of the high-quality, comfortable double bedrooms at the Blacksmiths Arms features en suite bathroom, flatscreen TV and tea and coffee-making facilities. All have recently been refurbished and are delightfully decorated. Downstairs, open log fires and a warm, relaxed atmosphere welcome you to the cosy bar, where excellent dinners and hearty breakfasts are freshly cooked to order. Evening diners can choose from the inventive brasserie-style menu, which draws from only the best local produce wherever possible, including fresh fish and seafood landed at local ports. Dishes here are much more than pub food, and might include roast local estate free-range venison, wild sea bass fillets in a seafood risotto with a lobster velouté drizzle, or Auntie Kate's fresh crispy roast duckling. Bernard Booker, the owner and chef of the Blacksmiths, has won awards for his seafood dishes, and award-winning, locally brewed Harveys Sussex Bitter is properly served in superb condition, another indication that the owners here like to do things properly.

Recommended in the area

Brighton; South Downs Way; Sheffield Park Gardens; Bluebell Railway; Glyndebourne Opera House

Battle Abbey

Wellington House

★★★★ BB

Address: Dixter Road, NORTHIAM, Rye TN31 6LB
Tel: 01797 253449
Email: fanny@frances14.freeserve.co.uk
Map ref: 4, TQ82
Directions: Into Northiam from S, turn left after Post Office signed Great Dixter Gardens. B&B 50yds up Dixter Rd on left
Rooms: 2 (2 en suite), S £50 D £70 **Parking:** 1
Notes: ⊘ in bedrooms 🐾 allowed in bedrooms 🧑‍🦽
Closed: Xmas & New Year

Set in the quiet village of Northiam, this charming Victorian house is perfect for a tranquil break. The spacious double bedrooms offer a high level of comfort with added extras such as home-made biscuits and hot water bottles cleverly disguised as teddy bears. The bathrooms have lots of pampering goodies. Enjoy afternoon tea by the open fire in the lounge. The hearty breakfast features home-made bread, local sausages and fish, and the freshest of free range eggs all served around one elegant table.

Recommended in the area

Battle Abbey; Rye; Great Dixter House and Gardens; Bodiam Castle; Camber Castle; Hastings Castles

Jeake's House

★★★★★ GA

Address: Mermaid Street, RYE TN31 7ET
Tel: 01797 222828
Fax: 01797 222623
Email: stay@jeakeshouse.com
Website: www.jeakeshouse.com
Map ref: 4, TQ92
Directions: Approach from High St or The Strand
Rooms: 11 (10 en suite), S £79 D £90–£124
Parking: 21 **Notes:** ⊘ in dining room 🐕 allowed on premises 👶 under 8yrs

A fine building in one of the most beautiful parts of Rye, Jeake's House dates from 1689 and during its colourful history it has been both a wool store and a Baptist school. In the early 20th century it was the home of American poet and author Conrad Potter Aiken, and was the setting for many literary get-togethers. The house is owned and run by Jenny Hadfield who offers relaxed hospitality and excellent accommodation of a high standard. The public rooms include an oak-beamed lounge and a book-lined bar where you can relax over a drink. The original galleried chapel has been converted into a dining room where a breakfast of fruit juices, fresh fruit, prunes, figs and cereals are followed by traditional cooked dishes, prepared from fresh local produce, and served with toast of your choice and home-made preserves. A vegetarian option is available. The bedrooms are individually styled with sumptuous furnishings including brass or mahogany bedsteads dressed with linen sheets. Ten rooms are en suite, and all offer TV, telephones, hospitality trays and luxuriously fluffy towels. There is a private car park nearby. Jenny is always happy to advise her guests on places to visit in the area and can recommend the local restaurants and friendly inns.

Recommended in the area

Bodiam Castle (NT); Battle; Sissinghurst Castle Garden (NT)

Manor Farm Oast

★★★★★ GA

Address: Windmill Lane, RYE TN36 4WL
Tel/Fax: 01424 813787
Email: manor.farm.oast@lineone.net
Website: www.manorfarmoast.co.uk
Map ref: 4, TQ92
Directions: 4m SW of Rye. A259 W past Icklesham
church, left at x-rds onto Windmill Ln, after sharp left
bend left into orchards
Rooms: 3 (2 en suite), S £59–£69 D £84–£94
Parking: 8 Notes: ⊗ on premises ⊗ in bedrooms ⤴under 11yrs Closed: 23 Dec–15 Jan

Built in 1860 and surrounded by a working orchard on the edge of the Icklesham, Manor Farm Oast is ideal for a quiet break. The oast house has been converted to keep the unusual original features both inside and out – the double bedroom in one tower is completely round. Your host Kate Mylrea provides a very friendly welcome. Kate is passionate about food: as well as a traditional English breakfast or a healthier alternative, she can prepare a top quality five-course dinner by arrangement.

Recommended in the area

Battle Abbey; historic Rye; Ellen Terry's House (NT)

Strand House

★★★★ GA

Address: Tanyards Ln, Winchelsea, RYE TN36 4JT
Tel: 01797 226276
Email: info@thestrandhouse.co.uk
Website: www.thestrandhouse.co.uk
Map ref: 4, TQ92
Directions: M20 junct 10 onto A2070 to Lydd. Follow
A259 to Rye. Through Rye, 2m outside Rye
Rooms: 10 (9 en suite), D £65–£120 Parking: 12
Notes: ⊗ ⊗ ⤴ under 12yrs

Strand House provides a calm retreat from the stresses of modern living, with elegant rooms set in a historic Tudor house full of period detail, such as low, oak-beamed ceilings, winding stairs and inglenook fireplaces in the large lounge. Bedrooms are full of good-quality furniture and include thoughtful extras such as hand-made biscuits. They include a ground-floor garden suite and a family room. Good, freshly made Sussex breakfasts are provided, as well as afternoon tea, packed lunches and evening meals on request – all incorporating organic locally reared meat and home-made cakes.

Recommended in the area

Great Dixter; Sissinghurst; Romney Hythe and Dymchurch Railway

White Vine House

★★★★ RR

Address: 24 High Street, RYE TN31 7JF
Tel: 01797 224748
Email: info@whitevinehouse.co.uk
Website: www.whitevinehouse.co.uk
Map ref: 4, TQ92
Directions: In the middle of Rye high street
Rooms: 7 en suite, S £70 D £125–£160
Notes: ⊘ on premises ⊗ in bedrooms ♦♦

Situated in the middle of the ancient town of Rye, delightful White Vine House retains much of its medieval and Elizabethan character, though it also boasts an impressive Georgian frontage. The bedrooms have all been refurbished and have period furniture as well as luxury bath or shower rooms. One extra-special bedroom boasts an antique four-poster. The meals offered here are made using locally grown organic produce where possible, and are served in the impressively restored dining rooms.

Recommended in the area

Camber Sands; the ancient town of Rye; Romney Marsh

The Gallery

★★★ GA

Address: Cliff Road, SEAFORD BN25 1BB
Tel: 01323 491755
Email: jackie@wrightplace.info
Website: www.wrightplace.info
Map ref: 3, TV49
Directions: Off A259 onto Marine Parade, E along esplanade to tower, left & 1st right
Rooms: 3 en suite, S D £55–£80 **Parking:** 3
Notes: ⊘ on premises ⊗ on premises ♦♦

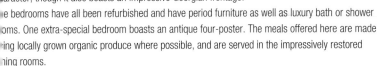

The Gallery is only a stroll from the beach and a short walk from Seaford town centre with its inns, restaurants and antique shops. A warm welcome is guaranteed at this refurbished house with wonderful sea views. The rooms, named after the French impressionists, are large, individually designed, beautifully furnished and well appointed with tea and coffee facilities and DVD televisions. Artwork by local artists adorn the walls of the breakfast room where an excellent meal is served. For a beautiful place to stay in a wonderful location The Gallery offers the ideal break.

Recommended in the area

Seven Sisters Country Park, Seaford; Clergy House (NT), Alfriston; Brighton

Crossways

★★★★ ◎◎ RR

Address: Lewes Road, WILMINGTON, Polegate BN26 5SG
Tel: 01323 482455
Fax: 01323 487811
Email: stay@crosswayshotel.co.uk
Website: www.crosswayshotel.co.uk
Map ref: 4, TQ50
Directions: On A27 between Lewes and Polegate, 2m E of Alfriston rdbt
Rooms: 7 en suite, S £70 D £105–£125 **Parking:** 30
Notes: ⊘ on premises ⊗ in bedrooms ⚑under 12yrs
Closed: 24 Dec–23 Jan

Under the watchful gaze of the famous Long Man of Wilmington, an impressive figure cut in the chalk hillside, this small country house is in a good location for all kinds of activities – walking on the downs, visiting the coast or touring the stately homes and gardens in the area. The building, surrounded by lovely grounds, has a chequered history. It was built for a London merchant as a home for his sisters, but they were later evicted for running it as a house of ill repute. Later it is thought to have been the home of Colonel and Mrs Gwynn, the parents of renowned cookery writer Elizabeth David. Appropriately, fine food is once again the main attraction, and the regularly changing menu might include seafood pancake, Stilton banana bake or hot savoury cheese peaches. Each evening is something of an occasion, with guests, local diners and the owners often chatting animatedly, in true country-house fashion. The bedrooms each have an individual decor, smart furnishings and an en suite bathroom, and guests can choose between the standard and superior rooms. The whole place exudes a delightfully warm atmosphere and it is little wonder that many guests return here time and time again

Recommended in the area

Eastbourne; Beachy Head Countryside Centre; Michelham Priory; Glyndebourne Opera House

WEST SUSSEX

West Dean College gardens

Arundel House Restaurant and Rooms

★★★★★ ◎ RR

Address: 11 High Street, ARUNDEL BN18 9AD
Tel: 01903 882136
Fax: 01903 881179
Email: mail@arundelhouseonline.co.uk
Website: www.arundelhouseonline.co.uk
Map ref: 4, TQ00
Directions: In town centre opp Post Office
Rooms: 5 en suite, D £80–£160 Notes: ⊗ ⊗ in bedrooms
👣 under 16yrs Closed: 2 wks end Feb

The high standard of accommodation is apparent from the moment you enter what is one of Arundel's newest places to stay. Its location, in the heart of this historic town, is another advantage because you can just stroll out to enjoy the attractions right on the doorstep. The building has been the subject of a major refurbishment and there is an atmosphere of luxury and indulgence you would expect to find in a top-class hotel. In the bedrooms the restful beds made up with Egyptian cotton bedlinen and original artwork enhances the stylish contemporary interior design. There are full-size writing desks, wireless internet access, direct-dial telephones, flat-screen TVs, and CD/clock/radios, and the bathrooms are equipped with 8-inch shower roses and Gilchrist and Soames toiletries. The food is a highlight of a stay here, with modern British cuisine (with an occasional French or Mediterranean influence) served in the intimate restaurant. Top quality wild, local and seasonal ingredients are cooked with considerable skill and there's an extensive wine list. Billy Lewis-Bowker and Luke Hackman are to be congratulated on their achievement in creating this exceptional establishment.

Recommended in the area

Arundel Castle; Wildfowl and Wetlands Trust, Arundel; Amberley Working Museum

The Townhouse

★ ★ ★ ◉ RR

Address: 65 High Street, ARUNDEL BN18 9AJ
Tel: 01903 883847
Website: www.thetownhouse.co.uk
Map ref: 3, TQ00
Directions: Follow A27 to Arundel onto High Street,
left at top of hill
Rooms: 4 en suite, D £85–£120 **Notes:** ⊗ ⊗ in
bedrooms ⊷ **Closed:** 2wks Jan & 2wks Oct

The Townhouse, an elegant Grade II listed building dating from around the 1800s, occupies a prime position opposite Arundel Castle. The spectacular carved ceiling in its dining room, however, is much older than the rest of the house; it originated in Florence and is a beautiful example of late Renaissance architecture. All of the en suite bedrooms here are sympathetically and tastefully decorated, and all benefit from TV with DVD/CD player, hairdryer and tea and coffee-making facilities. The restaurant, too, is stylish, though informal, with owner/chef Lee Williams offering a diverse menu based on local produce and featuring fresh bread made on the premises, earning The Townhouse an AA Rosette.
Recommended in the area
Glorious Goodwood; Arundel Castle; Chichester Theatre

White Barn Guest House

★ ★ ★ ★ GH

Address: Crede Lane, BOSHAM, Chichester PO18 8NX
Tel/Fax: 01243 573113
Email: chrissie@whitebarn.biz
Website: www.whitebarn.biz
Map ref: 3, SU80
Directions: A259 Bosham rdbt, turn S signed Bosham Quay,
.5m to T-junct, left signed White Barn, 0.25m turn left signed
White Barn, 50yds turn right
Rooms: 3 en suite, S £55–£65 D £65–£95 **Parking:** 3
Notes: ⊗ ⊗ ⊷ under 12yrs

The comfortable bedrooms at this guest house all have colour-co-ordinated soft furnishings and many thoughtful extras. The Goodwood Room is a mini-suite with its own access and is themed round the nearby Goodwood Estate, while the twin Honeysuckle Room has a small patio for rest and relaxation. The open-plan and glass-walled dining room overlooks an attractive garden, where breakfasts, made from fresh, locally sourced ingredients, are served if weather permits.
Recommended in the area
Chichester; Goodwood Race Circuit; Portsmouth; South Downs

West Stoke House

★★★★★ ◎◎ RR

Address: Downs Road, West Stoke,
CHICHESTER PO18 9BN
Tel: 01243 575226
Fax: 01243 574655
Email: info@weststokehouse.co.uk
Website: www.weststokehouse.co.uk
Map ref: 3, SU80
Directions: 3m NW of Chichester. Off B286 to West
Stoke, next to St Andrew's Church
Rooms: 8 (6 en suite), D £130–£225 Parking: 20 Notes: ⊘ ⚞ ⚟ Closed: 24–28 Dec

This fine country house, part Georgian and part medieval, with over five acres of manicured lawns and gardens, lies on the edge of the South Downs. Guests can enjoy a game of croquet on the lawns, or view the artworks exhibited in the semi-permanent West Stoke House Art Space. The large, uncluttered bedrooms at this exclusive restaurant-with-rooms have smart modern bathrooms and great country views, and parts of the original timber beams can still be seen in the attic bedrooms. Thoughtful touches include white linen bedding and fresh flowers in every room, as well as flatscreen televisions and DVD players. For those looking for something different, one room has a round double bed, providing Hollywood glamour. The restaurant has a relaxed atmosphere and produces very good food from a modern British menu with French influences; wines can be chosen from an interesting and varied list. Hearty breakfasts are made from local produce where possible, with eggs coming from West Stoke free-range hens. Public rooms, including the spacious Grand Ballroom, have a light-filled elegance and are adorned with an eclectic mix of period furniture and contemporary art. West Stoke House was a finalist for the AA Funkiest B&B of 2007 award.

Recommended in the area

The Witterings; Chichester Cathedral; Goodwood

The Lawn Guest House

★★★ GH

Address: 30 Massetts Rd, Gatwick Airport RH6 7DF
Tel: 01293 775751
Fax: 01293 821803
Email: info@lawnguesthouse.co.uk
Website: www.lawnguesthouse.co.uk
Map ref: 3, TQ24
Directions: M23 junct 9, signs to A23 (Redhill), 3rd exit at rdbt by Esso station, 300yds right at lights
Rooms: 12 en suite, S £45–£50 D £60–£65
Parking: 15 **Notes:** ⊘ on premises 🐾 allowed on premises 👥

Handy for Gatwick, this is an efficient well-run airport guest house. Thoughtful extras include scales to weigh luggage, airport parking, free airport transfers and an on-line computer. Bedrooms and bathrooms are fresh and bright, and include hairdryers, tea and coffee facilities, direct-dial phones, early call system, fans and internet access. A choice of hot and cold breakfast dishes is served in the attractive dining room, and there is a pretty garden. A good choice for the international traveller.
Recommended in the area
Hever Castle; Chessington World of Adventure; Leonardslee Gardens

Trumbles

★★★ GH

Address: Stan Hill, Gatwick Airport RH6 0EP
Tel: 01293 863418
Email: trumbles-gatwick@fsmail.net
Website: www.trumbles.co.uk
Map ref: 3, TQ24
Directions: 0.5m N of Charlwood. From village centre into Norwoodhill Rd, 1st left onto Stan Hill
Rooms: 6 en suite, S £50–£70 D £65–£70
Parking: 20 **Notes:** ⊘ ⊗ 👥 **Closed:** 24–26 Dec

This attractive house, within easy reach of Gatwick, enjoys a quiet and secluded setting in a charming village. The house was built in 1872 and was once a cottage hospital. Today, it combines modern facilities with period elegance and the bedrooms, including some family rooms, are spacious with a good range of facilities, such as wireless internet connection. The conservatory offers an ideal environment for guests to relax and enjoy either a continental or full English breakfast, overlooking the peaceful garden. Parking is available, along with airport transfers.
Recommended in the area
Kew Gardens; Windsor Castle; Legoland

Amberfold

★★★★ GA

Address: Amberfold, Heyshott, MIDHURST GU29 0DA
Tel: 01730 812385
Fax: 01730 813559
Email: erlingamberfold@aol.com
Website: www.amberfold.co.uk
Map ref: 3, SU82
Directions: Off A286 signed Graffham/Heyshott, after 1.5m pass pond, Amberfold on left
Rooms: 2 en suite, S £55–£75 D £75–£95
Parking: 2 **Notes:** ⊘ on premises ⊗ in bedrooms ❀ under 14yrs **Closed:** 16 Dec–8 Feb

This delightful 17th-century, Grade II listed cottage is set in mature and attractive gardens in idyllic countryside. It offers ample opportunities for peaceful walks on the doorstep. The charming accommodation here is provided in two very different private entrance units – a cottage annexe and a modern open-plan lodge. Each bedroom is tastefully appointed with many thoughtful extras such as T hospitality trolley, fridge and hairdryer. Breakfast is served in the Amberfold main house.

Recommended in the area

Singleton Open-Air Museum; Goodwood Estate; Cowdrey House

Rivermead House

★★★★★ BB

Address: Hollist Lane, MIDHURST GU29 9RS
Tel: 01730 810907
Email: mail@bridgetadler.com
Website: www.bridgetadler.com
Map ref: 3, SU82
Directions: 1m NW of Midhurst. Off A286 towards Woolbeding
Rooms: 1 en suite, D £70–£80 **Parking:** 2
Notes: ⊘ on premises ⊗ on premises ❀
Closed: 24–26 Dec

This gracious Sussex home is set in a semi-rural location on the edge of Midhurst, and the bedroom has glorious country views, with the South Downs in the distance. It is light and spacious, with room for a put-up bed or cot for children, and is equipped with TV, tea- and coffee-making facilities, hairdryer and radio alarm. A full English breakfast is served informally in the farmhouse-style kitchen, and evening meals are available if booked in advance. Pets are welcome, though not in the bedroom.

Recommended in the area

Weald and Downland Open-Air Museum; Goodwood; Chichester

Orchard Mead

★★★ BB

dress: Toat Lane, PULBOROUGH RH20 1BZ
l: 01798 872640
nail: siggy.rutherford@ukonline.co.uk
ap ref: 3, TQ01
ections: Off A29 1m N of Pulborough onto
ickgate Ln, left onto Pickhurst Ln & right onto Toat
, Orchard Mead at end
oms: 2 (2 en suite), S D £75–£80 **Parking:** 2
tes: ⊘ on premises ⊗ on premises ⚌ under
yrs **Closed:** Xmas & Etr

ong, winding road leads you to this delightful detached home. It is set in a peaceful rural location,
t is only a short drive from the local train station. The en suite bedrooms are comfortably furnished
d provide thoughtful touches, such as pure cotton sheets and fluffy towels. As well as breakfast, a
licious light supper or full dinner can be provided on request, and there are also many good eateries
arby. Guests at Orchard Mead are welcome to make use of the drawing room and the garden.
commended in the area
undel Castle; Pulborough Brooks RSPB Nature Reserve; Horsham Museum

The Beacons

★★★ GA

ldress: 18 Shelley Road, WORTHING BN11 1TU
l: 01903 230948
nail: thebeacons@btconnect.com
ap ref: 3, TQ10
ections: 0.5m W of town centre. Off A259
:hmond Rd onto Crescent Rd & 3rd left
oms: 8 en suite, S £38–£45 D £68–£76
rking: 8 **Notes:** ⊘ ⚌ allowed in bedrooms ⚌

e Beacons is conveniently situated for all local amenities, including the shopping centre, marine
rden, theatres, nightclubs, pier and promenade. The bowling greens at Beach House Park and
arine Gardens are only a short walk from the house. It is also well placed for touring the south coast
d the towns of Brighton, Chichester and Arundel are within easy reach. The bedrooms all have colour
', tea- and coffee-making facilities, hairdryer and clock. Breakfast, served at individual tables, is taken
the dining room and there is a comfortable lounge to relax in after a busy day sightseeing. There is
nple car parking on the premises. Dogs are allowed in rooms with prior arrangement.
commended in the area
ighton Pavilion; The Lanes, Brighton; South Downs

Moorings

★★★★ GA

Address: 4 Selden Road, WORTHING BN11 2LL
Tel: 01903 208882
Fax: 01903 236878
Email: themooringsworthing@hotmail.co.uk
Website: www.mooringsworthing.co.uk
Map ref: 3, TQ10
Directions: 0.5m E of pier off A259 towards Brighton
Rooms: 6 en suite **Notes:** ⊘ on premises ⊗ on premises ⋕

Colourful container plants and window boxes greet guests to this fine Victorian house, in a quiet residential area yet handy for the seafront and town centre. Inside, the spacious rooms are beautifully decorated, in keeping with the age of the house, and the good-sized bedrooms have co-ordinated colour schemes, original fireplaces, teddy bears on the beds and light flooding in from the big windows. Each has a TV and tea- and coffee-making facilities, and two are large enough to accommodate a family. In addition to the stylish dining room, there's a cosy lounge, with books, magazines and games.
Recommended in the area
Pier and seafront; Aquarena; Bowling Greens

Olinda Guest House

★★★★ GA

Address: 199 Brighton Road,
WORTHING BN11 2EX
Tel: 01903 206114
Email: info@olindaguesthouse.co.uk
Website: www.olindaguesthouse.co.uk
Map ref: 3, TQ10
Directions: 1m E of pier on Brighton Rd along Worthing seafront
Rooms: 6 (3 en suite), S £25–£35 D £50–£70
Notes: ⊘ on premises ⊗ on premises ⋕ under 12yrs

Olinda is a small, friendly guest house located on the seafront and just a walk away from the town centre. The cosy and comfortable bedrooms – some en suite – are furnished with TV and tea and coffee-making facilities and benefit from central heating. One single room has a balcony facing the sea. Breakfast, including f English and lighter choices, is taken in the attractively appointed dining room overlooking the seafront, and there are many places for lunchtime and evening dining just a short walk away.
Recommended in the area
Worthing Museum and Art Gallery; Beach House Park; Cissbury Ring

Warwick Castle

Fulready Manor

★★★★★ BB

Address: Fulready, ETTINGTON,
Stratford-upon-Avon CV37 7PE
Tel: 01789 740152
Fax: 01789 740247
Email: stay@fulreadymanor.co.uk
Website: www.fulreadymanor.co.uk
Map ref: 3, SP24
Directions: 2.5m SE of Ettington. 0.5m S off A422 at Pillerton Priors
Rooms: 3 en suite, D £105–£140 Parking: 6
Notes: ⊘ on premises ⊗ on premises ⋈ under 15yrs

Set in 125 acres, this brand new luxury home appears from afar to be a 16th-century castle. Full of character, the entrance hall has a stone fireplace and a floor-to-ceiling front window while one of the bedrooms has a four-poster bed with gold-embroidered muslin. The Manor offers old-fashioned comfort and the breakfasts are a feast. It was awarded AA Guest Accommodation of the Year 2006.
Recommended in the area
Warwick Castle; Warwick; Royal Shakespeare Theatre, Stratford-upon-Avon; The Cotswolds

The Fox & Hounds Inn

★★★★ ⊜ INN

Address: GREAT WOLFORD, Moreton-in-Marsh
CV36 5NQ
Tel: 01608 674220
Email: info@thefoxandhoundsinn.com
Website: www.thefoxandhoundsinn.com
Map ref: 3, SP23
Directions: Off A3400, 1.5m to Great Wolford
Rooms: 3 en suite, S £50 D £80 Parking: 12
Notes: ⊘ in bedrooms ⋈ allowed in bedrooms ⋈

This 16th-century village inn retains many original features. The mellow stone walls encompass roaring log fires, and a bar with blackboard menus, traditional ales and more than 180 varieties of whisky. Rustic furniture and memorabilia add to the character. Converted outbuildings house the thoughtfully furnished en suite bedrooms, with complimentary toiletries and tea and coffee facilities. Paul, Veronica, Gill, Sioned and Jamie serve freshly prepared breakfasts including home made sausages, breads and preserves before guests set out to explore the Cotswolds and Shakespeare country.
Recommended in the area
Batsford Arboretum; Cotswold Falconry Centre; Stratford-upon-Avon

The Old Coach House

★★★★★ BB

Address: GREAT WOLFORD, Shipston on Stour
CV36 5NQ
Tel: 01608 674152
Email: theoldcoachhouse@thewolfords.net
Website: www.theoldcoachhouseatthewolfords.co.uk
Map ref: 3, SP23
Directions: Off A44/A3400 to village centre
Rooms: 2 en suite, S £40–£50 D £60–£80
Parking: 2 **Notes:** ⊘ on premises ⊗ in bedrooms
🐾 under 8yrs

Only minutes from the thriving market town of Moreton-in-Marsh, this converted coach house is perfect for touring or walking in the north Cotswolds. Bedrooms have a wealth of thoughtful extras, and quality decor and furnishings enhance the intrinsic charm of the property. Exposed beams, a flagstone floor and wood-burning stove are features in the relaxing sitting room, which overlooks the delightful garden. All food is prepared using local produce and the pub next door serves excellent meals.

Recommended in the area

Chastleton House (NT); Hidcote Manor (NT); Royal Shakespeare Theatre, Stratford-upon-Avon

Victoria Lodge

★★★★ GA

Address: 180 Warwick Rd, KENILWORTH CV8 1HU
Tel: 01926 512020
Fax: 01926 858703
Email: info@victorialodgehotel.co.uk
Website: www.victorialodgehotel.co.uk
Map ref: 3, SP27
Directions: 250yds SE of town centre on A452 opp
St John's Church
Rooms: 10 en suite, S £49–£62 D £72–£80
Parking: 9 **Notes:** ⊘ on premises ⊗ on premises ⋔ **Closed:** 24 Dec–5 Jan

Victoria Lodge is a family-run establishment which has been extended to provide a range of well-equipped, individually styled bedrooms, two of which are located on the ground floor. The smart contemporary breakfast room serves up full English or vegetarian options, and there is a licensed bar and comfortable guest lounge. In addition, guests have access to private, off-road parking and wireless broadband internet connection.

Recommended in the area

Warwick Castle; NEC, Birmingham; NAC Royal Show Ground, Stoneleigh

Redlands Farm

★★★★ BB

Address: Banbury Road,
LIGHTHORNE CV35 0AH
Tel: 01926 651241
Fax: 01926 651241
Map ref: 3, SP35
Directions: Off B4100, 5m south of Warwick.
Located between junctions 12 and 13 of the M40
Rooms: 3 en suite, S £30–£40 D £60–£70
Parking: 7 Notes: ⊗ on premises ⊗ on premises
👫 Closed: Xmas

This delightful 400-year old farmhouse, set in one acre of well-kept gardens, is ideally placed for the north Cotswolds and has good road connections. The accommodation, with TV, broadband and tea and coffee facilities, includes a family suite of one room leading to another and boasts a four poster and twin beds. There is a wealth of exposed beams and two of the rooms have south-facing views onto open countryside. Outside in the attractive grounds is a swimming pool and barbeque area.
Recommended in the area
Stratford-upon-Avon; Heritage Motor Centre; Warwick Castle; National Agricultural Centre

The Adams

★★★★ GA

Address: 22 Avenue Road,
ROYAL LEAMINGTON SPA CV31 3PQ
Tel: 01926 450742
Fax: 01926 313110
Email: bookings@adams-hotel.co.uk
Website: www.adams-hotel.co.uk
Map ref: 3, SP36
Directions: 500yds W of town centre. Off A452
Adelaide Rd onto Avenue Rd

Rooms: 10 en suite, S £68.50 D £82–£85 Parking: 14 Notes: ⊗ on premises ⊗ in bedrooms 👫under 12 yrs Closed: 23 Dec–2 Jan

Built in 1827, The Adams is an elegant Regency townhouse, peacefully situated just a short level walk from the town centre. Public areas include a lounge bar with leather armchairs, as well as a pretty walled garden. The attractive en suite bedrooms, two of which are on the ground floor, are well appointed and include free internet access. Parking is available within the grounds.
Recommended in the area
Warwick Castle; Stratford-upon-Avon; The Cotswolds

Bubbenhall House

★★★★ GA

Address: Paget's Lane,
ROYAL LEAMINGTON SPA CV8 3BJ
Tel/Fax: 024 7630 2409
Email: wharrison@bubbenhallhouse.freeserve.co.uk
Website: www.bubbenhallhouse.com
Map ref: 3, SP36
Directions: 5m NE of Leamington. Off A445 at
Bubbenhall S onto Paget's Ln, 1m on single-track lane
(over 4 speed humps)
Rooms: 3 en suite, S £47–£49 D £67–£69 **Parking:** 12 **Notes:** ⊘ in bedrooms 🐾 👫

Located between Leamington Spa and Coventry, this large award-winning Edwardian house stands
in 5 acres of woodland and grounds. Inside, it features oak beams, a fine Jacobean-style staircase,
an elegant dining room serving first-class breakfasts and a choice of sumptuous lounges. Thoughtful
extras are provided in the large bedrooms, each with its own individual character and splendid views.
The owners are pet friendly and there is also a championship surface hard tennis court.
Recommended in the area
Stoneleigh Abbey; Ryton Organic Gardens; Warwick Castle

The Red Lion

★★★★ INN

Address: Main Street, Long Compton,
Nr SHIPSTON ON STOUR CV36 5JS
Tel: 01608 684221
Fax: 01608 684968
Email: info@redlion-longcompton.co.uk
Website: www.redlion-longcompton.co.uk
Map ref: 3, SP24
Directions: 5m S of Shipston on Stour on A3400
Rooms: 5 en suite, S £50 D £70–£100
Parking: 60 **Notes:** ⊘ in bedrooms 🐾 allowed in bedrooms 👫

This mid-18th-century Grade II listed posting house retains many
of its original features, highlighted by rustic furniture in the warm and inviting public areas. The newly
refurbished bedrooms are well appointed, with flatscreen TV, tea and coffee-making facilities, luxury
toiletries and hairdryer. Egyptian cotton bedding and fluffy towels add to the sense of luxury. The stylish
restaurant make good use of local produce and in summer, guests can sit in the delightful garden.
Recommended in the area
Stratford-upon-Avon; Warwick Castle; Hidcote Manor Garden

Holly End Bed & Breakfast

★★★★ BB

Address: London Road,
SHIPSTON ON STOUR CV36 4EP
Tel: 01608 664064
Email: hollyend.hunt@btinternet.com
Website: www.holly-end.co.uk
Map ref: 3, SP24
Directions: 0.5m S of Shipston on Stour on A3400
Rooms: 3 (2 en suite), S £45–£60 D £75–£90
Parking: 6 **Notes:** ⊘ on premises ⊗ on premises
⚕ under 9yrs

Holly End provides top-drawer accommodation on the edge of the Cotswolds, midway between Moreton-in-Marsh and Stratford-upon-Avon. Whether your preferences lie with long country hikes and exploring quaint Cotswold villages or discovering the history and culture of Shakespeare country, this bed and breakfast is suitably placed for both. The modern detached family house, immaculately maintained and spotlessly clean, is just a short walk from the centre of Shipston on Stour. Shipston, once an important sheep market town, was also an important stop for coaches, and many of the inns in the High Street date from that era. The spacious, comfortable bedrooms – king-size, twin and double – with subtle soft furnishings and decor have shower-baths, while dormer windows add to the character. You can pamper yourself with the Sanctuary spa products provided in each room. Colour televisions and tea- and coffee-making facilities are also provided. A comprehensive freshly cooked English breakfast uses the best of local produce (organic wherever possible). Afternoon tea or sherry and snacks are offered on arrival. There is a beautiful sunny garden with a lawn and patio dotted with many container plants.

Recommended in the area

Stratford-upon-Avon; Hidcote Manor (NT); Warwick Castle; Cotswold Falconry Centre

Ambleside Guest House

★★★★ GA

Address: 41 Grove Road,
STRATFORD-UPON-AVON CV37 6PB
Tel: 01789 297239
Fax: 01789 295670
Email: ruth@amblesideguesthouse.com
Website: www.amblesideguesthouse.com
Map ref: 3, SP25
Directions: On A4390 opp Firs Park
Rooms: 7 (5 en suite), S £25–£35 D £56–£80
Parking: 7 Notes: ⊘ on premises ⊗ on premises ⅙ under 5yrs

Ambleside is a comfortable guest house in the heart of Stratford-upon-Avon, where owners Ruth and Peter provide a warm welcome. A recent refurbishment has left the house in sparkling condition, and the accommodation can suit every need. Choose from the family rooms, one of which is situated on the ground floor, a double or twin. One room has a four-poster bed – ideal for that special occasion. Many rooms have shower rooms en suite, and each room is equipped with a colour TV, hairdryer and a hospitality tray. Ironing facilities are also available. The choice at breakfast ensures that everyone is satisfied and both the traditional full English breakfast and vegetarian options are freshly cooked. Breakfast is served in the bright and spacious dining room, which looks over the charming front patio garden. Ambleside stands opposite the attractive gardens of Firs Park and is just a short stroll into the town centre where there is a good choice of restaurants, cafés and inns. As well as the Shakespeare attractions Stratford-upon-Avon offers a wide range of shops and ancient buildings and the benefit of town trails to guide the visitor around this interesting town.

Recommended in the area

Shakespeare's birthplace; The Courtyard Theatre; Anne Hathaway's Cottage; Warwick Castle; Warwick; Charlecote Park (NT)

Twelfth Night

★★★★ GA

Address: 13 Evesham Place,
STRATFORD-UPON-AVON CV37 6HT
Tel: 01789 414595
Email: twelfthnight@fsmail.net
Website: www.twelfthnight.co.uk
Map ref: 3, SP25
Directions: In town centre off A4390 Grove Rd
Rooms: 6 en suite, S £35–£50 D £55–£70
Parking: 6 Notes: ⊘ ⊗ ♦♦ Closed: 11–25 Feb

Once owned by the governors of the Royal Shakespeare Company this delightful Victorian villa, built in 1897, is within easy walking distance of the town centre. Its high-quality decor and furnishings enhance the many charming original features throughout. Bedrooms are tastefully and traditionally decorated; all are en suite and are supplied with a host of thoughtful extras such as colour TV, ironing and beverage facilities and an information guide. Sumptuous breakfasts, including full English, vegetarian or continental options, are served on Wedgwood china in the elegant dining room.

Recommended in the area

Courtyard Theatre; Shakespeare's birthplace; Ann Hathaway's Cottage

Victoria Spa Lodge

★★★★ GA

Address: Bishopton Lane, Bishopton,
STRATFORD-UPON-AVON CV37 9QY
Tel: 01789 267985
Fax: 01789 204728
Email: ptozer@victoriaspalodge.demon.co.uk
Website: www.stratford-upon-avon.co.uk/
victoriaspa.htm
Map ref: 3, SP25
Directions: A3400 1.5m N to junct A46, 1st left onto
Bishopton Ln, 1st house on right Rooms: 7 en suite, 3 family rooms S £55 D £45 Parking: 12
Notes: ⊘ ⊗ ♦♦ Closed: Xmas & New Year

Opened in 1837 by Princess Victoria, whose coat-of-arms is built into the gables, this attractive house is in a peaceful country setting on the edge of town. The beautifully appointed bedrooms offer spacious comfort with quality furniture, stylish fabrics and thoughtful touches as well as Wi-fi internet access. Expect a warm welcome and high standards of service. Stratford is a gentle 20-minute walk away.

Recommended in the area

Warwick Castle; Shakespeare theatres & properties; The Cotswolds

WILTSHIRE

The Orangery at Bowood House

Home Farm

★★★★ BB

Address: Farleigh Road, Wingfield,
BRADFORD-ON-AVON BA14 9LG
Tel/Fax: 01225 764492
Email: info@homefarm-guesthouse.co.uk
Website: www.homefarm-guesthouse.co.uk
Map ref: 2, ST86
Directions: 2m S in Wingfield on A366
Rooms: 3 en suite, S D £60 Parking: 30
Notes: ⊗ on premises ⊗ on premises ⋅⋅

Home Farm is an imaginative conversion of what were originally cattle stalls, feeding rooms and a hay loft belonging to Wingfield House. It fronts onto the original farmyard, which provides ample private parking. There is a 2-acre garden and a large, comfortably furnished lounge to relax in. Breakfasts, cooked on an Aga, offer a wide selection including fish dishes, and home-made bread is a feature. Spacious bedrooms comprise a family room, a double, and a ground-floor twin. All rooms have dual-aspect windows, televisions, radios, hairdryers, trouser presses, bathrobes and hospitality trays.
Recommended in the area
Roman Baths, Bath; Longleat; Stonehenge

At the Sign of the Angel

★★★★ ⊜ ⇔ GA

Address: 6 Church Street, LACOCK,
Chippenham SN15 2LB
Tel: 01249 730230
Fax: 01249 730527
Email: angel@lacock.co.uk
Website: www.lacock.co.uk
Map ref: 2, ST86
Directions: Off A350 into Lacock, follow local signs
Rooms: 11 en suite, S £72–£85 D £105–£155
Parking: 7 Notes: ⊗ on premises ⋒ allowed on premises ⋅⋅ Closed: 23–30 Dec

Log fires, oak panelling and low beams create a wonderful atmosphere in this 15th-century house. The same family has owned this inn for over half a century and the restaurant is internationally renowned for its traditional cooking. Four bedrooms are in the cottage across the footbridge over a stream. Furnished with antiques, one has an enormous bed that was owned by the Victorian engineer Isambard Kingdom Brunel, another has a four-poster, and a third room has a French tented bed.
Recommended in the area
Lacock Abbey (NT); Fox Talbot Museum; Bowood House and Gardens

The Old Farmhouse

★★★★★ GA

Address: Bagbury Lane, Restrop,
PURTON, Swindon SN5 4LX
Tel: 01793 770130
Email: stay@theoldfarmhouse.net
Website: www.theoldfarmhouse.net
Map ref: 3, SU08
Directions: M4 junct 16, signs for Purton, right at 1st
x-rds, Bagbury Ln 1st left
Rooms: 6 en suite, S D £75–£160 **Parking:** 20
Notes: ⊗ on premises ⊗ on premises 🦮

The 18th-century Old Farmhouse is a wonderful place, set in tranquil countryside only a short distance from Swindon and the M4. Style and quality abound here, and the hospitality and housekeeping are also great strengths. Each bedroom is individually styled and very comfortable, and all are provided with a host of thoughtful knick-knacks. Four of the rooms are situated in lovingly converted cow stalls. One of these rooms, The Manger, has a large living area with a cottage-style three-piece suite and dining table, a kitchen area with an Aga and a separate bedroom. There are two suites in the main farmhouse. The Apple Rooms, which take up the first floor of the east wing, consist of a private drawing room, bedroom with a king-size four-poster and a bathroom, while the Cheese Room has a comfortable old French carved bed, and a living area with a sofa and dining room table and chairs. Soft furnishings and bed linen are sumptuous throughout and the bathing facilities verge on the sensual. An impressive continental breakfast is served in each room – ingredients are local, home-made or organic. There is a private, 9-hole golf course here for guests, and its free. Hot tubs and spa treatments are also available.

Recommended in the area

Cotswold Water Park; Wiltshire chalk horses; Avebury; Cirencester; Bowood House and Gardens

The Palladian Bridge, Wilton House

The Old House

★★★★ GA

Address: 161 Wilton Road, SALISBURY SP2 7JQ
Tel: 01722 333433
Fax: 01722 335551
Map ref: 3, SU12
Directions: 1m W of city centre on A36
Rooms: 7 en suite, S £38–£50 D £55–£60
Parking: 10 **Notes:** ⊗ on premises ⊗ on premises
🧒 under 7yrs

Charming accommodation is offered at this 17th-century house, located on the Wilton road within walking distance of Salisbury city centre. Ground-floor areas are beautifully furnished in keeping with the building's period character. The mature gardens are a lovely surprise, with three distinct areas providing privacy on summer evenings. Bedrooms have been tastefully decorated and equipped with modern facilities, including bath or shower rooms en suite. There are two rooms at ground-floor level and one room with a splendid four-poster bed, all the bedrooms are equipped with hairdryers and hospitality trays.

Recommended in the area
Stourhead (NT); Heale Garden; Wilton House

St Ann's House

★★★★ GA

Address: 32 Saint Ann Street, SALISBURY SP1 2DP
Tel: 01722 335657
Email: info@stannshouse.co.uk
Website: www.stannshouse.co.uk
Map ref: 3, SU12
Directions: From Brown St turn left onto St Ann St
Rooms: 8 en suite, S £65–£75 D £85–£110
Notes: ⊘ on premises ⊗ in bedrooms ⊶ under 9yrs
Closed: 23 Dec–2 Jan

St Ann's House is a newly refurbished Grade II Georgian townhouse offering boutique-style luxury accommodation close to the beautiful medieval city centre of Salisbury, and just two minutes' walk from the famous cathedral. Lovingly and sensitively restored with many original features, such as cast-iron fireplaces, chandeliers and sash windows, it blends beautiful antique furnishings with contemporary creature comforts such as flatscreen television, comfortable armchairs, good, locally produced toiletries, tea and coffee-making facilities with fresh milk, and fine Turkish bed linen in the en suite bedrooms. Double and single rooms make it a good option for business travellers as well as those just seeking rest and relaxation. The freshly prepared English and Mediterranean breakfasts are not to be missed, and owner-chef Michael Riley also draws on his wealth of experience to provide private bespoke dining for pre-booked parties of 12 or more in the intimate dining room, which boasts eye-catching floral displays. Dishes are made from the best local produce, and might include home-cured gravadlax, new-season lamb and smoked haddock in cream topped with Cheddar cheese soufflé. Formal butler service can even be arranged for extra-special occasions. This is a high-quality operation with a friendly host.

Recommended in the area

Stourhead; Salisbury Cathedral; Salisbury's twice-weekly market

Ardecca

★★★★ GA

Address: Fieldrise Farm, Kingsdown Lane,
Blunsdon, SWINDON SN25 5DL
Tel: 01793 721238
Email: chris-graham.ardecca@fsmail.net
Website: www.ardecca-bedandbreakfast.co.uk
Map ref: 3, SU18
Directions: Off A419 at Turnpike rdbt, left onto
Turnpike Rd, 1st right
Rooms: 4 en suite, S £35 D £55 **Parking:** 5
Notes: ⊘ on premises ⊗ on premises 📵 under 6yrs

Ardecca (the name is an amalgamation of the names Rebecca and Richard, the owners' children) has been the family home of Chris and Graham Horne for over 25 years. The large modern bungalow is immaculate inside and out and sits in 16 acres of pastureland on the edge of Blunsdon village, in a quiet rural setting in north Wiltshire within easy reach of Swindon and Cirencester, the Cotswolds and the Marlborough downs. A great find and an asset to the area, the bungalow offers spacious first-class accommodation in a friendly and relaxed atmosphere created by Chris and Graham. All the rooms are on the ground floor, larger than average and are equipped with modern amenities including Wi-fi access, TV, video, radio alarm and tea-and coffee-making facilities. A full English breakfast is provided and freshly cooked evening meals are available by arrangement, alternatively there are many good pubs and restaurants in the area. There is an outdoor patio area with seating and you can explore the immediate area on public footpaths leading through meadows. Ample parking is available. Please note that credit cards are not accepted. Arts and Crafts workshops are available on site.

Recommended in the area

Cotswold Water Park; Avebury stone circle; Marlborough, the Savernake Forest; Lydiard Park; Thames Path; Buscot Park (NT); Stonehenge

The Old Post Office Guest House

★★★ GH

Address:	Thornhill Road, South Marston, SWINDON SN3 4RY
Tel:	01793 823114
Fax:	01793 823441
Email:	theoldpostofficeguesthouse@yahoo.co.uk
Website:	www.theoldpostofficeguesthouse.co.uk
Map ref:	3, SU18
Directions:	A420 onto Thornhill Rd at Gablecross

About 0.75m on left before Old Vicarage Lane

Rooms: 5 en suite, S £45–£50 D £55–£75 **Parking:** 6

Notes: ⊗ on premises ⊗ on premises ♦♦

Sympathetically extended, this attractive property is about two miles from Swindon and makes an excellent base for touring the West Country, with places of interest at every point of the compass. Guests are welcomed by the enthusiastic owner, a professional opera singer with a wonderful sense of humour. It has been owned by the Sansum family for four generations and was originally a smallholding farm. A post office was added in the 1850s, and it became a focal point in the village. The comfortable and prettily decorated en suite bedrooms – including one family room – vary in size, and all come with numerous facilities, including freeview widescreen TV, free wireless internet connection and tea and coffee-making facilities. An extensive choice is offered at breakfast, from a sumptuous full English to a delicious continental. All dishes are freshly cooked using the best of local produce to make sure that no one leaves the table hungry. It is served in the breakfast room, which still contains the original well from the days when the Old Post Office was home to a bake house. Free off-street parking is available.

Recommended in the area

Cotswold Water Park; Lacock Abbey; Avebury Stone Circle

Stonehenge, Salisbury Plain

Eastbrook Cottage

★★★★ BB

Address: Hoopers Pool, Southwick,
TROWBRIDGE BA14 9NG
Tel: 01225 764403
Email: enquiries@eastbrookcottage.co.uk
Website: www.eastbrookcottage.co.uk
Map ref: 2, ST85
Directions: 2m SW of Trowbridge. Off A361 between
Rode & Southwick
Rooms: 3 (2 en suite), S £30–£45 D £60–£70
Parking: 5 Notes: ⊘ on premises ⊗ in bedrooms ⚹ under 10yrs

This pretty, traditional cottage set in 2 acres of grounds provides an ideal base for touring this beautiful part of the West Country. The bedrooms are cottage sized, finished to a high standard and equipped with many thoughtful extras. Guests always enjoy the snug lounge, with its wood-burning stove, books, games and puzzles. Breakfast, features local produce, including honey and eggs from the farm next door, is taken round a large oak refectory table.

Recommended in the area

Bath; Longleat; Stonehenge

WORCESTERSHIRE

Worcester Cathedral

The Boot Inn

★★★★ 🛏 INN

Address: Radford Road,
FLYFORD FLAVELL,
Worcester WR7 4BS
Tel: 01386 462658
Fax: 01386 462547
Email: enquiries@thebootinn.com
Website: www.thebootinn.com
Map ref: 2, SO95
Directions: In village centre, signed from A422
Rooms: 5 en suite, S £50 D £60–£80 **Parking:** 30
Notes: ⊘ on premises ⊗ in bedrooms ♦♦

An inn has occupied this site since the 13th century, though 'The Boot' itself, as it is called locally, dates from the Georgian period. It provides an ideal base for anyone wishing to explore Stratford-upon-Avon, the Cotswolds or the Malvern Hills. The inn has undergone modernisation, yet it has managed to retain much of its historic charm. The comfortable bedrooms in the converted coach house, furnished in antique pine, are equipped with practical extras such as tea- and coffee-making facilities, trouser press and radio alarm clock, and all have modern bathrooms. Two rooms have disabled access. Guests can relax and indulge in the range of options available at this family-run pub, which prides itself on its friendly staff and lively atmosphere. Traditional ales and an extensive wine list complement the varied and imaginative menus, which are adapted according to availability of ingredients, with everything from sandwiches to bar meals to full à la carte on offer. The award-winning food here, made from fine local produce, can be enjoyed in the cosy public areas, which include an attractive restaurant, a light and airy conservatory and a shaded patio area especially suited to summer dining.

Recommended in the area

Worcester Cathedral; Stratford-upon-Avon; Evesham

Gargoyle on All Saints Church, Evesham

The Dell House

★ ★ ★ ★ BB

Address:	Green Lane, Malvern Wells, MALVERN WR14 4HU
Tel:	01684 564448
Fax:	01684 893974
Email:	burrage@dellhouse.co.uk
Website:	www.dellhouse.co.uk
Map ref:	2, SO74
Directions:	2m S of Great Malvern on A449. Turn left off A449 onto Green Ln. House at top of road on right

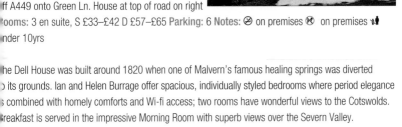

Rooms: 3 en suite, S £33–£42 D £57–£65 **Parking:** 6 **Notes:** ⊘ on premises ⊗ on premises ⅜ under 10yrs

The Dell House was built around 1820 when one of Malvern's famous healing springs was diverted to its grounds. Ian and Helen Burrage offer spacious, individually styled bedrooms where period elegance is combined with homely comforts and Wi-fi access; two rooms have wonderful views to the Cotswolds. Breakfast is served in the impressive Morning Room with superb views over the Severn Valley.

Recommended in the area

Malvern Hills; Three Counties Showground; Malvern Theatre

Lighthouse, Spurn Head

Burton Mount Country House

★★★★★ GA

Address: Malton Road, Cherry Burton,
BEVERLEY HU17 7RA
Tel: 01964 550541
Fax: 01964 551955
Email: pg@burtonmount.co.uk
Website: www.burtonmount.co.uk
Map ref: 8, TA03
Directions: 3m NW of Beverley. B1248 for Malton,
1m right at x-rds, house on left
Rooms: 3 en suite **Parking:** 20
Notes: ⊘ ⊗ in bedrooms 🐾 under 12yrs

Burton Mount is a charming country house 3 miles from Beverley, set in delightful gardens and offering luxurious accommodation. Nestling in a corner of the Yorkshire Wolds, it sits in its own secluded grounds and small woodland and makes a relaxing retreat for anyone travelling on business or for pleasure. Inside, a spacious hall leads up to the en suite bedrooms, all of which are located on the first floor and are well equipped with thoughtful extra touches, such as TV, hairdryer, tea- and coffee-making facilities, bathrobes and toiletries. Downstairs, the dining room has French windows that open onto a terrace, and this in turn leads through to the spacious and elegant drawing room, which has a blazing fire in the cooler months. A second large and comfortable sitting room has a TV and another log fire. An excellent, Aga-cooked Yorkshire breakfast is served in the morning room and includes smoked bacon, free-range eggs, home-made preserves and delicious bread, or a continental breakfast is available if preferred. The house is home to the Greenwood family, and Pauline Greenwood is renowned locally for her customer care, culinary skills and warm hospitality.

Recommended in the area

Beverley Minster; Bishop Burton Horse Trials; Wilberforce House, Kingston upon Hull

The Humber Bridge

The Royal Bridlington

★★★★ GA

Address: 1 Shaftesbury Road,
BRIDLINGTON YO15 3NP
Tel: 01262 672433
Fax: 01262 672118
Email: info@royalhotelbrid.co.uk
Website: www.royalhotelbrid.co.uk
Map ref: 8, TA16
Directions: A615 N to Bridlington (Kingsgate), right onto Shaftesbury Rd

Rooms: 17 (16 en suite), S £35–£40 D £60–£70 Parking: 7 Notes: ⊘ ⊗ in bedrooms ♦♦

In an ideal location, just 100 yards from the sea, this immaculate property also has a lovely, enclosed garden. The thoughtfully furnished bedrooms all have bathrooms and are very well equipped. Some rooms are ground floor with level access to the bar and restaurant. Many rooms have fine sea views, and wireless internet connection is available. The spacious public areas include a large dining room serving freshly cooked breakfasts and dinners, a conservatory-style sitting room and a cosy lounge.

Recommended in the area

Yorkshire Belle; Burton Agnes; Bridlington South Beach

taithes harbour, North Yorkshire Moors National Park

Shallowdale House

★★★★★ 🏠 🛏 GA

Address: West End, AMPLEFORTH YO62 4DY
Tel: 01439 788325
Fax: 01439 788885
Email: stay@shallowdalehouse.co.uk
Website: www.shallowdalehouse.co.uk
Map ref: 8, SE57
Directions: Off A170 at W end of village
Rooms: 3 (2 en suite), S £70–£80
D £87.50–£107.50 **Parking:** 3
Notes: ⊗ ⊗ on premises 🚸 under 12yrs **Closed:** Xmas & New Year

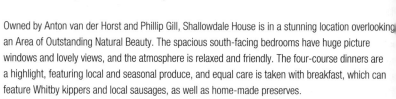

Owned by Anton van der Horst and Phillip Gill, Shallowdale House is in a stunning location overlooking an Area of Outstanding Natural Beauty. The spacious south-facing bedrooms have huge picture windows and lovely views, and the atmosphere is relaxed and friendly. The four-course dinners are a highlight, featuring local and seasonal produce, and equal care is taken with breakfast, which can feature Whitby kippers and local sausages, as well as home-made preserves.

Recommended in the area
Castle Howard; Rievaulx Abbey; Nunnington Hall (NT)

Elmfield House

★★★★ GH

Address: Arrathorne, BEDALE DL8 1NE
Tel: 01677 450558
Fax: 01677 450557
Email: stay@elmfieldhouse.co.uk
Website: www.elmfieldhouse.co.uk
Map ref: 7, SE28
Directions: 4m NW of Bedale. A684 from Bedale for Leyburn, right after Patrick Brompton towards Richmond, B&B 1.5m on right
Rooms: 7 en suite **Parking:** 7 **Notes:** ⊗ on premises ⊗ on premises 🚹

The former gamekeeper's cottage has been extended to provide spacious, well-equipped bedrooms with tea and coffee facilities. Two rooms have four-poster beds and two have easier access. There is a pleasant lounge area with an honesty bar, a conservatory-lounge and a games room. Relax in the gardens or stroll to the 14-acre wood and fishing lake for sightings of deer and kingfishers. The full English breakfast using local produce is a highlight; evening meals can be ordered by arrangement.

Recommended in the area
Bedale; Richmond; Yorkshire Dales and Moors

Orchard Lodge

★★★ GA

Address: North St, FLIXTON, Scarborough YO11 3UA
Tel/Fax: 01723 890202
Website: www.orchard-lodge.com
Map ref: 8, TA07
Directions: Off A1039 in village centre
Rooms: 6 en suite, S £45–£50 D £65–£80
Parking: 8 **Notes:** ⊗ No Pets
Closed: Jan–Feb

Located 6 miles south of Scarborough, in the heart of Flixton village and nestling beneath the Yorkshire Wolds, this purpose-built establishment makes a good base for touring the local countryside and coastline. It offers spacious and comfortable en suite bedrooms, all of which come with beverage tray, hairdryer and TV. Hearty breakfasts are served in the spacious dining room, with a varied menu that sometimes features home-made preserves made from home-grown raspberries, plums, blackberries and gooseberries.

Recommended in the area

Carr Starr archaeological site; Castle Howard; The Wolds Way

Ashfield House

★★★★★ 🛏 ☕ GA

Address: Summers Fold, GRASSINGTON,
Skipton BD23 5AE
Tel: 01756 752584
Fax: 07092 376562
Email: info@ashfieldhouse.co.uk
Website: www.ashfieldhouse.co.uk
Map ref: 7, SE06
Directions: B6265 to village centre Main St, left onto Summers Fold
Rooms: 8 (7 en suite), S £61–£115 D £85–£120 **Parking:** 8 **Notes:** ⊗ on premises ⊗ on premises ♦ under 5yrs

Owners, Joe Azzopardi and Elizabeth Webb, provide a warm welcome at Ashfield House, tucked away down a lane just off the cobbled village square. The furnishings and decor throughout the ground floor highlight the original features of the 17th-century building. Bedrooms are all equipped with thoughtful extras, dinner menus are imaginative and breakfasts set you up for a day exploring the Dales.

Recommended in the area

Bolton Abbey; Stump Cross Caverns; Aysgarth Falls

The Kings Head at Newton

★★★★ GA

Address:	The Green, GUISBOROUGH,
	Nr Great Ayton TS9 6QR
Tel:	01642 722318
Fax:	01642 724750
Email:	info@kingsheadhotel.co.uk
Website:	www.kingsheadhotel.co.uk
Map ref:	8, NZ61

Directions: A171 towards Guisborough, at rdbt onto A173 to Newton under Roseberry, under Roseberry Topping landmark

Rooms: 8 en suite, S £55–£65 D £69.50–£75 Parking: 96 Notes: ⊘ on premises ⊗ on premises
Closed: 25–26 Dec & 1 Jan

This family-owned establishment offers stylish, thoughtfully equipped bedrooms. The restaurant, next door, offers quality food with produce sourced from the local area. A full English or continental breakfast is served in the glass-roofed breakfast area with unspoiled views of Roseberry Topping.
Recommended in the area
Cleveland Way; North York Moors National Park; Whitby

Laskill Grange

★★★★ GA

Address:	HAWNBY YO62 5NB
Tel:	01439 798268
Fax:	01439 798498
Email:	laskillgrange@tiscali.co.uk
Website:	www.laskillgrange.co.uk
Map ref:	8, SE58

Directions: 6m N of Helmsley on B1257
Rooms: 4 en suite, D £60–£70 Parking: 20
Notes: ⊘ ⊯ ⊪ Closed: 25 Dec

Laskill is a charming 19th-century house in the North York Moors National Park. There are splendid walks in the surrounding countryside and fishing on the River Seph, which runs through the grounds. The elegant house has exposed beams and open fireplaces, and the immaculate bedrooms are decorated to a very high standard and come with hot-drink trays and flowers. Generous breakfasts are prepared using home-grown produce wherever possible. Across the courtyard from the farmhouse are converted barns for self catering. There is an activity centre for children too.
Recommended in the area
Rievaulx Abbey; Castle Howard; Nunnington Hall (NT)

Brickfields Farm

★★★ GA

ddress: Kirkby Mills, KIRKBYMOORSIDE
YO62 6NS

l: 01751 433074

nail: janet@brickfieldsfarm.co.uk

ebsite: www.brickfieldsfarm.co.uk

ap ref: 8, SE68

rections: A170 E from Kirkbymoorside, 0.5m right
o Kirby Mills (signed), farm 1st right

ooms: 6 en suite, S £40–£50 D £70–£100

rking: 8 **Notes:** ⊘ on premises ⊗ on premises ⱥ

ickfields Farm, set in open countryside close to the village of Kirkbymoorside, has been owned by
e same family for over 80 years. It is no longer a working farm, and recent dramatic renovations of
e farmhouse and barn have transformed it into a comfortable, spacious and stylish bed and breakfast
tablishment. En suite bedrooms, all on the ground floor, are located in the farmhouse or in the
inexe housed in the former barn. All of the rooms have bags of individual charm and are carefully
nished to a high standard – all have modern showers, fluffy bath sheets and bathrobes, flatscreen
eeview TV, DVD/CD player, fresh flowers, fridge with daily supplies of fresh milk and mineral water,
d well-stocked beverage-making facilities. One room is wheelchair accessible. The light and airy
est rooms have also been thoughtfully designed, with a mix of antiques, muted colours and plush
brics, and the conservatory is the place to enjoy the generous and appetising Yorkshire breakfasts.
arby there are a wealth of restaurants and dining pubs for evening dining, and the owners are happy
make recommendations and help with bookings. All in all, this is an ideal base for exploring the
rth York Moors.

commended in the area

istle Howard; North Yorks Moors and Steam Railway; Rievaulx Abbey

Fountains Abbey, National Trust

Gallon House

★★★★★ 🏠 🍽 GH

Address: 47 Kirkgate, KNARESBOROUGH HG5 8BZ
Tel: 01423 862102
Email: gallon-house@ntlworld.com
Website: www.gallon-house.co.uk
Map ref: 8, SE35
Directions: Next to railway station, in the centre of town
Rooms: 3 en suite, S £85 D £110 **Notes:** ⊘ in bedrooms 🐾 allowed in bedrooms ⋔⋔

Situated overlooking Nidd Gorge, Gallon House offers first-class accommodation and welcoming atmosphere. The stylish bedrooms are individually furnished with many extras, including CD players, bathrobes and superb refreshment trays. Rick Hodgson's culinary delights are not to be missed and he places strong emphasis on local ingredients. Dinner, by arrangement, features quality local bread, pâtés and chutneys and the beef casserole is prepared using local Yorkshire ale.

Recommended in the area

Leeds; York; Fountains Abbey (NT)

Newton House

★★★★ GA

Address: 5–7 York Place,
KNARESBOROUGH HG5 0AD
Tel: 01423 863539
Fax: 01423 869748
Email: newtonhouse@btinternet.com
Website: www.newtonhouseyorkshire.com
Map ref: 8, SE35
Directions: On A59 in Knaresborough, 500yds from town centre

Rooms: 11 (10 en suite), S £50–£85 D £75–£100 **Parking:** 10
Notes: ⊘ on premises 🦮 allowed in bedrooms ♦♦ **Closed:** 1wk Xmas

This delightfully elegant, Grade II listed former coaching inn, entered by an archway into a courtyard, is only a short walk from the river, castle and market square in the picturesque town of Knaresborough. Owners Mark and Lisa Wilson place the emphasis on relaxation, informality and comfort, and the generously proportioned and newly refurbished bedrooms, most of them en suite, include some four-posters and king-size doubles, as well as family rooms and a pair of interconnecting rooms. All are very well equipped, with Egyptian cotton bedding, Molton Brown toiletries, TV, minibar, a well-stocked refreshment tray, DAB radio with MP3 player input and free Wi-fi internet access coming as standard. There is a comfortable lounge offering guests newspapers, books, magazines, games, sweets and fresh fruit, while memorable breakfasts are served in the attractive dining room. Meals are freshly cooked and the sophisticated menu includes eggs Benedict, poached smoked haddock, and porridge with sultanas in malt whisky, as well as the traditional full English. Free-range eggs, sausages and bacon are sourced locally and complemented by seasonal fruit and home-made preserves.

Recommended in the area

Fountains Abbey; Yorkshire Dales; Newby Hall; RHS Harlow Carr Gardens

River House

★★★★ ≣ ⊜ GH

Address: MALHAM, Skipton BD23 4DA
Tel: 01729 830315
Email: info@riverhousehotel.co.uk
Website: www.riverhousehotel.co.uk
Map ref: 7, SD96
Directions: Off A65, N to Malham
Rooms: 8 en suite, S £45 D £45 Parking: 5 Notes: ⊘ on premises ⊁ allowed on premises ⋇ under 8yrs

This attractive, family-run Victorian guest house, parts of which date back to 1664, is set in the beautiful village of Malham, in the heart of the Yorkshire Dales. The surrounding countryside is excellent for walking, mountain-biking and horse-riding. Inside, the Victorian hallway has the original cornicing and archway moulding, while the newly decorated en suite bedrooms are all bright and comfortable, with a good selection of homely extras such as colour TV, large, luxury towels, well-stocked hospitality tray, good-quality toiletries and hairdryer. Some rooms have the original fireplace, and one large twin room on the ground floor is equipped with grab rails in the shower room. Public areas include a cosy, licensed lounge, with an extensive list of New World wines and a large, well-appointed dining room, where locally sourced produce, including the local butcher's scrumptious sausages and black pudding, is incorporated into the excellent breakfasts and imaginative evening meals that offer choice and quality above expectation, and make River House well worthy of its Breakfast and Dinner Award. Packed lunches can be made up on request, as can meals for vegetarian and those on special diets, and catering for walking parties, groups and family get-togethers is a speciality here.

Recommended in the area

Malham Cove and Gordale Scar; Yorkshire Dales; Pennine Way; Skipton; Settle to Carlisle Railway

Malham Cove, Yorkshire Dales National Park

Bank Villa Guest House

★★★★ ⬕ ⬌ GH

Address: MASHAM, Ripon HG4 4DB
Tel: 01765 689605
Email: bankvilla@btopenworld.com
Website: www.bankvilla.com
Map ref: 7, SE28
Directions: Enter on A6108 from Ripon, property on right
Rooms: 6 (4 en suite), S £45–£65 D £50–£95
Parking: 6 **Notes:** ⊘ on premises ⊗ on premises ⬥ under 5yrs

Graham and Liz Howard-Barker have created a welcoming atmosphere in their charming Georgian home, a great base for exploring the Dales. Relax in the lovely terraced gardens, in one of two comfortable lounges, or the conservatory, all of which have plenty of character. Individually decorated bedrooms feature beams, stripped pine period furniture and crisp white linens. Liz's cooking uses home-grown and local produce whenever possible, served in the relaxed licensed restaurant.

Recommended in the area

Black Sheep and Theakstons breweries; Rievaulx Abbey; Fountains Abbey; Yorkshire Dales

Three Tuns

★★★★ RR

Address: 9 South End, Osmotherley,
NORTHALLERTON DL6 3BN
Tel: 01609 883301
Fax: 01609 883988
Email: enquiries@threetunsrestaurant.co.uk
Website: www.threetunsrestaurant.co.uk
Map ref: 8, SE39
Directions: NE of Northallerton. Off A19 into
Osmotherley village
Rooms: 7 en suite, S £55 D £75 Parking: 2 Notes: ⊘ on premises ⊗ on premises ♦♦

This family-run establishment, situated in the picturesque village of Osmotherley in the North Yorkshire Moors, is full of character. With its friendly, informal atmosphere and great food, it is a popular destination for business travellers, tourists and locals alike. The Charles Rennie Mackintosh-inspired decor sets it apart, and the bedrooms – some situated above the bar, some located in an adjoining annexe – vary in size but are stylishly furnished in pine throughout. All rooms are en suite, including one family room and one on the ground floor, and have colour TV, large beds, fluffy pillows and tea and coffee-making facilities; some rooms enjoy stunning views of the Cleveland Hills. The homely lounge contains a video and CD player, and there's a film and music collection available for guests to browse through and enjoy. The restaurant is a real draw, offering an imaginative range of wholesome, modern British dishes with the emphasis on fine local produce and with fine wines and traditional cask-conditioned ales to wash it all down. A hearty breakfast, early-morning snacks, lunch, afternoon tea and dinner are all on offer, and evening meals might include smoked haddock on spring onion mash followed by chargrilled amaretto peaches with clotted cream.

Recommended in the area

The Forbidden Corner; Wensleydale Railway; Mount Grace Priory

17 Burgate

★ ★ ★ ★ ★ GA

Address: 17 Burgate, PICKERING YO18 7AU
Tel: 01751 473463
Email: info@17burgate.co.uk
Website: www.17burgate.co.uk
Map ref: 8, SE78
Directions: From A170 follow sign to Castle. On right
Rooms: 5 en suite, S £66–£76 D £85–£105
Parking: 7 Notes: ⊘ ⊗ in bedrooms 🔥 under 10 yrs

This elegant market town house, situated close to the town centre and the castle, has been expertly renovated, and the owners have gone the extra mile to make sure you enjoy your stay here. Guests will enjoy the comfortable, individually designed bedrooms, all with modern facilities including free broadband, flatscreen TV, DVD player and a range of spa cosmetics and aromatic candles. Public areas include a comfortable lounge bar with a log-burning stove and well-stocked bar, and breakfast includes a wide choice of local, healthy foods. Guests are encouraged to make use of the peaceful garden, which includes a terrace on which to relax and enjoy a bottle of wine.

Recommended in the area

Flamingo Land; Castle Howard; North Yorkshire Moors Railway

Whashton Springs Farm

★ ★ ★ ★ FH

Address: RICHMOND DL11 7JS
Tel: 01748 822884
Fax: 01748 826285
Email: whashtonsprings@btconnect.com
Website: www.whashtonsprings.co.uk
Map ref: 7, NZ10
Directions: In Richmond N at lights towards Ravensworth, 3m down steep hill, farm at bottom left
Rooms: 8 en suite, S £36–£40 D £64–£72
Parking: 10 Notes: ⊘ on premises ⊗ on premises 🔥 under 5yrs Closed: late Dec–Jan

This family-run, working farm in the heart of the countryside makes a perfect base for exploring the Yorkshire Dales. The lambing season is a particularly good time to visit when the farm's new arrivals are on show. Accommodation is either in the large farmhouse or within the delightful courtyard rooms. Jane Turnbull serves a hearty breakfast in the dining room overlooking the garden, and is on hand to chat and answer questions. The stylish lounge provides somewhere to contemplate the day ahead.

Recommended in the area

Richmond; Swaledale; York; Yorkshire Dales; the Lake District; North Yorkshire Moors

Mallard Grange

★★★★★ FH

Address: Aldfield, RIPON HG4 3BE
Tel/Fax: 01765 620242
Email: maggie@mallardgrange.co.uk
Website: www.mallardgrange.co.uk
Map ref: 7, SE37
Directions: B6265 W fom Ripon, Mallard Grange 2.5m on right
Rooms: 4 en suite, D £70–£90 Parking: 6
Notes: ⊗ on premises ⊗ in bedrooms
👪 under 12yrs Closed: Xmas & New Year

Set in glorious countryside and ideally placed for touring the Yorkshire Dales and Moors, this fine 16th-century Yorkshire farmhouse retains many original features. Each room is en suite and has a distinct character with quality furnishings and extra touches to ensure luxury, comfort and convenience. There are two ground floor bedrooms in the converted smithy. As an AA Breakfast Award winner, breakfast is high standard and a real farmhouse treat using locally sourced produce such as Whitby kippers.

Recommended in the area

Fountains Abbey (NT); Harrogate; Newby Hall

St George's Court

★★★★ FH

Address: Old Home Farm, Grantley, RIPON HG4 3PJ
Tel: 01765 620618
Email: stgeorgescourt@bronco.co.uk
Website: www.stgeorges-court.co.uk
Map ref: 7, SE37
Directions: B6265 W from Ripon, right signed Grantley, up hill 1m past Risplith sign & next right
Rooms: 5 (5 en suite), S £45–£55 D £65–£75
Parking: 12 Notes: ⊗ on premises ⊁ in bedrooms 👫

Warm hospitality is the hallmark of this renovated farmhouse complex on the edge of Wensleydale and close to Fountains Abbey World Heritage Site. The elegant house is set in 20 acres that includes a small lake. The ground floor rooms, each with their own front door, are located around a pretty central courtyard, and have quality beds, refreshment trays and spacious bathrooms. One unit with two bedrooms is ideal for families. Imaginative breakfasts, using fine local ingredients, are served in the conservatory-dining room.

Recommended in the area

Fountains Abbey (NT); Brimham Rocks; Newby Hall

The Blackwell Ox Inn

★★★★ ◉ INN

Address: Huby Road, SUTTON-ON-THE-FOREST
YO61 1DT
Tel: 01347 810328
Fax: 01904 691529
Email: enquiries@blackwellinns.com
Website: www.blackwelloxinn.co.uk
Map ref: 8, SE56
Directions: Off A1237, onto B1363 to
Sutton-on-the-Forest. Left at T-junct, 50yds on right

Rooms: 5 en suite, S £90 D £90 **Parking:** 18 **Notes:** ⊘ on premises ⊗ on premises ♦♦

Picturesque Sutton-on-the-Forest is only 7 miles from York, making it a good base for exploring the city and the surrounding countryside. This refurbished inn offers attractive, individually designed bedrooms and pleasing public rooms. Chef Steven Holding prepares excellent dishes in the restaurant using local produce to create French-inspired dishes and the bold flavours of Spain's Catalan region. Tasty puddings round off the experience. Children welcome but only guide dogs please.

Recommended in the area

Castle Howard; Jorvic Centre, York; Railway Museum, York

Spital Hill

★★★★★ ⌂ ⌂ GA

Address: York Road, THIRSK YO7 3AE
Tel: 01845 522273
Fax: 01845 524970
Email: spitalhill@spitalhill.entadsl.com
Website: www.spitalhill.co.uk
Map ref: 8, SE48
Directions: 1.5m SE of town, set back 200yds from
A19, driveway marked by 2 white posts

Rooms: 5 (4 en suite), S £60–£65 D £90–£100
Parking: 6 **Notes:** ⊘ on premises ⊗ on premises ♦♦under 12yrs

Robin and Ann Clough warmly welcome guests to their beautiful home, a fine country house set in its gardens and parkland surrounded by open countryside. Ann produces an excellent set dinner each evening as an optional extra, using good fresh produce, much of which comes from the garden. Breakfast is also a highlight. Bedrooms are furnished with quality and style, and thoughtfully equipped with many extras; there is no tea making equipment as Ann prefers to offer tea as a service.

Recommended in the area

Herriott Centre, Thirsk; Byland Abbey; York Minster

Woodhouse Farm

★★★★ FH

Address: WESTOW, York YO60 7LL
Tel: 01653 618378
Email: stay@wood-house-farm.co.uk
Website: www.wood-house-farm.co.uk
Map ref: 8, SE76
Directions: Off A64 to Kirkham Priory & Westow. Right at T-junct, farm drive 0.5m out of village on right
Rooms: 3 en suite, S £30–£40 D £60–£80
Parking: 12 Notes: ⊗ on premises ⊗ on premises ⋔ Closed: Xmas, New Year & Mar–mid Apr

This 500-acre family-run working farm is set in rolling countryside nestled between the Vale of York, the Yorkshire Wolds and the Howardian Hills. The 18th-century farmhouse has been sympathetically restored retaining original beams and open log fires to provide a homely feel. All rooms are well equipped and consist of king-size and family rooms. Start the day with a delicious country breakfast sourced from locally produced sausages and bacon, plus home-made preserves, cakes and scones.
Recommended in the area
Castle Howard; York Minster; North Yorkshire Moors

Corra Lynn

★★★★ GA

Address: 28 Crescent Avenue, WHITBY YO21 3EW
Tel: 01947 602214
Fax: 01947 602214
Map ref: 8, NZ81
Directions: Corner A174 & Crescent Av
Rooms: 5 en suite, S £25 D £54 Parking: 5
Notes: ⊗ in bedrooms ⊗ in bedrooms ⋔
Closed: 21 Dec–5 Jan

Bruce and Christine Marot have a passion for what they do, mixing traditional values of cleanliness, comfort and friendly service with a modern trendy style. The house is set in a prominent corner position on the West Cliff within easy walking distance of the town of Whitby and its picturesque harbour. The bedrooms are thoughtfully equipped with colour TV, radio alarm and hospitality tray, and are individually furnished and colourfully decorated. The delightful dining room, with a corner bar and a wall adorned with clocks, really catches the eye. Breakfasts at Corra Lynn are hearty, with a vegetarian option, and the menu changes with the seasons. There is off-street parking.
Recommended in the area
Whitby Abbey; Captain Cook Memorial Museum; Robin Hood's Bay

Estbek House

★★★★ 🛏 ❀ RR

Address: East Row, Sandsend, WHITBY YO21 3SU
Tel: 01947 893424
Fax: 01947 893625
Email: info@estbekhouse.co.uk
Website: www.estbekhouse.co.uk
Map ref: 8, NZ81
Directions: On Cleveland Way, within Sandsend, next to East Beck
Rooms: 4 (3 en suite), S £60–£90 D £90–£130
Parking: 6 **Notes:** ⊘ on premises ⊗ in bedrooms ⊮ under 14yrs

Estbek House, a beautiful Georgian establishment located in a small coastal village north-west of Whitby, is a restaurant-with-rooms that specialises in seafood. Here, diners can indulge themselves in the first-floor restaurant while listening to the relaxing break of the waves from the nearby Yorkshire Moors coastline. Chef/co-proprietor Tim Lawrence has nearly 30 years' experience of seafood cookery and he and his team present a range of mouth-watering dishes, including non-fish alternatives, on daily-changing menus. An innovative wine chalk board shows a large selection of bottles and wines by the glass, especially notable for the large Australian contingent, with over 100 wines listed. Surroundings in the restaurant are modern and stylishly simple – airy and bright by day, thoughtfully lit in the evenings; when the weather allows, diners may eat outside in the flower-bordered courtyard. On the ground floor is a small bar and breakfast room, while above are the individually decorated and luxurious bedrooms. Each has its own name – such as Florence or Eva – and character, and comes with a wealth of thoughtful extras such as flatscreen TV, CD/radio alarm clock, hairdryer, tea and coffee-making facilities and complimentary guest pack.

Recommended in the area

Mulgrave castles; Mulgrave woods; Cleveland Way

Appleton-Le-Moors, North York Moors National Park

Netherby House

★★★★ ➡ GA

Address: 90 Coach Road, Sleights,
WHITBY YO22 5EQ
Tel/Fax: 01947 810211
Email: info@netherby-house.co.uk
Website: www.netherby-house.co.uk
Map ref: 8, NZ81
Directions: In village of Sleights, off A169 (Whitby–Pickering road)
Rooms: 11 en suite, S £37–£44 D £74–£88
Parking: 17 **Notes:** ⊘ on premises ⊗ on premises ⋕ **Closed:** 25–26 Dec

For owners Lyn and Barry Truman their bed and breakfast business is a labour of love; the beautifully kept gardens and the delightful day rooms and bedrooms, all contribute to a restful stay. Hospitality is another strength of Netherby House, and imaginative evening meals using fresh garden produce are served in the candlelit dining room. There are twin, double and family rooms, and a four-poster room adds that extra touch of luxury. There is a lounge-bar and a conservatory for relaxing in.

Recommended in the area

Historic Whitby; North Yorkshire Moors National Park; North Yorkshire Moors Railway

Ascot House

★★★★ GA

Address: 80 East Parade, YORK YO31 7YH
Tel: 01904 426826
Fax: 01904 431077
Email: admin@ascothouseyork.com
Website: www.ascothouseyork.com
Map ref: 8, SE65
Directions: 0.5m NE of city centre. Off A1036 Heworth Green onto Mill Ln, 2nd left
Rooms: 13 (12 en suite), S £45–£70 D £60–£76
Parking: 14 **Notes:** ⊘ in bedrooms 🐾 allowed on premises 👫 **Closed:** 21–28 Dec

This Victorian villa was built for a prominent family in 1869 close to the city centre. The owners have retained many original features, yet they have improved the building to provide modern standards of comfort. Bedrooms are equipped with period furniture, and most of the spacious rooms on the first floor have four-poster or canopy beds. Two rooms are on the ground floor, and most have en suites along with hospitality trays and colour TV. The curved stained-glass window on the landing is a particularly attractive feature. There is a spacious and comfortable lounge where you can relax, watch television or enjoy a drink from the Butlers Pantry. Tea and coffee are also served in the lounge throughout the day. Delicious traditional, vegetarian and continental breakfasts are served in the dining room; the generous portions are sure to set you up for the day. Ascot House is a welcoming property that can be reached from the city by bus in just a few minutes, or by a short brisk walk. It has an enclosed car park, and the public park next door has two tennis courts and two bowling greens. A nearby pub serves good food, and there are also many restaurants, wine bars and theatres within walking distance.

Recommended in the area

Jorvik Viking Centre; National Railway Museum; York Minster

Burswood Guest House

★★★★ GH

Address: 68 Tadcaster Road,
Dringhouses, YORK YO24 1LR
Tel: 01904 702582
Fax: 01904 708377
Email: george@burswoodguesthouse.co.uk
Website: www.burswoodguesthouse.co.uk
Map ref: 8, SE65
Directions: Tadcaster Rd A1036 opposite
racecourse, from the A64 on S side of the city
Rooms: 5 en suite, D £70–£85 Parking: 6
Notes: ⊗ on premises ⊗ in bedrooms ♦♦

Guests can be sure of a warm welcome indeed at this modern dormer bungalow, with attractive window-boxes, whose owner strives to offer a level of excellence that he believes is not usually found outside of a five-star hotel. Bedrooms are richly furnished and very well equipped – providing guests with numerous home comforts such as fridges supplied with milk and bottled water, air-conditioning, ceiling fans, feather pillows, comfortable armchairs, ironing board stations, bathmats, velour bathrobes and slippers and digital television. Chocolate biscuits, sweets and good-quality toiletries add to the feeling that you are being well looked after. Good, freshly cooked breakfasts are on offer, and are served in the conservatory/breakfast room, which overlooks the guest house's well-tended garden. Ample car parking is available at the front of the house and Burswood is easily accessible for visiting the walled city of York, with its host of world-class attractions, such as York Minster, the York Dungeon, the Shambles shopping centre, York Castle Museum, and the racecourse, as well as the countless restaurants, pubs, tea rooms and coffee shops the city has to offer.

Recommended in the area

Medieval York; National Railway Museum; York Races

York Minster

The Heathers Guest House

★★★★ GA

Address: 54 Shipton Rd, Clifton Without,
YORK YO30 5RQ
Tel/Fax: 01904 640989
Email: reservations@heathers-guest-house.co.uk
Website: www.heathers-guest-house.co.uk
Map ref: 8, SE65
Directions: N of York on A19, halfway between
A1237 ring road & York city centre
Rooms: 6 (4 en suite), S £48–£126 D £52–£130
Parking: 9 **Notes:** ⊘ ⊗ ⛄ under 10yrs **Closed:** Xmas

Recent remodelling and refurbishment at this large 1930s house has resulted in a most comfortable and welcoming establishment. Heather and Graham Fisher have designed each room individually using quality fabrics and decor and there is a feeling of luxury in the bedrooms, all of which have en suite or private facilities and benefit from TV and well-stocked tea and coffee-making facilities. The light and airy breakfast room looks out onto a well-tended garden area, and off-street parking is available.

Recommended in the area

North York Moors; Castle Howard; Ryedale Folk Museum

Langsett, South Yorkshire

Padley Farm B&B

★★★★ GA

Address: Dungworth Green, SHEFFIELD S6 6HE
Tel/Fax: 0114 285 1427
Email: aandlmbestall@btinternet.com
Website: www.padleyfarm.co.uk
Map ref: 8, SK38
Directions: M1 onto A61 to Loxley, B6077 to Bradfield & B6076 to Dungworth **Rooms:** 7 en suite, S £27–£37 D £54–£60 **Parking:** 8
Notes: ⊗ on premises ⊗ on premises ♦♦

Padley Farm is just 10 minutes from Sheffield by car, while enjoying a peaceful village setting with panoramic views over the Loxley Valley. This lovely barn conversion has retained much character, including its great oak beams, while providing high quality accommodation. Bedrooms, which benefit from under-floor heating, have shower rooms, televisions with DVD players, tea- and coffee-making facilities and an information folder. Two rooms are on the ground floor and accessible to wheelchair-users. There are seats in the lovely garden, and inside there's a full-size snooker table.

Recommended in the area

Country walks; Sheffield museums and entertainment venues; Abbeydale Industrial Hamlet

The Huddersfield Central Lodge

★★★★ GA

Address: 11/15 Beast Market,
HUDDERSFIELD HD1 1QF
Tel: 01484 515551
Fax: 01484 432349
Email: enquiries@centrallodge.com
Website: www.centrallodge.com
Map ref: 7, SE11
Directions: In town centre off Lord St, Signs for Beast Market from ring road
Rooms: 22 en suite, S £45–£55 D £55–£65 **Parking:** 50 **Notes:** ⊗ ♠ allowed on premises ♦♦

The Huddersfield Central Lodge, in the town centre, is independently run by the Marsden family who have a reputation for providing smart, friendly accommodation. Some bedrooms are in the main house, with others, many with kitchenettes, situated across a courtyard. All are spacious, en suite and very well equipped with every convenience. Public rooms include a fully licensed bar with plasma-screen TV and a large conservatory, where breakfast, based on local and organic produce, is served.

Recommended in the area

Galpharm Stadium; Holmfirth (setting for *Last of the Summer Wine*); The National Mining Museum

CHANNEL ISLANDS

Moulin Huet Bay, near St Martin, Guernsey

The Panorama

★★★★★ GA

Address: La Rue du Crocquet, ST AUBIN JE3 8BZ
Tel: 01534 742429
Fax: 01534 745940
Email: info@panoramajersey.com
Website: www.panoramajersey.com
Map ref: 13
Directions: In village centre
Rooms: 14 en suite, S £35–£61 D £70–£122
Notes: ⊘ on premises ⊗ on premises ⚲ under 18
rs Closed: mid Oct–mid Apr

The Panorama is aptly named indeed, with its spectacular views across St Aubin's Bay. A long-established favourite with visitors, not least because of the genuinely warm welcome, it is situated on a pretty seafront street. Inside are antiques aplenty, including a number of elegant fireplaces, and the hotel is well known for its collection of over 500 teapots. Wireless internet access is now also available. A feature of the recently upgraded bedrooms is the luxurious pocket-sprung beds, most well over six feet long. The breakfasts, each individually cooked to order, are another draw, with dishes such as Grand Slam and Elegant Rarebit among the inventive choices on the lengthy menu. For lunch or dinner there are many restaurants in close proximity, providing ample opportunity to sample the best produce that Jersey has to offer. Many are within walking distance, and the owners will happily make recommendations. The hotel is a good base for walking, cycling (a cycle track along the promenade leads to St Helier) or travelling around the island by bus. Day trips by boat are available to the neighbouring islands of Guernsey, Herm and Sark, and also to St Malo in Brittany. The accommodation is unsuitable for children.

Recommended in the area

Picturesque village of St Aubin; Railway Walk to Corbière; Beauport and Les Creux Country Park

ISLE OF MAN

Snaefell Mountain Railway, Laxey

Corrin's Folly, Peel

Aaron House

★ ★ ★ ★ ★ GH

Address: The Promenade, PORT ST MARY IM9 5DE
Tel: 01624 835702
Website: www.aaronhouse.co.uk
Map ref: 5, SC26
Directions: Signs for South & Port St Mary, left at Post Office, house in centre of Promenade overlooking harbour
Rooms: 4 en suite, S £59–£98 D £70–£98
Notes: ⊘ on premises ⊗ on premises ⚶ under 4yrs **Closed:** 21 Dec–3 Jan

This family-run establishment lovingly recreates the property's original Victorian style, with exquisite interior design, cast-iron fireplaces in the public rooms and sparklingly polished period furniture. Delicious home-made cakes served on arrival and the luxurious bedrooms have a hot water bottle placed in your bed at night. Breakfast is a treat and evening meals are offered in the winter only (Monday–Friday). Smoking and alcohol are not permitted. There is free parking 70 yards away.

Recommended in the area

Cregneash Folk Village; Victorian Steam Railway; Sound and Calf of Man (bird sanctuary)

SCOTLAND

Loch an Eilean

Callater Lodge Guest House

★★★★ GH

Address: 9 Glenshee Road, BRAEMAR,
Aberdeenshire AB35 5YQ
Tel: 013397 41275
Email: hampsons@hotel-braemar.co.uk
Website: www.callaterlodge.co.uk
Map ref: 12, NO19
Directions: Next to A93, 300yds south of Braemar town centre
Rooms: 6 en suite, S £32–£35 D £60–£66
Parking: 6 **Notes:** ⊘ on premises ⊗ on premises ⋔

Callater Lodge, built of local granite in 1861, stands in spacious and attractive grounds at the south end of this pretty village with its royal connections. A warm welcome is assured at any time, but especially in the winter when this beautifully kept house is heated round the clock. Sink into deep leather chairs in the lounge after a day walking, climbing, golfing, cycling, fishing or skiing. The individually-styled en suite bedrooms have lovely soft furnishings, colour TV, tea- and coffee-making facilities, thermostatically controlled heating, hairdryer and bathrobes and the bathrooms contain a good selection of toiletries. Callater Lodge is also fully licensed. Breakfast is served in the bright dining room and offers a wide choice. Later, soup of the day, snacks and a variety of tasty sandwiches are served between 5–8pm. Surrounded by fine hills, magnificent Braemar Castle can be reached by one of many pretty walks. There are also a number of local trails including the Victorian Heritage Trail and the Whisky Trail. For guests returning from a day out on the hills or ski slopes there is a drying room available to hang up wet clothing and boots; there is also secure storage for bicycles, golf clubs and skis.

Recommended in the area

Balmoral Castle; Cairngorm National Park; Glenshee Ski Centre, Cairnwell

Bealach Country House

★★★★★ ⊝ GH

Address: Duror, APPIN, Argyll & Bute
PA38 4BW
Tel: 01631 740298
Email: info@bealach-house.co.uk
Website: www.bealach-house.co.uk
Map ref: 9, NM94
Directions: Off A828, 2m S of Duror. 1.5m into
the Glen
Rooms: 3 en suite, S £40–£55 D £70–£80
Parking: 6 **Notes:** ⊘ on premises ⊗ on premises ⋇ under 14yrs **Closed:** 19 Dec–Jan

Nestling in the heart of Salachan Glen, between Oban and Fort William, is Bealach House, the only surviving house here. It is surrounded by mountains, forest and sea and makes an ideal starting point for exploring the west coast of Scotland and the spectacular mountains, glens and lochs of the Highlands. The meandering drive up the track to the property is well worth the journey – you will be offered home-made tea and biscuits with tea or coffee on arrival. The bedrooms and bathrooms here are very comfortable, catering well for the needs of the modern guest. King-size beds, heated towel rails, fluffy towels, power showers and hospitality trays with fresh milk all come as standard. Public areas are a home away from home, with the spacious lounge offering comfortable leather sofas and a wood-burning stove, and the conservatory stocked with many books and games for guests to enjoy. Excellent, fairly formal dinners are available with prior notice, with as much made on the premises as possible, and the breakfast is also very impressive. Although Bealach is not licensed, a complimentary glass or two of wine is offered with dinner, and guests are welcome to bring their own bottle.

Recommended in the area

Glencoe; Barcaldine Castle; Loch Ness

Kirkton House

★★★★★ GA

Address: Darleith Road, CARDROSS,
Argyll & Bute G82 5EZ
Tel: 01389 841951
Fax: 01389 841868
Email: aa@kirktonhouse.co.uk
Website: www.kirktonhouse.co.uk
Map ref: 9, NS37
Directions: 0.5m N of village, turn N onto Darleith Rd
at W end of village. Kirkton House 0.5m on right

Rooms: 6 en suite, S £35–£45 D £55–£70 **Parking:** 12 **Notes:** ⊗ on premises 🐾 allowed on premises ♥♥ **Closed:** Dec–Jan

Guests feel at ease here thanks to Gillian and Stewart Macdonald's warm hospitality and their comfortable home. The converted 18th-century farmhouse stands in peaceful countryside with panoramic views of the River Clyde. Stone walls and large fireplaces give a cosy, rustic atmosphere, while the mainly spacious bedrooms are individually styled. The full Scottish breakfast is a high point.

Recommended in the area

Loch Lomond; The Hill House, Helensburgh (NTS); Burrell Collection, Glasgow

---

Dunvalanree

★★★★ ⊛ GA

Address: Port Righ Bay, CARRADALE, Argyll & Bute
Campbeltown PA28 6SE
Tel: 01583 431226
Fax: 01583 431339
Email: stay@dunvalanree.com
Website: www.dunvalanree.com
Map ref: 9, NR83
Directions: From centre of Carradale, turn right at
x-rds and continue to end of road

Rooms: 5 en suite, D £130–£150 **Parking:** 8 **Notes:** ⊗ on premises ⊗ in bedrooms ♥♥

Stunningly situated on the Mull of Kintyre, Dunvalanree has been welcoming guests for over 70 years. It stands in delightful gardens on the edge of Port Righ Bay, and enjoys splendid views over Kilbrannan Sound, to the Isle of Arran. Most of the en suite bedrooms, all individually decorated and one of which is on the ground floor, enjoy panoramic sea views, and all have many extras, such as a Fairtrade hospitality tray and a set of binoculars. The restaurant menu uses local seafood and farm produce.

Recommended in the area

Campbeltown; Springbank Distillery; Carradale Nature Reserve

Coylet Inn

★★★★ INN

Address: Loch Eck, DUNOON,
Argyll & Bute PA23 8SG
Tel: 01369 840426
Email: reservations@coylet-locheck.co.uk
Website: www.coylet-locheck.co.uk
Map ref: 9, NS17
Directions: N from Dunoon on A815
Rooms: 4 en suite, S £42.50 D £75 **Parking:** 35
Notes: ⊘ on premises ⊗ on premises ♙
Closed: 25 Dec

This charming 17th-century coaching inn on the shore of Loch Eck is an ideal base for hill walking, golf, water sports and pony trekking, and boats are available for fishing on the loch. The bedrooms offer a high standard of comfort – one room has an enormous bath in the window, perfect for watching the world go by. Delicious and imaginative food using fine local produce is served in the dining room and there is a well-stocked bar with a fine selection of malt whiskies and real ale.

Recommended in the area

Dunoon; Benmore Botanical Gardens; Quadmania Outdoor Adventure Centre

Lethamhill

★★★★★ GA

Address: West Dhuhill Drive, HELENSBURGH,
Argyll & Bute G84 9AW
Tel: 01436 676016
Fax: 01436 676016
Email: Lethamhill@talk21.com
Website: www.lethamhill.co.uk
Map ref: 9, NS28
Directions: 1m N of pier/town centre. Off A818 onto
West Dhuhill Dr. Cross Upper Colquhoun St, 3rd on r
Rooms: 3 en suite, S £55–£60 D £75–£80 **Parking:** 6 **Notes:** ⊘ on premises ⊗ on premises ♙

This large spacious property with lovely well-tended gardens offers superb hospitality and impressive bedrooms that ensure guests return time and again; Jane's delicious breakfasts made from fresh Scottish produce are another lure. The rooms come with superb bathrooms, great beds and flat-screen televisions, along with many thoughtful extras. Public areas are equally comfortable, with a spacious lounge and a delightful dining room that looks out to the garden. Minimum stay two nights.

Recommended in the area

The Hill House, Helensburgh (NTS); Loch Lomond; Glasgow Airport

Alltavona House

★★★★ GH

Address: Corran Esplanade, OBAN, Argyll & Bute PA34 5AQ
Tel: 01631 565067
Fax: 01631 565067
Email: carol@alltavona.co.uk
Website: www.alltavona.co.uk
Map ref: 9, NM82
Directions: From Oban centre along seafront past cathedral, 5th house from the end of Esplanade
Rooms: 6 en suite, S £35–£70 D £60–£80 **Parking:** 6
Notes: ⊗ on premises ⊗ on premises ✙under 12yrs
Closed: 12–30 Dec

An elegant Victorian villa within a 10-minute walk of central Oban, Alltavona House has the added benefit of stunning views over Oban Bay to the islands of Lismore and Kererra. Alltavona offers a warm and friendly family atmosphere, and your hosts Allan and Carol take every care to cater to their guests' individual requirements. The attractive en suite bedrooms are individually styled and feature quality furnishings, all in harmony with the age and style of the property. The rooms come equipped with colour TV and tea- and coffee-making facilities. The public areas, some with tartan carpets, include an elegant dining room and a small, cosy reading room. You will be unable to resist the delicious breakfasts that feature the best of local produce. Choose from traditional porridge, cereals or fruit and then treat yourself to a full Scottish breakfast complete with Stornoway black pudding, sausages direct from the local butcher and haggis. If a lighter option is preferred there are free-range eggs, Mull smoked salmon or fresh poached local smoked haddock. A continental-style breakfast of cold baked ham, a selection of cheeses served with warm, freshly baked croissants or rolls and bread is another tasty alternative.

Recommended in the area

Oban Rare Breeds Farm Park; Scottish Sea Life Sanctuary; Dunstaffnage Castle; Barcaldine Castle

Glenburnie House

★★★★ GH

Address: The Esplanade, OBAN,
Argyll & Bute PA34 5AQ
Tel: 01631 562089
Email: graeme.strachan@btinternet.com
Website: www.glenburnie.co.uk
Map ref: 9, NM82
Directions: On Oban seafront. Follow signs for Ganavan
Rooms: 12 en suite, S £45–£49 D £74–£100
Parking: 12 **Notes:** ⊘ on premises ⊗ on premises 🚼 under 12yrs **Closed:** Nov–Mar

From its prime position on the Esplanade, this handsome establishment has dazzling views across the Firth of Lorne to the Isle of Mull. The bedrooms, including a superior four-poster and a mini-suite, are beautifully decorated and equipped with modern facilities. Delicious breakfasts feature the best of local produce and home-made preserves. The Strachans are happy to advise you on the restaurants in the town centre, which is just a stroll away. AA Landlady of the Year finalist 2004–2005. Private parking.

Recommended in the area

Crarae and Arduaine gardens; fishing and golf; boat hire and cruises

Craigadam

★★★★ 🏆 🍽 GH

Address: Craigadam, CASTLE DOUGLAS,
Dumfries and Galloway DG7 3HU
Tel/Fax: 01556 650233
Email: inquiry@craigadam.com
Website: www.craigadam.com
Map ref: 5, NX76
Directions: From Castle Douglas E on A75 to Crocketford. In Crocketford turn left on A712 for 2m. House on hill
Rooms: 10 en suite, S £42–£84 D £84 **Parking:** 12 **Notes:** ⊘ 🐴 🚼 **Closed:** Xmas & New Year

Set on a working farm, this elegant country house offers gracious living in a relaxed environment. The strikingly individual and large en suite bedrooms are housed in a converted 18th-century farmstead, with antique furnishings and French windows opening out onto a courtyard. Public areas include a well-furnished lounge with a log fire and a snooker room with comprehensive honesty bar. The dining room features a magnificent 15-seater table, the setting for Celia Pickup's delightful meals. .

Recommended in the area

Dalton Pottery; Cream o' Galloway; Mill on the Fleet

Caerlaverock Castle, Dumfries and Galloway

Southpark House

★★★★ GA

Address: Quarry Road, Locharbriggs, DUMFRIES,
Dumfries and Galloway DG1 1QG
Tel: 01387 711188
Fax: 01387 711155
Email: info@southparkhouse.co.uk
Website: www.southparkhouse.co.uk
Map ref: 5, NX97
Directions: 3.5m NE of Dumfries. Off A701 in
Locharbriggs onto Quarry Rd, last house on left
Rooms: 4 en suite S £30 D £49.50 **Parking:** 13 **Notes:** ⊘ on premises ⊗ on premises ⊷

Southpark House, a substantial and well-maintained property in a peaceful location on the edge of town, is renowned for its comfortable accommodation, good food and hospitality. It offers stunning views across five valleys, yet is only a short drive from the centre of the bustling market town of Dumfries with all its amenities. All of the en suite bedrooms here, including one family room as well as doubles and twins, are comfortable, attractively decorated and well equipped. There is a relaxing lounge for the use of guests with the added comfort of a roaring log fire when the weather is cold outside. Email and fax facilities are also available, as well as a laundry room – making this an ideal choice for business travellers as well as those simply visiting for pleasure. The friendly proprietor, Ewan Maxwell, personally oversees the hearty Scottish breakfast, which offers a wide range of cereals, traditionally made porridge, a choice of breads and fruit juice as well as a full cooked breakfast menu to choose from. Breakfast is served in the light and airy conservatory breakfast room, a recently built addition to the house that offers beautiful views over the surrounding countryside. There is ample secure parking for guests.

Recommended in the area

Mabie Park Farm; Farmers Den; Kippford beach

Wallamhill House

★★★★ BB

Address: Kirkton, DUMFRIES, Dumfries and
Galloway DG1 1SL
Tel: 01387 248249
Email: wallamhill@aol.com
Website: www.wallamhill.co.uk
Map ref: 5, NX97
Directions: 3m N of Dumfries. Off A701 signed
Kirkton, 1.5m on right
Rooms: 3 en suite, S £35–£38 D £56–£60
Parking: 6 **Notes:** ⊗ ⊗ on premises ♦♦

Hospitality is a real strength at Wallamhill House, a very nice house set in well-tended gardens and peaceful countryside 3 miles from Dumfries. The large bedrooms are extremely well equipped and there is a drawing room and a mini health club, with sauna, steam shower and gym equipment. Evening meals (by arrangement) are served in the dining room around one large table, and you can bring your own wine. The area offers great walking, cycling, or mountain biking in the Ae and Mabie forests.
Recommended in the area
Nithdale; Sweetheart Abbey, New Abbey; Caerlaverock Castle

Hartfell House

★★★★ GH

Address: Hartfell Crescent, MOFFAT,
Dumfries and Galloway DG10 9AL
Tel: 01683 220153
Email: enquiries@hartfellhouse.co.uk
Website: www.hartfellhouse.co.uk
Map ref: 10, NT00
Directions: Off High St at war memorial onto Well St
& Old Well Rd, Hartfell Crescent on right
Rooms: 8 (7 en suite), S £35 D £60 **Parking:** 6
Notes: ⊗ on premises ⊗ on premises ♦♦ **Closed:** Xmas

A stunning example of Victorian architecture, this 'B' Listed property is set in a designated 'Outstanding Conservation Area' yet is only three miles from the M74 (J15). Rob and Mhairi will make every effort to use their combined 20 years experience of 5 star hotels to make your stay in this licensed guest house as comfortable and enjoyable as possible. All rooms are equipped with TV, radio alarm, hairdryer and tea/coffee making facilities. The residents' lounge on the first floor enjoys views of the Moffat hills.
Recommended in the area
Galloway Forest Park; Dumfries; Carlisle

Limetree House

★★★★ GA

Address: Eastgate, MOFFAT, Dumfries and Galloway
DG10 9AE
Tel: 01683 220001
Email: info@limetreehouse.co.uk
Website: www.limetreehouse.co.uk
Map ref: 10, NT00
Directions: Off High St onto Well St, left onto Eastgate,
house 100yds
Rooms: 6 en suite, S £37.50 D £65–£75 **Parking:** 3
Notes: ⊘ on premises 🐾 allowed on premises 👶under 5yrs

This quiet property near Moffat's High Street has high standards of accommodation with many original features, where Katherine and Derek make you feel as comfortable as possible. The rooms, smartly furnished, include refreshment trays and hairdryers. Derek's legendary pancakes and a wide choice of buffet and cooked dishes are offered at breakfast time.

Recommended in the area

Craigieburn Gardens; Grey Mare's Tail waterfall; St Mary's Loch

Gillbank House

★★★★★ GA

Address: 8 East Morton Street, THORNHILL,
Dumfries and Galloway DG3 5LZ
Tel: 01848 330597
Fax: 01848 331713
Email: hanne@gillbank.co.uk
Website: www.gillbank.co.uk
Map ref: 5, NX89
Directions: In town centre off A76
Rooms: 6 en suite, S £40–£45 D £60–£65
Parking: 8 **Notes:** ⊘ on premises ⊗ in bedrooms 👶 under 8yrs

Once the home of a wealthy Edinburgh merchant, Gillbank is a charming late Victorian house located in a quiet street close to the centre of the picturesque town of Thornhill, and easily accessible from the A76 Dumfries bypass or off the M74 at Elvanfoot. The comfortable, spacious and recently refurbished bedrooms have en suite shower rooms and are well equipped. Breakfast is served at individual tables in the bright, airy dining room. Bicycle storage is available for cyclists.

Recommended in the area

Drumlanrig Castle; River Nith (salmon fishing); Thornhill Golf Course

Allison House

★★★★ GA

Address: 17 Mayfield Gardens,
EDINBURGH EH9 2AX
Tel: 0131 667 8049
Fax: 0131 667 5001
Email: info@allisonhousehotel.com
Website: www.allisonhousehotel.com
Map ref: 10, NT27
Directions: Off A701 heading south from centre of the city
Rooms: 11 (10 en suite), S £45–£65 D £55–£105 **Parking:** 6
Notes: ⊗ in dining room 🐾 allowed on premises ♦♦

A good choice for both business travellers and those simply
on vacation, Allison House offers a range of modern comforts within a splendid Georgian building.
Located on the south side of Edinburgh in a residential area, this family-run establishment is on
the main bus route and is convenient for the city centre and its host of amenities. Valuable off-road
parking is available for those with cars. Inside, the attractive and elegant bedrooms, all with en suite
shower room, have been tastefully refurbished to include Black Watch and Lindsey tartan fabrics. The
rooms are generally spacious here and very well equipped, offering TV, writing desk, wireless internet
connection, trouser-press, ironing facilities, hairdryer, refreshment tray and a complementary drink
from the decanters of whisky and sherry. For special occasions, you can arrange to have champagne,
chocolates or flowers in your room on arrival. Breakfast is served at individual tables in the ground
floor dining room and provides a range of options, including a traditional full cooked Scottish plate, or
an extensive continental buffet, with fruit juices, fresh fruit, cereals, croissants, pastries and cheeses.
Allison House specialises in organising a selection of golf, shopping, city, sporting and theatre breaks.

Recommended in the area

Dynamic Earth; Edinburgh Zoo; The Museum of Scotland

Ellesmere House

★★★★ GH

Address: 11 Glengyle Terrace,
EDINBURGH EH3 9LN
Tel: 0131 229 4823
Email: ruth@edinburghbandb.co.uk
Website: www.edinburghbandb.co.uk
Map ref: 10, NT27
Directions: S of city centre off A702
Rooms: 4 en suite, S £45–£70 D £90–£140
Notes: ⊗ on premises ⊗ on premises ♦♦

This Victorian terraced town house overlooks the famous Bruntsfield Links golf course, reputed to be the oldest golf course in the world, and is close to the Golf Tavern, dating from 1456. The terrace on which this delightful establishment stands was built in 1869 by William and Duncan McGregor, and the name 'Glengyle' has associations with the Clan McGregor. Ellesmere House is within walking distance of Edinburgh city centre and all of its attractions and, as such, would make an ideal base for visiting Scotland's capital city, whether for business, a weekend break or a longer holiday. Edinburgh has excellent shopping facilities and offers no shortage of entertainment. Guests are treated to an exceptional level of comfort here, in a clean and friendly environment. The attractive and individually decorated en suite bedrooms vary in size and have many thoughtful touches, such as flatscreen colour TV, wireless internet connection and tea and coffee-making facilities. There is a family room is available and one of the bedrooms boasts a four-poster bed. A superb breakfast, featuring the best of local produce and all freshly prepared, is served in the elegant lounge-dining room, from a menu full of delicious choices. In the evening, there are many excellent and varied restaurants from which you can choose, all within easy walking distance.

Recommended in the area

Edinburgh Castle; Princes Street; Holyrood Palace

Elmview

★★★★★ GA

Address: 15 Glengyle Terrace, EDINBURGH EH3 9LN
Tel: 0131 228 1973
Email: nici@elmview.co.uk
Website: www.elmview.co.uk
Map ref: 10. NT27
Directions: 0.5m S of city centre. Off A702 Leven St onto ValleyField St, one-way to Glengyle Ter
Rooms: 3 en suite, S £60–£95 D £80–£120 **Notes:** ⊘ on premises ⊗ on premises 👪 under 15yrs **Closed:** Dec–Feb

Elmview is situated in the heart of Edinburgh in a delightful Victorian terrace within easy walking distance of Edinburgh Castle and Princes Street (0.6 miles). The spacious and quiet en suite bedrooms have been furnished to include everything a guest could want. Fresh flowers, complementary sherry and elegant furnishings all add to the feeling of a personal home. Elmview overlooks a large urban park, which includes a free, 36-hole, pitch and putt golf course. The highlight of a stay is the excellent breakfast taken at one large table.

Recommended in the area

Edinburgh Castle; Edinburgh Old Town; Museum of Scotland

The International Guest House

★★★★ GH

Address: 37 Mayfield Gardens,
　　　　　 EDINBURGH EH9 2BX
Tel: 0131 667 2511
Fax: 0131 667 1112
Email: intergh1@yahoo.co.uk
Website: www.accomodation-edinburgh.com
Map ref: 10, NT27
Directions: On A701 1.5m S of Princes St
Rooms: 9 en suite, S £55–£75 D £55–£135
Parking: 3 **Notes:** ⊘ on premises ⊗ on premises 👫

This attractive Victorian terrace house, on the south side of the city, 1.5 miles from Edinburgh Castle, is on a main bus route to the city centre. All the bedrooms, decorated and fitted in matching period floral prints, have fresh flowers and modern en suites. Some rooms have magnificent views across to the extinct volcano known as Arthur's Seat. A hearty Scottish breakfast is served on fine bone china at separate tables in the dining room which features a lovely marble fireplace.

Recommended in the area

Edinburgh Castle; Palace of Holyroodhouse; University of Edinburgh

Kew House

★★★★★ GA

ddress: 1 Kew Terrace, Murrayfield,
EDINBURGH EH12 5JE
el: 0131 313 0700
ax: 0131 313 0747
mail: info@kewhouse.com
ebsite: www.kewhouse.com
ap ref: 10, NT27
irections: 1m W of city centre A8
ooms: 6 en suite, S £75–£85 D £85–£150
arking: 6 Notes: ⊘ on premises 🐎 allowed on premises 👫

ew House forms part of a listed Victorian terrace dating from 1860, located a mile west of the city
entre, convenient for Murrayfield Rugby Stadium, and just a 15-minute walk from Princes Street.
egular bus services from Princes Street pass the door. The house is ideal for both business travellers
nd holidaymakers, with secure private parking. While many period features have been retained,
e interior design is contemporary, and the standards of housekeeping are superb. Expect
omplementary sherry and chocolates on arrival, and you can order supper in the lounge. Full Scottish
reakfast with an alternative vegetarian choice is included in the room tariff, and light snacks, with
om service, are available all day. Bedrooms, including some on the ground floor, are en suite and
ell equipped with remote control television with digital channels, direct-dial telephones, modem
oints, hairdryers, trouser presses, fresh flowers and tea and coffee facilities. The superior rooms also
ave thier own fridge. Kew House also offers two very comfortable serviced apartments accommodating
o to five people.

ecommended in the area

dinburgh Castle; Edinburgh International Conference Centre; Murrayfield Rugby Stadium; National
allery of Scotland; National Museum of Scotland; Princes Street and its spacious gardens

The Royal Mile, Edinburgh

The Lodge

★★★★ GH

Address: 6 Hampton Terrace, West Coates,
EDINBURGH EH12 5JD
Tel: 0131 337 3682
Fax: 0131 313 1700
Website: www.thelodgehotel.co.uk
Map ref: 10, NT27
Directions: On A8, 0.75m W of Princes St
Rooms: 12 en suite, S £75 D £110 **Parking:** 8
Notes: ⊘ on premises ⊗ on premises ♦♦

Set in Edinburgh's West End, this fine Georgian house is within walking distance of the city centre and also on the main bus route. The comfortable en suite bedrooms, including ground-floor and family rooms, are carefully decorated and well-equipped for leisure and business travellers, with wireless internet connection in some rooms. Guests are well looked after, with a glass of wine in the room on arrival. The Lodge is bedecked with floral displays, and there is an elegant ground-floor lounge and an attractive dining room serving hearty breakfasts and evening meals by arrangement.

Recommended in the area

Edinburgh Castle; Rosslyn Chapel; Holyroodhouse

Southside Guest House

★ ★ ★ ★ GH

Address: 8 Newington Road,
EDINBURGH EH9 1QS
Tel: 0131 668 4422
Fax: 0131 667 7771
Email: info@southsideguesthouse.co.uk
Website: www.southsideguesthouse.co.uk
Map ref: 10, NT27
Directions: E end of Princes St onto North Bridge to Royal Mile,
continue S 0.5m, house on right
Rooms: 8 en suite, S £50–£70 D £70–£140
Notes: ⊘ on premises ⊗ on premises ✤ under 10yrs

Built in 1865, Southside Guest House is an elegant Victorian sandstone terraced house in the centre of Edinburgh, only a few minutes from Holyrood Park. The owners Lynne and Franco have been involved in the hotel trade for many years and have happily made their home in the capital. Lynne is from the Highlands, and Franco hails from Florence. They offer individually designed, stylish, well-equipped bedrooms, with direct-dial telephones, DVD players, free wireless internet access, and many other comforts including quality mattresses and crisp fine linen to ensure a good night's sleep. Two of the rooms have four-poster beds and comfortable sofas, and the remaining rooms come in a variety of colour schemes and bed sizes. Breakfast at Southside is guaranteed to satisfy with its great choice of traditional freshly cooked Scottish dishes, cheeses, oatcakes, fresh fruit and real coffee. Guests sit at separate tables in the attractive dining room. Southside Guest House has recently enhanced its facilities with a new self-contained apartment.

Recommended in the area

Edinburgh Castle; Edinburgh Festival Theatre; The Palace of Holyroodhouse; Old Town; Holyrood Park; Princes Street shops and gardens

The Witchery by the Castle

★★★★★ ◉ RR

Address: 352 Castlehill, The Royal Mile,
EDINBURGH EH1 2NF
Tel: 0131 225 5613
Fax: 0131 220 4392
Email: mail@thewitchery.com
Website: www.thewitchery.com
Map ref: 10, NT27
Directions: Top of Royal Mile at gates of Castle
Rooms: 7 en suite, S £295 D £295 **Notes:** ⊘ on
premises ⊗ in bedrooms ⊁ under 12yrs **Closed:** 25–26 Dec

A-list celebrities often choose to stay in this quirky, luxurious, romantic little place that is tucked away in a group of historic buildings right at the gates of Edinburgh Castle. And it's not just the perfect central location that appeals to guests, they are drawn by the fantastic – in the truest sense of the word – suites that could easily be the lavish set of some big-budget medieval movie. Massive four-poster beds, rich red and gold fabrics, oak panelling and tapestries set the scene, and each of the rooms has its own individuality, such as the military uniforms in The Guardroom. The bathrooms are simply stunning. The one belonging to The Library is lined with bookshelves; the Old Rectory's bathroom is in the style of a Gothic chapel; that of the Inner Sanctum is in red laquer, with a huge antique bathtub; Sempill's bathroom has oak-panelling and Vestry's is a riot of red trompe-l'oeil drapery. The food served in the oak-panelled Witchery restaurant and the elegant Secret Garden is equally renowned – hardly surprising since the establishment was the brainchild of Scotland's most famous restaurateur, James Thomson. The room rates include a continental breakfast and a bottle of champagne; absolutely free is the chance of being neighbour to some member of the Hollywood elite.

Recommended in the area

Edinburgh Castle; the Royal Mile; Museum of Scotland; National Gallery of Scotland

St Andrews Castle, Fife

The Spindrift

★ ★ ★ ★ GH

Address:	Pittenweem Road, ANSTRUTHER, Fife KY10 3DT
Tel:	01333 310573
Fax:	01333 310573
Email:	info@thespindrift.co.uk
Website:	www.thespindrift.co.uk
Map ref:	10, NO50
Directions:	Entering town from W on A917, 1st building on left

Rooms: 8 (7 en suite), S £40–£48.5 D £60–£76 **Parking:** 12 **Notes:** ⊘ on premises 🐾 allowed on premises 👶under 10yrs **Closed:** Xmas–late Jan

A unique feature of this house is the top-floor Captain's Room, made to resemble a shipmaster's cabin by the original owner – the east-facing window looks towards Anstruther harbour. All the individually furnished, spacious bedrooms are brightly decorated and have a wide range of extras. The lounge has an honesty bar for a pre-dinner drink, and enjoyable, home-cooked fare is served in the dining room.

Recommended in the area

Scottish Fisheries Museum; St Andrews; East Neuk coastal villages

The Roods

★★★★ BB

Address:	16 Bannerman Avenue,
	INVERKEITHING, Fife KY11 1NG
Tel:	01383 415049
Fax:	01383 415049
Email:	isobelmarley@hotmail.com
Website:	www.the-roods.co.uk
Map ref:	10, NT18

Directions: N of town centre off B981 Church St-Chapel Pl

Rooms: 2 en suite, S £26–£30 D £50–£60 **Parking:** 4 **Notes:** ⊗ on premises ⊗ on premises ⡗

In a secluded setting, this delightful house is within easy reach of both the railway station and the town centre. The individually furnished bedrooms are on the ground floor and have smart new bathrooms. Thoughtful touches bring a personal feel to the rooms, which have direct-dial telephones, central heating and tea and coffee facilities. The lounge has an inviting open fire and breakfast is served at individual tables in the pretty conservatory. Evening meals by arrangement. No dogs please.

Recommended in the area

Culross Palace, Town House and The Study; Pittencrieff House Museum; Aberdour Castle

---

Dunclutha Guest House

★★★★ GH

Address:	16 Victoria Road, LEVEN, Fife KY8 4EX
Tel:	01333 425515
Fax:	01333 422311
Email:	pam.leven@blueyonder.co.uk
Website:	www.dunclutha.myby.co.uk
Map ref:	10, NO30

Directions: A915, B933 Glenlyon Rd into Leven, rdbt left onto Commercial Rd & Victoria Rd, Dunclutha opp church on right

Rooms: 4 (3 en suite), S from £35 D £60–£80 **Parking:** 3 **Notes:** ⊗ on premises ⊗ on premises ⡗

The original splendour of this former Victorian rectory sits well with modern trappings, making this an impressive place to stay. Three spacious bedrooms and a cosy fourth room make up the excellent accommodation. All of the rooms are smartly decorated. The lounge is filled with interesting items as well as a piano, and is a sociable place in the evenings. The adjoining dining room is the setting for hearty breakfasts, which include delicious home-made preserves and bread.

Recommended in the area

St Andrews; Levens Links golf course; Fife Coastal Path

The Peat Inn

★★★ ◉◉ RR

Address: PEAT INN, Fife KY15 5LH
Tel: 01334 840206
Fax: 01334 840530
Email: stay@thepeatinn.co.uk
Website: www.thepeatinn.co.uk
Map ref: 10, NO40
Directions: At junct of B940 and B941 5m SW of St Andrews
Rooms: 8 en suite, S £125 D £175 **Parking:** 24
Notes: ⊘ on premises 🐾 allowed in bedrooms 🚫 **Closed:** 25–26 Dec & 1–15 Jan

The Peat Inn is consistently one of the best restaurants in Scotland, holder of two AA Rosettes and renowned for its use of fresh, Scottish produce for over 30 years. Chef Geoffrey Smeddle ensures it remains a real haven for food lovers. Set in a 300-year-old former coaching inn, this restaurant-with-rooms enjoys a rural location yet is close to St Andrews. With three intimate dining areas and luxurious and spacious suite accommodation – this is the perfect blend of cuisine and comfort.

Recommended in the area

Falkland Palace; St Andrews Cathedral; Scotland's Secret Bunker

Glenderran Guest House

★★★ GH

Address: 9 Murray Park, ST ANDREWS, Fife KY16 9AW
Tel: 01334 477951
Email: info@glenderran.com
Website: www.glenderran.com
Map ref: 10, NO51
Directions: In centre. Off North St onto Murray Park
Rooms: 5 (4 en suite), S £38–£45 D £76–£100
Notes: ⊘ ⊗ on premises 🚫 under 12yrs

This immaculately presented guest house is centrally located in beautiful St Andrews. All the bedrooms have recently been fully refurbished to a very high standard, offering subtle contemporary comforts while maintaining all the character of this beautiful Victorian house. All bedrooms have flat-screen TVs, hospitality trays and a full range of high quality bathroom accessories. The house has free wi-fi internet throughout and a laptop computer for guests' use. The excellent breakfasts are freshly cooked to order from a varied menu, and make great use of locally-sourced fresh produce.

Recommended in the area

University of St Andrews; St Andrew's Links; Cathedral

The Inn at Lathones

★★★★ ◉◉ INN

Address: Largoward, ST ANDREWS, Fife KY9 1JE
Tel: 01334 840494
Fax: 01334 840694
Email: lathones@theinn.co.uk
Website: www.theinn.co.uk
Map ref: 10, NO51
Directions: 5m S of St Andrews on A915, 0.5m on left before village of Largoward just after hidden dip
Rooms: 13 en suite, S £120 D £180 **Parking:** 35
Notes: ⊘ on premises ⌁ allowed in bedrooms ⁙ **Closed:** 26 Dec & 3–16 Jan

The Inn dates back to c1603 and over the last 10 years it has been sympathetically restored to provic comfortable light, cosy bedrooms. Facilities include a hospitality tray, satellite TV, radio, direct-dial telephone and computer access. The restaurant is widely acclaimed and the Inn welcomes the return of the former chef Marc Guilbert after a short break, during which he has further honed his special skills. Marc's style of cooking is clean and modern European with slight Asian influences.

Recommended in the area

St Andrews Old Course, British Golf Museum; Castle and Visitor Centre; St Andrews

The Kelvingrove

★★★★ GA

Address: 944 Sauchiehall Street,
GLASGOW G3 7TH
Tel: 0141 339 5011
Fax: 0141 339 6566
Email: info@kelvingrovehotel.com
Website: www.kelvingrove-hotel.co.uk
Map ref: 9, NS56
Directions: M8 junct 18, 0.5m along road signed Kelvingrove Museum, on left
Rooms: 22 en suite, S £40–£70 D £70–£100 **Notes:** ⊘ on premises ⌁ allowed on premises ⁙

This friendly terraced establishment, is in Glasgow's lively West End and close to the town centre. Ru by three generations of the same family it is very well maintained. All of the bedrooms, including triple and several good family rooms, are well equipped for guest comfort and convenience. The en suite bathrooms have power showers and luxuriously soft towels. Free wireless internet connection is also available. Breakfast is served in the bright breakfast room and the reception lounge is always open.

Recommended in the area

Kelvingrove Museum and Art Gallery; Botanic Gardens; SECC

Dell Druie Guest House

★ ★ ★ ★   BB

Address: Inverdruie, Rothiemurchus,
AVIEMORE, Highland PH22 1QH
Tel: 01479 810934
Email: enquiries@delldruieguesthouse.com
Website: www.delldruieguesthouse.com
Map ref: 12, NH81
Directions: 0.75m S of Aviemore. Off B9152 onto
B970 to Coylumbridge and Cairngorm Mountain,
sharp left after Rothiemurchus Visitor Centre, last
house in cul-de-sac
Rooms: 3 (2 en suite), S £60–£70 D £70–£110 **Parking:** 6
Notes: ⊘ on premises ⊗ on premises ✸ under 14yrs

Dell Druie is an impressive modern house set in a riverside location in the heart of the Cairngorm National Park. Less than a mile from the centre of Aviemore and three minutes' walk from The Rothiemurchus Visitor Centre, Dell Druie offers easy access to the abundance of activities that make the Cairngorms and Aviemore so special. This guest house offers immaculate, stylish, contemporary bedrooms with tea and coffee making facilities, Sky TV, DVD player, and free broadband wireless internet connection in all rooms. The fresh flowers, white cotton bed linen, fluffy white towels and bathrobes along with many other thoughtful extra comforts such as Arran Aromatics bath products all help make your stay relaxing and memorable. Full cooked breakfasts are served including free-range farm eggs and other local produce including Rothiemurchus Honey with Whisky, and Scottish Salmon. There is a spacious lounge where you can watch red squirrels, pheasants and many other species of local birds in the garden, or relax by the river in the private picnic paradise.

Recommended in the area

Cairngorm National Park; RSPB Nature Reserve

Craiglinnhe House

★★★★ ⌂ ⊜ GH

Address: Lettermore, BALLACHULISH,
Highland PH49 4JD
Tel: 01855 811270
Email: info@craiglinnhe.co.uk
Website: www.craiglinnhe.co.uk
Map ref: 9, NN05
Directions: From village A82 onto A828, Craiglinnhe
1.5m on left
Rooms: 5 (5 en suite), S £42–£63 D £50–£84
Parking: 5 **Notes:** ⊗ on premises ⊗ on premises 🚼 under 13yrs **Closed:** 24–26 Dec, Feb

Craiglinnhe House was built in 1885 by the owner of the local slate quarry, and though it retains all of its Victorian style and character, it has been modernised to provide the utmost comfort. A perfect place for walking, climbing and skiing in the winter. The elegant lounge has stunning views of the loch and is a lovely place to relax, while the dining room provides a fine setting for the superb meals cooked by owner David Hughes. The stylish en suite bedrooms are all attractive and very well equipped.

Recommended in the area

Glencoe; Fort William; Whisky distillery

Lyn-Leven Guest House

★★★★ GH

Address: West Laroch,
SOUTH BALLACHULISH PH49 4JP
Tel: 01855 811392
Fax: 01855 811600
Email: macleodcilla@aol.com
Website: www.lynleven.co.uk
Map ref: 9, NN05
Directions: Off A82 signed on left West Laroch
Rooms: 12 en suite, S £30–£50 D £50–£64
Parking: 12 **Notes:** ⊗ on premises ⌖ allowed on premises 🚼 **Closed:** Xmas

Beautifully situated, this guest house maintains high standards in all areas. Highland hospitality puts guests at their ease, and the spectacular views of Loch Leven guarantee plenty to talk about. Bedrooms vary in size, are prettily decorated, and have showers and some thoughtful extras. The spacious lounge and smart dining room make the most of the scenic outlook, and delicious home-cooked evening meals (£9 per person) and breakfasts are served at separate tables. There is ample parking.

Recommended in the area

Ballachulish Country House Golf Course; Glencoe Visitor Centre and Museum

Glenaveron

★★★★★ BB

Address: Golf Road, BRORA, Highland KW9 6QS
Tel: 01408 621601
Email: alistair@glenaveron.co.uk
Website: www.glenaveron.co.uk
Map ref: 12, NC90
Directions: A9 NE into Brora, right onto Golf Rd, 2nd house on right
Rooms: 3 en suite, S £45–£55 D £64–£70
Parking: 6 **Notes:** ⊘ on premises ⊗ on premises
⁼↟ Closed: 8–23 Oct, Xmas & New Year

This beautiful Edwardian house, set amid extensive mature gardens, is a delightful family home where guests are welcomed into a friendly and relaxing atmosphere. The bedrooms are spacious and well-equipped, with a ground floor bedroom available for easier access. Breakfast is served in the elegant dining room, house-party style. Glenaveron is an ideal base for touring the northern Highlands and for crossing to Orkney; the world famous Royal Dornoch golf club is just 20 minutes' drive away.

Recommended in the area

Royal Dornoch Golf Club; Orkney Islands

Shorefield House

★★★★ ⌂ GA

Address: Edinbane, EDINBANE,
Isle of Skye Highland IV51 9PW
Tel: 01470 582444
Fax: 01470 582414
Email: shorefieldhouse@aol.com
Website: www.shorefield-house.com
Map ref: 11, NG35
Directions: 12m from Portree & 8m from Dunvegan, off A850 into Edinbane, 1st on right

Rooms: 4 en suite, S £36–£46 D £70–£84 **Parking:** 10 **Notes:** ⊘ on premises ⊗ on premises ⁼↟
Closed: Oct–Etr

The Prall family settled on Skye eleven years ago to provide modern accommodation in family, double, twin and single bedrooms and ground floor rooms with ramped access. Traditional Highland breakfasts or a lighter buffet alternative are served in the dining room (special diets are catered for). The adjoining conservatory has books, games and a TV. There are excellent local restaurants for evening meals.

Recommended in the area

Dunvegan Castle and seal colony; The Three Chimneys Restaurant; Talisker Whisky Distillery

Ashburn House

★★★★★ GA

Address: 8 Achintore Road,
FORT WILLIAM Highland PH33 6RQ
Tel: 01397 706000
Fax: 01397 702024
Email: christine@no-1.fsworld.co.uk
Website: www.scotland2000.com/ashburn
Map ref: 12, NN17
Directions: 500yds S of town centre on A82
Rooms: 7 en suite, S £45–£50 D £90–£100
Parking: 8 Notes: ⊘ on premises ⊗ on premises ⋫ under 12yrs Closed: Xmas

Wonderful views of Loch Linnhe and the Ardgour Hills can be enjoyed from many of the bedrooms at this imposing Victorian property just a 5-minute walk from the centre of Fort William. A loving restoration has brought the house back to its former glory. Bedrooms are individually designed and spacious, with little luxuries, hairdryers and hospitality trays. Wake up to the aroma of Christine MacDonald's freshly baked scones and plan your day out consulting the knowledgeable Willie.

Recommended in the area

Nevis Range Gondola; Ben Nevis; Jacobite steam train

The Grange

★★★★★ GA

Address: Grange Road, FORT WILLIAM
Highland PH33 6JF
Tel: 01397 705516
Email: info@thegrange-scotland.co.uk
Website: www.thegrange-scotland.co.uk
Map ref: 12, NN17
Directions: A82 S from Fort William, 300yds from rdbt left onto Ashburn Ln, at top on left
Rooms: 3 en suite, S D £98–£110 Parking: 3
Notes: ⊘ on premises ⊗ on premises ⋫ under 13yrs Closed: Nov–Mar

Years of careful planning and hard work have gone into the restoration of this lovely property, which provides only the highest standards. Meticulous attention to detail is evident throughout the house, and warm Highland hospitality is assured. Attractive decor and pretty fabrics are used to stunning effect in the charming bedrooms. From its hillside position The Grange enjoys magnificent views over Loch Linnhe and the highland scenery.

Recommended in the area

Ben Nevis; Jacobite steam train; Loch Ness

Inveraray Castle Park

Mansefield Guest House

★★★★ GH

Address: Corpach, FORT WILLIAM,
Highland PH33 7LT

Tel: 01397 772262

Email: mansefield@btinternet.com

Website: www.fortwilliamaccommodation.com

Map ref: 12, NN17

Directions: 2m N of Fort William A82 onto A830,
house 2m on A830 in Corpach

Rooms: 6 en suite, S £24–£35 D £48–£70

Parking: 7 **Notes:** ⊗ on premises ⊗ on premises 🚼 under 12yrs

Mansefield Guest House is a former manse set in mature gardens overlooking Loch Linnhe, with great mountain views. The friendly, family-run guest house provides bedrooms with country-style decor and Laura Ashley furnishings, plus complementary toiletries and hospitality trays. You can even request blankets if you prefer them to duvets. The cosy sitting room overlooks the garden, and a roaring coal fire burns on cold evenings as you browse the many books, magazines and tourist brochures.

Recommended in the area

Treasures of the Earth Exhibition, Corpach; Ben Nevis; boat trips to Seal Island, Loch Linnhe

Foyers Bay House

★★★ GH

Address: Lochness, FOYERS
Highland IV2 6YB
Tel: 01456 486624
Fax: 01456 486337
Email: enquiries@foyersbay.co.uk
Website: www.foyersbay.co.uk
Map ref: 12, NH42
Directions: Off B852 into Lower Foyers
Rooms: 6 en suite, S £55–£75 D £70–£90
Parking: 6 **Notes:** ⊗ on premises ⊗ on premises ⚑ under 16yrs

Set on the quiet, undeveloped side of Loch Ness, midway between Inverness and Fort Augustus, among hillside woodlands with a colourful abundance of rhododendrons, this delightful house offers stunning views as well as forest walks and nature trails. It makes a perfect choice for a relaxing break away from it all. Foyers Bay was originally built as a family home in the late 1890s and today it still offers many of the delights of a Victorian villa, though it has been thoughtfully and comfortably refurbished. There is a comfortable residents' bar and lounge adjacent to an airy, plant-filled conservatory cafe-restaurant, where traditional Scottish breakfasts and delicious evening meals are served against a backdrop of magnificent, unspoilt views of the loch. The attractive bedrooms, which vary in size and one of which is on the ground floor, all have en suite bath or shower rooms, direct-dial telephones, hairdryer, colour TV, tea and coffee-making facilities and fresh fruit. Some of the rooms have loch views. Self-catering lodges with large balconies are also available, set in 4 acres of grounds.

Recommended in the area

Inverness; Loch Ness; Glen Affric

An Cala Guest House

★★★★★ GH

Address: Woodlands Terrace, GRANTOWN-ON-
SPEY Highland PH26 3JU
Tel: 01479 873293
Fax: 01479 873610
Email: ancala@globalnet.co.uk
Website: www.ancala.info
Map ref: 12, NJ02
Directions: From Aviemore on the A95 bear left
on the B9102 at the rdbt outside Grantown. After
400yds, 1st left & An Cala opp
Rooms: 4 en suite, D £66–£84 **Parking:** 6 **Notes:** ⊘ ⛔ under 3yrs **Closed:** Xmas

This large Victorian house is surrounded by well-tended gardens and overlooks woods, yet is just a 12 minute walk from the town centre. Val and Keith Dickinson provide an attractive setting where you can really relax. They offer beautifully decorated bedrooms, with king or superking-size beds – one room has a lovely kingsize four-poster bed.

Recommended in the area

The Malt Whisky Trail; Ballindalloch Castle; Osprey Centre, Boat of Garten

The Ghillies Lodge

★★★★ BB

Address: 16 Island Bank Road, INVERNESS
Highland IV2 4QS
Tel: 01463 232137
Fax: 01463 713744
Email: info@ghillieslodge.com
Website: www.ghillieslodge.com
Map ref: 12, NH64
Directions: 1m SW from town centre on B862
Rooms: 3 en suite, S £35–£45 D £55–£65
Parking: 4 **Notes:** ⊘ on premises ⛔ allowed on premises ⛔

Built in 1847 as a fisherman's lodge, the Ghillies Lodge lies on the River Ness with fine views over the Ness Islands and just a mile from Inverness centre, making it an ideal base for touring the Highlands. The attractive and peaceful en suite bedrooms, (including one on the ground floor) are individually styled, well equipped and wireless internet connection is available. There is a comfortable lounge-dining room and a conservatory over looks the river.

Recommended in the area

Loch Ness; Speyside distilleries; Isle of Skye

The Kessock Bridge, north of Inverness

Daviot Lodge

★★★★★ GA

Address: Daviot Mains, DAVIOT, Inverness
Highland IV2 5ER
Tel: 01463 772215
Fax: 01463 772099
Email: margaret.hutcheson@btopenworld.com
Website: www.daviotlodge.co.uk
Map ref: 12, NH64
Directions: Off A9 5m S of Inverness onto B851
signed Croy. 1m on left
Rooms: 7 en suite, S £45–£50 D £80–£100 **Parking:** 10 **Notes:** ⊘ on premises ⌀ allowed on
premises ⌀ under 5yrs

This lovely small country house offers luxury accommodation just south of Inverness amid 80 acres of
pastureland. The Hutcheson family have been welcoming guests for 20 years and won the AA Guest
Accommodation of the Year for Scotland 2005. The attractive bedrooms have co-ordinated furnishings
and the master bedroom has a four-poster bed. One room is on the ground floor for easy access.
Recommended in the area
Loch Ness; Culloden Battlefield (NTS); Cawdor Castle

Moyness House

★★★★ GA

Address: 6 Bruce Gardens, INVERNESS
Highland IV3 5EN
Tel: 01463 233836
Fax: 01463 233836
Email: stay@moyness.co.uk
Website: www.moyness.co.uk
Map ref: 12, NH64
Directions: Off A82 Fort William road, almost opp Highland
Regional Council headquarters
Rooms: 6 en suite, S £50–£60 D £72–£96 **Parking:** 10
Notes: ⊘ on premises ♦♦

Built in 1880 this gracious villa, once the home of acclaimed Scottish author Neil Gunn, has been sympathetically restored to its full Victorian charm by Jenny and Richard Jones, and has many fine period details. The six stylish en suite bedrooms, named after Gunn's novels, are enhanced by contemporary amenities and thoughtful extra touches. Breakfasts served in the elegant dining room include a wide range of delicious Scottish choices, as well as vegetarian and healthy options, using fresh local produce. The inviting sitting room overlooks the garden to the front, and a pretty walled garden to the rear is a peaceful retreat in warm weather. Free wireless internet connection is available throughout the house. Moyness House has ample parking within the grounds, and is well located in a quiet residential street, less than 10 minutes walk from the city centre where there are several highly recommended restaurants, the Eden Court Theatre and delightful riverside walks. Jenny and Richard are happy to advise on local eateries and to make dinner reservations for their guests. They will also be glad to provide touring advice and help guests make the most of their stay in the beautiful Highlands.

Recommended in the area

Culloden Battlefield; Loch Ness and the Caledonian Canal; Urquhart Castle and Cawdor Castle

Trafford Bank

★★★★★ GH

Address: 96 Fairfield Road, INVERNESS
Highland IV3 5LL
Tel: 01463 241414
Email: enquiries@invernesshotelaccommodation.co.uk
Website: www.traffordbankhotel.co.uk
Map ref: 12, NH64
Directions: Off A82 at Kenneth St, Fairfield Rd 2nd left, 600yds on right
Rooms: 5 en suite, S £60–£75 D £80–£104 **Parking:** 8
Notes: ⊗ on premises ⊗ on premises ⛟

Luxurious accommodation and Highland hospitality go hand in hand at this guest house, run by Lorraine Freel and Koshal Pun. This multilingual pair can welcome you in *Italian*, *French*, *Hindi* and *Swahili*. Located within walking distance of the city centre and the Caledonian Canal, Trafford Bank, built in 1873, was once the local bishop's home. Lorraine's flair for interior design has produced a pleasing mix of antique and contemporary wherever you come from furnishings, some of which she has designed herself; the dining-room chairs are a special feature, and there is unusual lighting and original art throughout the house. The bright bedrooms are individually themed; all are en suite and have enticing extras like Arran aromatic products and organic soap from the Strathpeffer Spa soap company. Each bedroom is superbly decorated with fine bed linen, hairdryers, fairtrade tea and coffee, flat screen digital TVs , DVD players, CD /radio alarms, iPod docking stations and silent fridges. Breakfast is prepared using the best Highland produce and served on Anta pottery in the stunning conservatory. There are two spacious lounges and the house is surrounded by mature gardens that you are welcome to enjoy. Wi-fi is available throughout the house.

Recommended in the area

Cawdor Castle; Culloden Battlefield (NTS); Loch Ness; Moniack Castle (Highland Winery)

Westbourne Guest House

★★★★ GA

Address: 50 Huntly Street, INVERNESS
Highland IV3 5HS
Tel: 01463 220700
Fax: 01463 220700
Email: richard@westbourne.org.uk
Website: www.westbourne.org.uk
Map ref: 12, NH64
Directions: A9 onto A82 at football stadium, over 3 rdbts & Friars Bridge, 1st left onto Wells & Huntly St
Rooms: 10 en suite, S £35–£45 D £64–£84 **Parking:** 6 **Notes:** ⊘ on premises ⌖ allowed on premises ⋕ **Closed:** Xmas & New Year

This splendid guest house, overlooking the River Ness to the city centre, is Scottish through and through, with a tartan-theme decor in most of the bedrooms and good old Scottish family names given to the larger rooms. The best traditions of Scottish hospitality are also maintained, and these have earned Westbourne a place in the national finals of the 2006 AA Landlady of the Year awards. Deceptively spacious, the guesthouse was built in 1998 to provide the highest standards of comfort and convenience and includes two particularly large bedrooms sleeping six adults and four adults respectively. There is also a bedroom on the ground floor with easy access to the car park and dining room. The lounge has a range of books, games and puzzles, plus internet access. The thoughtful approach of owner Richard Paxton includes an impressive range of facilities in the bedrooms, all designed to ensure entertainment and every comfort and convenience. Some rooms also have a safe. A full Highlanders breakfast would suit anyone preparing for a day tramping over the mountains, and the kitchen can also cater for vegetarian and other special diets.

Recommended in the area

Loch Ness; Inverness Castle; Culloden Battlefield

Spey Bay, Moray

Smiddy House

★★★★ ◎◎ GH

Address: Roy Bridge Road, SPEAN BRIDGE,
Highland PH34 4EU
Tel: 01397 712335
Fax: 01397 712043
Email: enquiry@smiddyhouse.co.uk
Website: www.smiddyhouse.co.uk
Map ref: 12, NN28
Directions: In village centre, A82 onto A86
Rooms: 4 (en suite), S £55–£70 D £65–£80
Parking: 15 **Notes:** ⊘ on premises ✈ allowed on premises ⊪ **Closed:** Nov

Located in the village of Spean Bridge within The Great Glen, which forms 60 miles of splendour from Fort William to Inverness, Smiddy House offers genuine Scottish hospitality in luxurious surroundings. The well-appointed guest rooms are attractive with fresh flowers and bottled water. Delicious dinners are served in Russell's 2 AA Rosette restaurant located on the ground floor. A residents lounge, offering a place to unwind and relax, is scheduled.

Recommended in the area
Ben Nevis; Loch Ness; Glencoe

Catalina

★★★★ BB

Address: Aultivullin, STRATHY POINT KW14 7RY
Tel: 01641 541395
Fax: 0871 900 2537
Email: catalina.bandb@virgin.net
Website: www.a1tourism.com/uk/catalina.html
Map ref: 12, NC86
Directions: A836 at Strathy onto Strathy Point Rd,
1.5m then left & 1m to end
Rooms: 1 en suite, S £35 D £50 **Parking:** 2
Notes: ⊗ on premises ⊗ on premises ⊀

This former croft house has a tranquil setting close to the sea and is perfect for getting away from it all. Guests can enjoy peace, perfect peace in their own private suite, comprising a self-contained twin bedroom, located in a wing for guests' exclusive use that includes a dining room and a cosy lounge, and offers satellite TV and central heating, as well as tea and coffee-making facilities. Everything here, breakfast and three-course meals, is home-cooked and meal times are flexible.

Recommended in the area

Strathy Point Lighthouse; Caithness's beaches and mountains; Orkney islands

The Haughs Farm

★★★ FH

Address: KEITH, Moray AB55 6QN
Tel: 01542 882238
Email: jiwjackson@aol.com
Website: www.haughsfarmbedandbreakfast.net
Map ref: 10, NJ45
Directions: 0.5m NW of Keith off A96, signed
Inverness
Rooms: 3 en suite, S £30–£33 D £44–£48
Parking: 11 **Notes:** ⊗ on premises ⊗ on premises
⊀ **Closed:** Oct/Etr

You are assured of a warm welcome at this comfortable farmhouse on the outskirts of town. The land of this mixed farm is now rented to a neighbouring farmer, but you will always enjoy a traditional farmhouse stay here. The large en suite bedrooms, offer a comprehensive range of accessories including tea-making facilities. The large lounge has scenic views of the surrounding countryside, and meals are served in the sunroom overlooking the garden.

Recommended in the area

Whisky Trail, Keith; Baxters Visitor Centre, Fochabers; Moray coast

Allandale Guest House

★★★★ GH

Address: BRODICK, Isle of Arran,
North Ayrshire, KA27 8BJ
Tel/Fax: 01770 302278
Email: info@allandalehouse.co.uk
Website: www.allandalehouse.co.uk
Map ref: 9, NS03
Directions: 500yds S of Brodick Pier, off A841 to
Lamlash, up hill 2nd left at Corriegills sign
Rooms: 6 (5 en suite), D £68–£74 **Parking:** 6
Notes: ⊗ ⊗ in bedrooms ♦♦ **Closed:** Nov–Feb

This comfortable guest house, set in delightful gardens in beautiful countryside, occupies one of the finest spots in Brodick, close to the CalMac ferry terminal yet in a peaceful location, with beautiful views. Bedrooms vary in size (one twin, two doubles, two family rooms and a triple, and have pleasing colour schemes and thoughtful extras. With its long established reputation for a warm, friendly welcome, personal attention, a good breakfast and comfortable rooms, guests return year after year.
Recommended in the area
Brodick; Lamlash Bay

Whin Park

★★★★ GH

Address: 16 Douglas Street, LARGS
North Ayrshire, KA30 8PS
Tel: 01475 673437
Email: enquiries@whinpark.co.uk
Website: www.whinpark.co.uk
Map ref: 9, NS25
Directions: N of Largs off A78 signed Brisbane Glen
Rooms: 4 en suite, S £36–£38 D £64–£68
Parking: 4 **Notes:** ⊗ on premises ⊗ on premises
♦♦ **Closed:** Feb

This comfortable guest house is situated close to the seafront in a quiet residential area of Largs. It is within easy reach of the promenade and the town centre with its excellent choice of restaurants. The bedrooms come well equipped with toiletries, quality towels, hospitality tray, TV, hairdryer and ironing facilities. The bright spacious breakfast room, with individual tables, is a fine setting for the hearty and delicious breakfast featuring the best of local produce.
Recommended in the area
Islands of the Firth of Clyde; Loch Lomond; Culzean Castle

Tigh Na Leigh Guesthouse

★ ★ ★ ★ ★ 🛏 🍽 GA

Address:	22–24 Airlie Street, ALYTH, Perth and Kinross PH11 8AJ
Tel:	01828 632372
Fax:	01828 632279
Email:	bandcblack@yahoo.co.uk
Website:	www.tighnaleigh.co.uk
Map ref:	10, NO24

Directions: In town centre on B952

Rooms: 5 en suite, S £37.50 D £80–£110

Parking: 5 **Notes:** ⊘ on premises 🐾 allowed on premises 👶 under 12yrs **Closed:** Dec–Feb

Winner of the AA Guest Accommodation of the Year for Scotland 2006/2007 award, this guest house in the heart of the country town of Alyth is an absolute delight. Tigh Na Leigh is Gaelic for 'The house of the Doctor or Physician', and although it may look rather sombre from the outside, the property is superbly modernised and furnished with an eclectic mix of modern and antique furniture. The large, luxurious and individually decorated bedrooms, one of which is on the ground floor, are very well equipped, and some rooms have spa baths. All rooms have TV/DVD player, tea and coffee-making facilities, hairdryer and bathrobes. For extra luxury, one room has a grand four-poster, while the suite has its own lounge with very comfortable sofa. The public rooms comprise three entirely different lounges, one of which has a log fire for cooler evenings and another of which provides broadband internet connection. Delicious home-cooked dinners have an international flavour, and these, as well as the hearty breakfasts, are all made from the best of Scottish produce – vegetables come from the kitchen garden or surrounding (organic) farms where possible. Meals are served in the huge conservatory/dining room overlooking the spectacular landscaped garden.

Recommended in the area

Scone Palace; Glamis Castle; Dunkeld Cathedral

Gilmore House

★★★★ BB

Address: Perth Road, BLAIRGOWRIE,
Perth and Kinross PH10 6EJ
Tel/Fax: 01250 872791
Email: jill@gilmorehouse.co.uk
Website: www.gilmorehouse.co.uk
Map ref: 10, NO14
Directions: On A93 S
Rooms: 3 en suite, D £50–£60 **Parking:** 3
Notes: ⊘ ♉ ♟ **Closed:** Xmas

Built in 1899, this deceptively spacious late-Victorian detached house is the perfect base from which to explore all that Perthshire has to offer, being conveniently located for Glamis Castle, Scone Palace and Dunkeld. The three comfortable en suite rooms include a cosy king, a twin and a very spacious superking. There are two beautiful lounges for guests' use, with plenty of reading material to plan your activities. A full Scottish breakfast or something lighter is served in the elegant dining room overlooking the front garden, and the owners pride themselves on the relaxed, warm and friendly ambience.
Recommended in the area
Glamis Castle; Blair Castle; Perth races

Merlindale

★★★★ BB

Address: Perth Road, CRIEFF,
Perth and Kinross PH7 3EQ
Tel: 01764 655205
Fax: 01764 655205
Email: merlin.dale@virgin.net
Website: www.merlindale.co.uk
Map ref: 10, NN82
Directions: On A85 350yds from E end of High St
Rooms: 3 en suite, S £45–£65 D £65–£78
Parking: 3 **Notes:** ⊘ on premises ⊗ on premises ♟ **Closed:** 9 Dec–10 Feb

First impressions of this stylish detached house and its neat garden are pleasing indeed, and once through the door this is reinforced at every turn. There is a spacious lounge, an impressive library and an elegant dining room where delicious evening meals are available (with 24 hours' notice) in addition to the traditional Scottish breakfasts. Bedrooms are pretty and comfortable. In a quiet residential area, Merlindale is within walking distance of the town centre.
Recommended in the area
Drummond Castle; Perth; Scone

An Lochan Tormaukin

★★★★ ◉ INN

Address: GLENDEVON,
Perth and Kinross FK14 7JY
Tel: 0845 371 1414
Email: info@anlochan.co.uk
Website: www.anlochan.co.uk
Map ref: 10. NN90
Directions: On A823 north of Dunfermline
Rooms: 13 en suite, S £95 D £120 **Parking:** 50
Notes: ⊘ on premises 🐾 allowed in bedrooms

This delightful and stylish coaching inn, dating from the 17ᵗʰ century and set in the lovely Perthshire hills, is just five minutes away from Gleneagles, with its famous championship golf courses. It is perfectly located for getting away from it all, set on a quiet road that wends its way through a glen, yet only an hour from Glasgow and Edinburgh. Great attention is paid to guests' comfort by the friendly and welcoming team and the establishment is undergoing a rolling programme of refurbishment. Open log fires and stone walls add to the character and comfort of the interior. Each of the en suite bedrooms is individually furnished and decorated; they are very well equipped and the bathrooms come with warm slate tiles and a plentiful supply of extra-fluffy towels and Purdies hand-made toiletries. Food is taken seriously at An Lochan, with the emphasis on delicious meals made from locally sourced ingredients, including Highland beef raised specially for the inn, Perthshire lamb, wild boar, venison and shellfish, all served with home-made bread. Breakfast is equally varied and impressive and meals can be taken in a choice of dining areas, including an airy conservatory. There is plenty to do in the area and every opportunity to enjoy the scenery, and burn off the effects of inevitable indulgence, with some good walking nearby.

Recommended in the area

Stirling Castle; Scone Palace; Crieff

The Earl's Tower, Kinnoull Hill

Cherrybank Guesthouse

★★★★ GA

Address: 217–219 Glasgow Road,
PERTH, Perth and Kinross PH2 0NB
Tel: 01738 451982
Fax: 01738 561336
Email: m.r.cherrybank@blueyonder.co.uk
Map ref: 10, NO12
Directions: 1m SW of town centre on A93
Rooms: 5 (4 en suite), S £35–£45 D £50–£58
Parking: 4 **Notes:** ⊗ ⊗ on premises ♦♦

Suited to business travellers and holidaymakers, Cherrybank is located in central Perth, convenient
for the motorway network and close to the many attractions the area and the town itself have to offer.
Maggie and Robert extend a warm welcome at their home, which offers bedrooms with TV, video, radio
alarm, hairdryer and a welcome tray. All are beautifully presented with an emphasis on good linen and
home comforts. Enjoy a quieter moment in the tastefully furnished lounge, and satisfy your appetite
with a delicious traditional Scottish breakfast served at individual tables in the bright dining room.
Recommended in the area
Scone Palace; Glamis Castle; Pitlochry

Westview Guest House

★★★★ BB

Address: 49 Dunkeld Road, PERTH,
Perth and Kinross PH1 5RP
Tel: 01738 627787
Fax: 01738 447790
Email: angiewestview@aol.com
Map ref: 10, NO12
Directions: On A912, 0.5m NW from town centre
opp Royal Bank of Scotland
Rooms: 5 (3 en suite) **Parking:** 4 **Notes:** ⊗ on
premises ⌇ allowed on premises ⋔

Expect a warm welcome from enthusiastic owner Angie Livingstone at this B&B situated on the outskirts of the pretty town of Perth, with all its amenities. She is a fan of Victoriana, and her house captures that period, with one notable feature being the teddies on the stairs. The best possible use is made of available space in the bedrooms, including a ground-floor and a family room, which are full of character. Public areas include an inviting lounge and a dining room. Some parking is available.

Recommended in the area

Scone Palace; The Black Watch Museum; Perth Museum and Art Gallery

Crailing Old School B&B

★★★★ ⌂ ⌇ GH

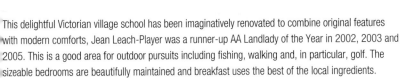

Address: CRAILING, Nr Jedburgh,
Scottish Borders TD8 6TL
Tel: 01835 850382
Email: jean.player@virgin.net
Website: www.crailingoldschool.co.uk
Map ref: 10, NT62
Directions: A698 onto B6400 signed Nisbet, Crailing
Old School also signed
Rooms: 4 (2 en suite), S £30–£35 D £60–£70
Parking: 7 **Notes:** ⊗ on premises ⊗ in bedrooms ⋔ under 9yrs **Closed:** 24–27 Dec & 2 wks Feb
and Nov

This delightful Victorian village school has been imaginatively renovated to combine original features with modern comforts, Jean Leach-Player was a runner-up AA Landlady of the Year in 2002, 2003 and 2005. This is a good area for outdoor pursuits including fishing, walking and, in particular, golf. The sizeable bedrooms are beautifully maintained and breakfast uses the best of the local ingredients.

Recommended in the area

St Cuthbert's Way; Teviot and Tweed rivers; Roxburghe Championship Golf Course

Fauhope House

★★★★★ GH

Address: Gattonside, MELROSE,
Scottish Borders TD6 9LU
Tel: 01896 823184
Fax: 01896 823184
Email: fauhope@bordernet.co.uk
Map ref: 10, NT53
Directions: 0.7m N of Melrose over River Tweed.
N off B6360 at Gattonside 30mph sign (E)
Rooms: 3 en suite, S £55–£65 D £80–£90
Parking: 10 **Notes:** ⊘ on premises ⊗ on premises ♦♦

Fauhope House is a fine example of the arts and crafts style of architecture of the 1890s, designed by
Sidney Mitchell, who was also responsible for Edinburgh's much-admired Ramsey Gardens property.
It is perched high on a hillside on the northeast edge of the village of Gattonside, and provides the
kind of breathtaking views of the River Tweed and the Eildon Hills that have inspired artists and writers
down the years. It offers discerning guests comfortable seclusion and the space to relax, yet is just a
ten-minute walk from the Borders town of Melrose, with its shops, restaurant and small theatre. A short
drive will take you to Abbotsford, home of Sir Walter Scott, and the Robert Adam-designed Mellerstain
House, The hospitality provided by experienced host Sheila Robson is first class, and the delightful
country house boasts a splendid interior, furnished and decorated to the highest possible standard.
Stunning floral displays enhance the overall interior design, and lavish drapes and fine furniture grace
the drawing room and the magnificent dining room, where full Scottish or a continental breakfast is
served. The generously sized bedrooms are luxurious and superbly equipped, each with individual
furnishings and thoughtful extras.
Recommendedin the area
Melrose Abbey; Roxburghe Golf Course; River Tweed

Bressay Sound, Lerwick, Shetland

Glen Orchy House

★★★★ GH

Address: 20 Knab Road, LERWICK,
Shetland ZE1 0AX
Tel: 01595 692031
Fax: 01595 692031
Email: glenorchy.house@virgin.net
Website: www.guesthouselerwick.com
Map ref: 13
Directions: Next to coastguard station
Rooms: 24 en suite, S £50 D £80 **Parking:** 10
Notes: ⊗ on premises 🐾 allowed on premises 👫

Once an Episcopalian convent, this smart guest house has swapped an austere past for the modern comforts expected by discerning guests. All rooms are non-smoking and have Freeview and air conditioning. One of the lounges has an honesty bar, and there are plenty of books and games for wet days. Authentic Thai cuisine is served 6.30–9pm and substantial breakfasts are also provided in the dining room. Fax and VCR facilities are available on request.

Recommended in the area

Shetland scenery; Pictish broch on the Island of Mousa; St Ninian's Isle

Daviot House

★★★★ GH

Address: 12 Queens Terrace, AYR,
South Ayrshire KA7 1DU
Tel: 01292 269678
Email: daviothouse@hotmail.com
Website: www.daviothouse.com
Map ref: 9, NS32
Directions: Off A719 onto Wellington Sq & Bath
Place, turn right
Rooms: 5 (4 en suite), S £32–£40 D £56–£62
Parking: 0 **Notes:** ⊗ on premises ⊗ in bedrooms ⚄

In a quiet residential area, a short distance from the beach and town centre with its many amenities, Daviot House is a well-maintained, comfortable Victorian terraced home that retains many original features, such as stained-glass windows and intricate cornices. Bedrooms, including one family room, are modern in style, bright and prettily decorated with a tartan theme, and come equipped with thoughtful extras such as hospitality tray, alarm clock, hairdryer, ironing facilities, fluffy towels and LCD television with DVD. Drying facilities are also available, as are free parking permits. Public areas include a dining room, where guests congregate around one big table to start the day with a cooked Scottish breakfast, including black pudding and tattie scones; also on offer are other options such as pancakes with scrambled eggs, bacon and maple syrup or eggs Benedict. Snacks and packed lunches can also be provided with notice, and the friendly owners are happy to offer recommendations for good local evening dining. There are over 30 golf courses in Ayrshire, and Daviot House is a member of Golf South Ayrshire Hoteliers golf booking service for local municipal courses.

Recommended in the area

Burns Cottage; Royal Troon and Turnberry golf courses; Culzean Castle and Country Park (NTS)

Dunduff Farm

★ ★ ★ ★ FH

Address: Dunure, DUNURE,
South Ayrshire KA7 4LH
Tel: 01292 500225
Fax: 01292 500222
Email: gemmelldunduff@aol.com
Website: www.gemmelldunduff.co.uk
Map ref: 9, NS21
Directions: On A719 400yds past village school
Rooms: 3 (2 en suite) **Parking:** 10
Notes: ⊗ on premises ⊗ on premises ♦ **Closed:** Nov–Feb

There are panoramic sea views from all rooms at this working farm, parts of which date back to the 15th and 17th centuries. From its position above the Firth of Clyde, the sheep and beef farm looks out towards Arran and the Mull of Kintyre, and over to Ailsa Craig. Thoughtful touches are evident throughout the house, and the modern bedrooms are well equipped. Specialities such as locally smoked kippers are served at breakfast, and there is a choice of places to eat in nearby Ayr.

Recommended in the area

Dunure Castle; Burns Cottage; Culzean Castle and Country Park (NTS)

Ladyburn

★ ★ ★ ★ ★ 🛏 🍽 GA

Address: MAYBOLE, South Ayrshire KA19 7SG
Tel: 01655 740585
Fax: 01655 740580
Email: jh@ladyburn.co.uk
Website: www.ladyburn.co.uk
Map ref: 9, NS20
Directions: A77 (Glasgow/Stranraer) at Maybole turn to B7023 to Crosshill and right at War Memorial. In 2m turn left for approx 1m on right
Rooms: 5 en suite, S £65 D £100 **Parking:** 12 **Notes:** ⊗ on premises

This charming country house, sitting in open countryside and dating from the 1600s is the home of the welcoming Hepburn family. There are antiques throughout and the classically styled bedrooms, two with four-poster beds, are comfortable and full of character, with luxurious fabrics, pictures and prints. These are complemented by the library, with its wood fire, and the drawing room. Dinner, by arrangement, comprises a three-course set menu, served in a gracious candlelit setting.

Recommended in the area

Alloway, birthplace of Robert Burns; Culzean Castle (NTS); Croy Brae (Electric Brae)

Annfield Guest House

★★★★ GH

Address: 18 North Church Street,
CALLANDER, Stirling FK17 8EG
Tel: 01877 330204
Email: reservations@annfieldguesthouse.co.uk
Website: www.annfieldguesthouse.co.uk
Map ref: 10, NS79
Directions: Off A84 Main St onto North Church St
Rooms: 7 (4 en suite), S £30–£40 D £50–£60
Parking: 7 **Notes:** ⊗ on premises ⊗ in bedrooms
⋕ under 6yrs **Closed:** Xmas & New Year

Quietly situated just two minutes' walk from Callander's bustling main street, this is a beautiful Victorian villa. Recently fully renovated to the highest standards, Annfield retains all the charm of a bygone age. The owners pride themselves on their attention to detail, from fresh flowers and goosedown duvets to silver cutlery and soft fluffy towels. Breakfast is a highlight; there's a large choice from the sideboard buffet or cooked to order from the extensive menu, all prepared with the freshest of local ingredients.

Recommended in the area

Falkirk Wheel; Loch Lomond and Trossachs National Park; Stirling Castle; Loch Katrine;

Arden House

★★★★ GA

Address: Bracklinn Road, CALLANDER,
Stirling FK17 8EQ
Tel: 01877 330235
Email: ardenhouse@onetel.com
Website: www.ardenhouse.org.uk
Map ref: 10, NS79
Directions: Off A84 Main St onto Bracklinn Rd, house
200yds on left
Rooms: 6 en suite, S £35 D £65–£75 **Parking:** 10
Notes: ⊗ on premises ⊗ on premises ⋕ under 14yrs **Closed:** Nov–Mar

The fictional home of Doctors Finlay and Cameron, in a peaceful area of the town, is now owned by Ian and William, who offer a genuine welcome with tea and home-made cake on arrival. The comfortable en suite bedrooms have been refurbished and provided with thoughtful extras. A stylish lounge and bright dining room are inviting, and traditional Scottish breakfasts are a definite high spot of any visit.

Recommended in the area

Loch Lomond and Trossachs National Park; Stirling Castle; Loch Katrine; Falkirk Wheel

Loch Lomond

Bomains Farm Guest House

★ ★ ★ ★ GH

Address: Near Bo'ness, LINLITHGOW,
West Lothian EH49 7RQ
Tel: 01506 822188
Fax: 01506 824433
Email: bunty.kirk@onetel.net
Website: www.bomains.co.uk
Map ref: 10, NS97
Directions: A706 1.5m N towards Bo'ness, left at
golf course x-rds, 1st farm on right

Rooms: 5 (4 en suite), S £30–£40 D £50–£70 **Parking:** 8 **Notes:** ⊘ 🐎 allowed on premises ♦♦

This friendly farmhouse has stunning views of the Firth of Forth, Linlithgow and the hills beyond.
The warmth of the Kirks' welcome is apparent from the moment you step into the hallway with its
impressive galleried staircase. The beautifully decorated bedrooms are enhanced by quality fabrics and
modern hand-painted furniture. The traditional Scottish breakfast is served at a mahogany table. The
working farm is next to a golf course with fishing nearby, and is convenient for Edinburgh Airport.

Recommended in the area

Falkirk Wheel; Linlithgow Palace; Bo'ness Steam Railway

WALES

Morfa Nefyn, Gwynedd

Hafod Country House

★★★★ BB

Address: CEMAES BAY, Isle of Anglesey, LL67 0DS
Tel: 01407 711645
Email: hbr1946@aol.com
Map ref: 5, SH39
Directions: 0.5m S of Cemaes. Off A5025 Cemaes rdbt signed Llanfechell, Hafod 500yds on left
Rooms: 3 en suite, S £35 D £60 **Parking:** 3
Notes: ⊘ on premises ⊗ on premises ⋌ under 7yrs **Closed:** Oct–Mar

Set in extensive gardens with sea views, this large and spacious Edwardian house is quietly located on the outskirts of Cemaes, with its picturesque harbour and beaches. Guests are greeted on arrival with a welcoming pot of tea and Welsh cakes, and the pampering continues in the en suite bedrooms, which are very well equipped and have fine countryside or sea views. Guests are welcome to use the comfortable lounge. A good breakfast, using local and homemade produce, including free-range eggs from Hafod's own chickens and home-made preserves, is served in the breakfast room.

Recommended in the area

Anglesey Coastal Path; Melin Llynnon (working) flour mill; South Stack Lighthouse; Bull Bay Golf Club

The Bull

★★★★ INN

Address: Bulkley Square, LLANGEFNI,
Isle of Anglesey LL77 7LR
Tel: 01248 722119
Email: bull@welsh-historic-inns.com
Website: www.welsh-historic-inns.com
Map ref: 5, SH47
Directions: 5 mins from A55 junct 6
Rooms: 22 en suite, S £50–£75 D £50–£110
Parking: 15 **Notes:** ⊘ ⊗ in bedrooms ⋌⋌

This town-centre hostelry was built in 1817 and makes an ideal base for exploring North Wales as well as a good stopover for ferry travellers crossing to or from Ireland. Inside it provides a range of well-equipped, tastefully furnished en suite accommodation both in the main building and the annexe, including a room with a four-poster bed, some rooms on the ground floor and family rooms. Public areas offer a choice of bars and a spacious and traditional restaurant open for dinner, together with a comfortable, relaxing lounge.

Recommended in the area

Snowdonia National Park; Maritime Museum, Holyhead; Beaumaris Castle (Cadw)

Capel Dewi Uchaf Country House

★★★★ GA

Address: Capel Dewi, CARMARTHEN,
Carmarthenshire SA32 8AY
Tel: 01267 290799
Email: uchaffarm@aol.com
Website: www.walescottageholidays.uk.com
Map ref: 1, SN42
Directions: On B4300 between Capel Dewi &
junct B4310
Rooms: 3 en suite, S £48 D £70 **Parking:** 10 **Notes:**
⊗ on premises ⊗ on premises ♦♦
Closed: Xmas

Featuring a relaxed and easy-going atmosphere, this beautiful Grade II listed farmhouse stands in 34 acres of lush grazing meadow by the River Towy. A welcoming fire and period decor enhance the property's original features and the lovely garden includes a terrace. Fresh local produce, including home-grown vegetables, is a feature of the memorable dinners and generous Welsh breakfasts.

Recommended in the area

National Botanic Garden of Wales; Aberglasney; Newton House (NT)

Sarnau Mansion

★★★★ GA

Address: Llysonnen Road, CARMARTHEN,
Carmarthenshire SA33 5DZ
Tel: 01267 211404
Email: fernihough@so1405.force9.co.uk
Website: www.sarnaumansion.co.uk
Map ref: 1, SN42
Directions: 5m W of Carmarthen. Off A40 onto
B4298 & Bancyfelin road, Sarnau on right
Rooms: 3 en suite, S £45 D £60–£70 **Parking:** 10
Notes: ⊗ on premises ⊗ in bedrooms ♦♦ under 5yrs

This fine Grade II listed Georgian mansion is set in the heart of the Carmarthen countryside, in 16 acres of grounds, which include a tennis court. It's not far from here to the many attractions and beaches of south and west Wales, and it is a delightful place to return to each evening. Many original features have been retained and the public areas are both comfortable and elegant. Bedrooms are large and nicely decorated, and all of the rooms have stunning rural views.

Recommended in the area

National Botanic Garden of Wales; Aberglasney Gardens; Dylan Thomas Boathouse, Laugharne

River Tywi, Rhandirmwyn

Allt Y Golau Farmhouse

★★★★ FH

Address: Allt Y Golau Uchaf, FELINGWM UCHAF,
Carmarthenshire SA32 7BB

Tel: 01267 290455

Fax: 01267 290743

Email: alltygolau@btinternet.com

Website: www.alltygolau.com

Map ref: 1, SN52

Directions: A40 onto B4310, N for 2m. 1st on left
after Felingwm Uchaf

Rooms: 3 (2 en suite), S £40 D £60 **Parking:** 3 **Notes:** ⊘ on premises ⊗ in bedrooms ⋔
Closed: 20 Dec–2 Jan

Enjoying panoramic views over the Tywi Valley and the dramatic Black Mountains, this delightful
Georgian farmhouse has been restored, furnished and decorated to a high standard. The comfortable
bedrooms have many thoughtful extras and the lounge is well stocked with books and games. Served at
a communal table breakfast is sumptuous with home-baking and excellent local produce.

Recommended in the area

The National Botanic Garden of Wales; Aberglasney Gardens; Carreg Cennen Castle

Coedllys Country House

★★★★★ BB

Address:	Llangynin, ST CLEARS,
	Carmarthenshire SA33 4JY
Tel:	01994 231455
Fax:	01994 231441
Email:	coedllys@btinternet.com

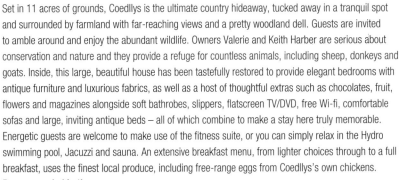

Website: www.coedllyscountryhouse.co.uk
Map ref: 1, SN21
Directions: A40 to St Clears rndbt. Take 3rd exit
down to lights & left. 100 yards on, turn r where road
forks (sign Llangynin). 3m to Llangynin, after 30mph signs turn l. After 300 yards l, signed Coedllys Uchaf
Rooms: 3 en suite, S £52.50–£62.50 D £80–£100 **Parking:** 6 **Notes:** ⊗ ⋔ ⋋ under 10yrs
Closed: Xmas

Set in 11 acres of grounds, Coedllys is the ultimate country hideaway, tucked away in a tranquil spot
and surrounded by farmland with far-reaching views and a pretty woodland dell. Guests are invited
to amble around and enjoy the abundant wildlife. Owners Valerie and Keith Harber are serious about
conservation and nature and they provide a refuge for countless animals, including sheep, donkeys and
goats. Inside, this large, beautiful house has been tastefully restored to provide elegant bedrooms with
antique furniture and luxurious fabrics, as well as a host of thoughtful extras such as chocolates, fruit,
flowers and magazines alongside soft bathrobes, slippers, flatscreen TV/DVD, free Wi-fi, comfortable
sofas and large, inviting antique beds – all of which combine to make a stay here truly memorable.
Energetic guests are welcome to make use of the fitness suite, or you can simply relax in the Hydro
swimming pool, Jacuzzi and sauna. An extensive breakfast menu, from lighter choices through to a full
breakfast, uses the finest local produce, including free-range eggs from Coedllys's own chickens.
Recommended in the area
Dylan Thomas Boathouse, Laugharne; Millennium Coastal Path; National Botanical Gardens

Bodalwyn Guest House

★★★★ GH

Address: Queen's Avenue, ABERYSTWYTH,
Ceredigion SY23 2EG
Tel: 01970 612578
Fax: 01970 639261
Email: enquiries@bodalwyn.co.uk
Website: www.bodalwyn.co.uk
Map ref: 2, SN58
Directions: 500yds N of town centre. Off A487 Northgate St onto North Rd to end
Rooms: 8 en suite, S £35–£47.50 D £55–£70
Notes: ⊘ on premises ⊗ on premises ♦♦
Closed: 24 Dec–1 Jan

This restored Edwardian house is ideal for a relaxing break by Cardigan Bay or as a base for exploring the countryside. The spacious bedrooms have stylish modern bathrooms and plenty of homely features, such as bottled water and a hospitality tray. Breakfast is a hearty Welsh spread.

Recommended in the area

National Library of Wales; Llanerchaeron (NT); Vale of Rheidol Railway

Yr Hafod

★★★★ GH

Address: 1 South Marine Terrace, ABERYSTWYTH,
Ceredigion SY23 1JX
Tel: 01970 617579
Email: johnyrhafod@aol.com
Website: www.yrhafod.co.uk
Map ref: 2, SN58
Directions: On south promenade between harbour and castle
Rooms: 7 (2 en suite), S £27–£28 D £54–£70
Parking: 1 **Notes:** ⊘ on premises ⊗ on premises ♦♦
Closed: Xmas & New Year

Yr Hafod is an immaculately maintained end-of-terrace Victorian house in a commanding location at the quieter end of the promenade. Most of the well equipped and comfortable bedrooms have panoramic sea views of Cardigan Bay. The extensive breakfast menu, including full Welsh, is served in the dining room facing the sea, where you may spot a dolphin or two and guests can use the comfortable lounge.

Recommended in the area

Devil's Bridge Steam Train; Ceredigion Museum; Constitution Hill

Cwmanog Isaf Farm

★★★★ FH

Address: Fairy Glen, BETWS-Y-COED,
　　　　　Conwy LL24 0SL
Tel: 　　01690 710225
Email: 　heather.hughes3@tesco.net
Website: www.cwmanogisaffarmholidays.co.uk
Map ref: 5, SH75
Directions: 1m S of Betws-y-Coed off A470 by Fairy
Glen Hotel, 500yds on farm lane
Rooms: 3 (2 en suite), S £32–£50 D £56–£60
Parking: 4 **Notes:** ⊘ on premises ⊗ on premises 🜂under 15yrs

Hidden away, yet only a 20-minute stroll from the Victorian village of Betws-y-Coed, Cwmanog Isaf ,a 200-year-old house on a working livestock farm, is set in 30 acres of undulating land, including the renowned Fairy Glen, and has stunning views of the surrounding countryside. It provides comfortably, furnished and well equipped bedrooms (one on the ground floor). and serves wholesome Welsh farmhouse cuisine using home-reared and local organic produce, home-made bread and preserves.
Recommended in the area
Bodnant Gardens; Fairy Glen; Portmeirion

Park Hill

★★★★ GH

Address: Llanrwst Road, BETWS-Y-COED,
　　　　　Conwy LL24 0HD
Tel: 　　01690 710540
Email: 　welcome@park-hill.co.uk
Website: www.park-hill.co.uk
Map ref: 5, SH75
Directions: 0.5m N of Betws-y-Coed on A470
Rooms: 9 en suite, S £53–£78 D £56–£78 **Parking:**
11 **Notes:** ⊘ on premises ⊗ in bedrooms 🜂under 8yrs

The Park Hill, a fine Victorian building, is situated in the Snowdonia National Park, and has breathtaking views over the River Conwy. It makes an ideal base for walkers. You will find teddy bears here, there and everywhere, as the owners have a collection of 200. Guests can enjoy a swim in the splendid indoor heated swimming pool, relax in the whirlpool bath or take a sauna, before retiring to the bar or the comfortable and well-equipped en suite bedrooms. Breakfasts and dinners are freshly made from local produce.
Recommended in the area
Mount Snowdon; Tree Top Adventure, Snowdonia; Conwy Castle

Penmachno Hall

★★★★★ 🍴 GA

Address: Penmachno, BETWS-Y-COED
Conwy LL24 0PU
Tel/ Fax 01690 760410
Email: stay@penmachnohall.co.uk
Website: www.penmachnohall.co.uk
Map ref: 5, SH75
Directions: 5m S of Betws-y-Coed. A5 onto B4406 to
Penmachno, over bridge, at Eagles pub signed Ty Mawr
Rooms: 3 en suite, S D £75–£90 **Parking:** 3 **Notes:** ⊘ on
premises ⊗ on premises ♦♦ **Closed:** Xmas & New Year

Penmachno Hall, a lovingly restored Victorian rectory, is situated
in over 2 acres of mature grounds in the secluded Glasgwm Valley in Snowdonia National Park. With
its breathtaking views and quiet forest tracks leading to secluded waterfalls, the valley is a haven of
tranquillity within easy reach of bustling Betws-y-Coed. This is an establishment that prides itself on
catering for the visitor's every need. Stylish decor and quality furnishings highlight the many original
features throughout the ground-floor areas, while the bedrooms come with a wealth of thoughtful
extras, and each benefits from panoramic views. The spacious Morning Room has comfortable sofas
and large bay windows overlooking the garden; it houses a large collection of books, maps, walking
guides and tourist information, as well as games and puzzles. The slightly more formal dining room
is the venue for award-winning evening meals, served dinner-party style round a central dining table.
The set five-course menu is prepared daily, based on the preferences of that night's diners and using
only the finest, fresh local produce. An extensive wine list complements the meal, and expert advice is
available to help guests select the most appropriate wine for their tastes and the food being served.
Recommended in the area

Snowdon; Bodnant Garden (NT); Portmeirion

Tan-y-Foel Country House

★ ★ ★ ★ ★ ◉◉◉ GH

Address: Capel Garmon, BETWS-Y-COED,
Conwy LL26 0RE
Tel: 01690 710507
Fax: 01690 710681
Email: enquiries@tyfhotel.co.uk
Website: www.tyfhotel.co.uk
Map ref: 5, SH75
Directions: 1.5m E of Betws-y-Coed. Off A5 onto A470 N, 2m
right for Capel Garmon, establishment signed 1.5m on left
Rooms: 6 en suite, S £110–£155 D £125–£170
Parking: 14 **Notes:** ⊘ on premises ⊗ in bedrooms ⊁
under 12yrs **Closed:** Dec

The 17th-century Welsh stone exterior of this country house gives no hint of the interior, where a series
of intimate and immaculately designed rooms unfold. Bold ideas fuse the traditional character of the
building with contemporary style, giving it an elegant simplicity that goes hand-in-hand with luxurious
facilities. Tan-y-Foel is aimed at the discerning traveller looking for a gourmet hideaway in a peaceful,
location in the heart of Snowdonia National Park. The surrounding countryside is delightful, with the
opportunity for some lovely walks. Independent and family run, this place offers a highly original
country house experience, with the owners' influence clearly in evidence throughout. There is a range
of options, not only in bedroom size but in the style of decor too, and many of the regular guests have
their own favourites. Naturally, each bedroom has its own bathroom, and each is well decorated and
furnished, with a selection of welcoming extras. A major highlight of a stay here is the food, and dinner
is a memorable occasion, consisting of carefully chosen fresh ingredients, skilfully prepared.

Recommended in the area

Bodnant Garden (NT); Snowdon Mountain Railway; Conwy Castle

Hafod Elwy Hall

★★★★ FH

Address: BYLCHAU, Denbigh, Conwy LL16 5SP
Tel: 01690 770345
Fax: 01690 770266
Email: enquiries@hafodelwyhall.co.uk
Website: www.hafodelwyhall.co.uk
Map ref: 5, SH96
Directions: A5 onto A543, 5.5m right onto track signed Hafod Elwy Hall
Rooms: 3 (2 en suite), S £30–£70 D £60–£90
Parking: 4 **Notes:** ⊘ on premises ⊗ in bedrooms 👶 under 16yrs

Hafod Elwy Hall is steeped in history, having first been referred to in the 1334 'survey of the honour of Denbighshire'. Today many of the original features remain at this peaceful property, surrounded by the hills and lakes of Mynydd Hiraethog, and with the spectacular backdrop of the Snowdonia Mountains. There's a sun room, a spacious lounge and a gun room, and real log fires are lit when it's chilly outside. Guests are encouraged to enjoy the grounds – this is a 60-acre sheep and pig-rearing holding – and Hafod Elwy has its own private fishing rights. The spacious and comfortable bedrooms here are all well appointed and individually decorated, and all enjoy stunning views of the mountains and moorlands. As well as a substantial suite and a pretty twin room, there is also a four-poster room with the original Edwardian bathroom and its own separate 'thunderbox'. Delicious breakfasts and dinners are served in the oldest part of the hall, expertly prepared using meat from Hafod Elwy's own livestock, home-grown vegetables and locally caught fish where possible. Environmental concerns are taken seriously here – the owners hold the Green Dragon environmental certificate and won Green Snowdonia's 'best sustainable tourism business award 2007'.

Recommended in the area

Mount Snowdon; Betws-y-Coed; the magnificent castles of Wales

The Old Rectory Country House

★ ★ ★ ★ ★ GA

Address: Llanrwst Road, Llansanffraid Glan Conwy, CONWY LL28 5LF

Tel: 01492 580611

Email: info@oldrectorycountryhouse.co.uk

Website: www.oldrectorycountryhouse.co.uk

Map ref: 5, SH77

Directions: 0.5m S from A470/A55 junct on left, by 30mph sign

Rooms: 6 en suite, S £79–£109 D £99–£159 **Parking:** 10

Notes: ⊘ on premises 🐾 allowed on premises 👶 under 5yrs

Closed: 14 Dec–15 Jan

The house, which is situated in two and a half acres of glorious gardens, certainly lives up to its Welsh motto 'Hardd Hafen Hedd' which translates as 'Beautiful Haven of Peace'. The Old Rectory has stunning views over the wide Conwy estuary, the Conwy RSPB reserve, the historic walled town of Conwy (now a World Heritage site) and across to the mountains of Snowdonia. The view alone merits a stay in this long etsablished and highly-acclaimed country house. The house, originally dating from Tudor times, was remodelled in the Georgian period and has traditional day rooms furnished with antiques and Victorian watercolours. The bedrooms are extremely comfortable and have stylish modern bath or power shower rooms. Hospitality trays, bath robes and quality toiletries demonstrate the thoughtful attention to detail. The atmosphere is friendly and relaxing and help is willingly given with touring routes. There are a wide selection of AA rated restaurants, inns and bistros within four miles and assistance will be given with making reservations and obtaining transport if required. In Llandudno, some restaurants provide pre-theatre dinners for those who wish to visit the excellent theatre, cinemas or enjoy seeing Welsh choirs in concert.

Recommended in the area

Bodnant Garden (NT); Conwy; Llandudno

Sychnant Pass Country House

★★★★★ ◉ GA

Address: Sychnant Pass Road, CONWY LL32 8BJ
Tel: 01492 596868
Fax: 01492 585486
Email: bre@sychnant-pass-house.co.uk
Website: www.sychnant-pass-house.co.uk
Map ref: 5, SH77
Directions: 1.75m W of Conwy. Off A547 Bangor Rd in town onto Mount Pleasant & Sychnant Pass Rd, 1.75m on right near top of hill

Rooms: 12 en suite, S £75–£160 D £95–£180 **Parking:** 30 **Notes:** ⊘ on premises ⋔ allowed on premises ♦♦ **Closed:** 24–26 Dec & Jan

There are fine views from this Edwardian house, set in three acres of luxuriant gardens with lawns, trees and a wild garden with ponds and a stream. Nestling in the foothills of the Snowdonia National Park, it was awarded the AA's Best Guest Accommodation in Wales in 2003–2004 and it continues to impress. Guests at this exceptional establishment, which offers country house luxury, can unwind and enjoy the superb health and leisure facilities, with salt-treated (no chlorine) indoor pool, fitness equipment, sauna, and hot tub. The range of bedrooms are imaginative and stylish, and include four-poster rooms, suites with galleried bedrooms and two suites with their own private terrace and hot tub. They are all superbly comfortable and equipped with a range of thoughtful extras such as dressing gowns, big fluffy towels and refrigerator. Lounges, warmed by open fires in chillier months, are comfortable and inviting, and imaginative meals created from locally sourced seasonal produce by owner Graham, a trained chef who has worked at Gleneagles and Turnberry, are served in the attractive dining room. High teas are available for younger children.

Recommended in the area

Conwy; Bodnant Garden (NT); Penrhyn Castle

The Lion Inn Gwytherin

★★★★ INN

Address: GWYTHERIN, Nr Betws-y-Coed,
Conwy LL22 8UU
Tel: 01745 860123
Fax: 01745 860556
Email: info@thelioninn.net
Website: www.thelioninn.net
Map ref: 5, SH86
Directions: From A470 heading north, turn r onto
A548. Signs to Pandy Tudur and then Gwytherin
Rooms: 6 en suite, S £39 D £79 **Parking:** 8
Notes: ⊘ on premises ⊁ allowed in bedrooms ♦♦

The Lion Inn is set in the picturesque village of Gwytherin, through which the River Cledwen flows. Quiet and off the beaten track, it makes an ideal place in which to relax and get away from the pressures of everyday life. All of the cosy en suite bedrooms have been tastefully refurbished to a high standard and complement the character of this 16th-century inn. Each room has been decorated in an individual style and includes a wealth of home comforts, including sumptuous beds with traditional colourful, hand-woven Welsh throws, DVD player, and use of an extensive collection of films, and tea and coffee-making facilities. All of the rooms have a charming country outlook, and one room boasts its own private balcony, from which to admire the view and the local wildlife, including red kites. Full English breakfasts include fresh Gwytherin eggs and a cafetiere of coffee or pot of tea. In the evening, guests can relax in front of a log fire with a glass of wine, chosen by Master of Wine Julia Harding, or try the locally brewed real ale before moving to the dining room to enjoy the freshly cooked Welsh produce, expertly and imaginatively prepared.

Recommended in the area

Bodnant Gardens; Conwy Falls; Conwy Castle

Abbey Lodge

★★★★ GH

Address: 14 Abbey Road, LLANDUDNO,
Conwy LL30 2EA
Tel: 01492 878042
Fax: 01492 878042
Email: enquiries@abbeylodgeuk.com
Website: www.abbeylodgeuk.com
Map ref: 5, SH78
Directions: Turn left off the promenade into Gloddaeth St. Take the 2rd right into Arvon Ave. Turn left at the top of the road into Abbey Rd
Rooms: 4 en suite, S £37.50 D £75 **Parking:** 3 **Notes:** ⊘ on premises ⊗ ✺ under 12yrs **Closed:** Dec–1 Feb

Built in 1840 and set on a leafy avenue within easy walking distance of the promenade, Abbey Lodge retains all the charm of a Victorian townhouse. This Grade II building is under the personal supervision of its owners, Dennis and Janet, who welcome guests with a complimentary pot of tea or coffee in the comfortable guest lounge or in the pretty walled garden that shelters beneath the Great Orme. The charming, en suite bedrooms are well equipped with generous hospitality trays, hairdryers, TV, magazines, books, towels and bathrobes. Internet access is available throughout the house. The owners have a fine collection of local interest books and maps to help guests plan outings. The ingredients for breakfast are mostly sourced from the local farmers market, and packed lunches can be ordered. Abbey Lodge endeavours to have due regard for the environment and offers a discount to guests arriving by public transport. Abbey Road is quiet, yet only 5 minutes walk from the pier and the Victorian High Street with a good choice of shops and cafés. A variety of restaurants are only a five minutes walk.

Recommended in the area

Bodnant Gardens; Conwy Castle; Snowdonia Mountains

Conwy Castle

Can-Y-Bae

★★★ GA

Address: 10 Mostyn Crescent, Central Promenade,
LLANDUDNO, Conwy LL30 1AR
Tel: 01492 874188
Fax: 01492 868376
Email: canybae@btconnect.com
Website: www.can-y-baehotel.com
Map ref: 5, SH78
Rooms: 16 en suite, S £30–£40 D £60–£70 **Notes:** ⊗ on
premises ↗ allowed in bedrooms ♦♦

Since the late 19th century, the Can-Y-Bae, meaning 'song of
the bay', has provided an elegant escape from everyday life and offers guest accommodation at the
centre of Llandudno's gently curving promenade. Bedrooms are well equipped for guest comfort and
convenience and the upper floors are serviced by a modern lift. Day rooms include a panoramic lounge,
cosy bar and an attractive basement dining room, serving full breakfasts using fresh, local produce,
afternoon tea and a varied dinner menu.

Recommended in the area

Bodnant Garden; Conwy; Snowdonia

The Hilary Guesthouse

★★★★ GH

Address: 32 St David's Road, LLANDUDNO,
Conwy LL30 2UL
Tel: 01492 875623
Email: thehilary@fsmail.net
Website: www.thehilaryguesthouse-llandudno.co.uk
Map ref: 5, SH78
Directions: A470 to town centre, take the first left
after train station, then the 4th right
Rooms: 8 en suite, S £35–£60 D £58–£80
Parking: 6 **Notes:** ⊗ on premises ⊗ in bedrooms 🐾

Situated in one of Llandudno's quietest and loveliest roads, Hilary Guesthouse is an easy stroll to all th
town has to offer. It is beautifully appointed and provides a host of thoughtful extras in the individually
decorated en suite bedrooms including free wireless broadband. Breakfasts are delicious and hosts,
Colin and Deborah, pride themselves on the motto that 'nothing is too much trouble'; guests may even
make use of the on-site beauty therapy service.

Recommended in the area

The Great Orme Tramway; Conwy Castle; Snowdon

St Hilary Guest House

★★★★ GA

Address: The Promenade, 16 Craig-Y-Don Parade,
LLANDUDNO Conwy LL30 1BG
Tel: 01492 875551
Fax: 01492 877538
Email: info@sthilaryguesthouse.co.uk
Website: www.sthilaryguesthouse.co.uk
Map ref: 5, SH78
Directions: 0.5m E of town centre. On B5115 seafront road
Rooms: 10 (9 en suite), S £31–£41.5 D £44–£60 **Notes:** ⊗ on
premises ⊗ in bedrooms 🐾 **Closed:** mid Nov–early Feb

An elegant Victorian seafront guest house, commanding
magnificent views of Llandudno's sweeping bay. The owners have created a wonderful combination
of comfortable, well equipped, contemporary rooms together with a very warm welcome and friendly
atmosphere. Whether you choose a "Hearty Welsh Grill" or a lighter alternative, the breakfasts are
always appreciated and are served in the lovely breakfast room overlooking the sea.

Recommended in the area

The Great Orme Tramway; Conwy Castle; Snowdon

Plas Rhos

★★★★ GA

Address: Cayley Promenade, RHOS-ON-SEA,
Conwy LL28 4EP
Tel: 01492 543698
Fax: 01492 540088
Email: info@plasrhos.co.uk
Website: www.plasrhos.co.uk
Map ref: 5, SH88
Directions: A55 junct 20 onto B5115 for Rhos-on-Sea, right at rdbt onto Whitehall Rd to promenade
Rooms: 8 en suite, S £45–£55 D £70–£98 **Parking:** 4 **Notes:** ⊘ on premises ⊗ on premises ⚹ under 12yrs **Closed:** 21 Dec–Jan

A yearning to live by the sea and indulge their passion for sailing brought Susan and Colin Hazelden to the North Wales coast. Running a hotel in Derbyshire for many years was the ideal preparation for looking after guests at their renovated Victorian home. Built as a gentleman's residence in the late 19th century, Plas Rhos is situated on Cayley Promenade, where it enjoys panoramic views over the bay, beach and coast. Breakfast, a particularly memorable meal, is taken overlooking the pretty patio garden. It consists of cereals, fresh fruit, juices and yoghurt followed by free-range eggs cooked to your liking with Welsh sausage, local back bacon, tomato, mushrooms, beans and fried bread or your choice of a number of other hot options including kippers or scrambled eggs with smoked salmon.
The two sumptuous lounges have spectacular sea views, comfy chairs and sofas, and interesting memorabilia, while the modest-size bedrooms are individually decorated and have plenty of thoughtful extras. One period room is furnished with a romantic half-tester and antiques, and enjoys those same stunning views. Wireless broadband internet access is available in all rooms– just bring your laptop.

Recommended in the area

Conwy Castle; Bodnant Garden (NT); Snowdonia National Park

Hafod Country House

★★★★ GA

Address: TREFRIW, Conwy LL27 0RQ
Tel: 01492 640029
Email: stay@hafod-house.co.uk
Website: www.hafod-house.co.uk
Map ref: 5, SH76
Directions: On B5106 entering Trefriw from S, house second on right
Rooms: 6 en suite, S £40–£52.5 D £70–£95
Parking: 14 **Notes:** ⊗ on premises ⚬ allowed in bedrooms ⚬under 11yrs **Closed:** Jan

Situated in the beautiful Conwy Valley, Yr Hafod ('the summer dwelling') is a former farmhouse that dates back to the Middle Ages. Now a comfortable, personally run guest house, it has a wealth of charm and character and is extensively furnished with antiques throughout. The en suite bedrooms, which all have access to the balcony, are on the first floor and also feature tasteful period furnishings; each comes with a wealth of extra touches, including cut flowers, fresh fruit, a decanter of dry oloroso sherry, mineral water and fresh milk to help make your stay as comfortable as possible. Downstairs, the public areas include a small but well-stocked bar, fashioned from Victorian chapel fittings, and a comfortable lounge with a large fireplace. There's also an extensive garden for guests to enjoy – all this on top of the surrounding countryside, which provides a wealth of walks. Food is an important part of your stay here, particularly breakfast, with thick sliced dry-cured Cheshire bacon, duck and goose eggs from Hafod's own birds, and home-baked sourdough bread on offer. The extensive and imaginative dinner menu provides up to four courses with choices on each. All of the food is completely home-cooked.

Recommended in the area

Snowdonia; Bodnant Gardens; Conwy Castle

Bron-y-Graig

★★★★★  GH

Address: CORWEN, Denbighshire LL21 0DR
Tel: 01490 413007
Fax: 01490 413007
Email: info@north-wales-hotel.co.uk
Website: www.north-wales-hotel.co.uk
Map ref: 5, SJ04
Directions: On A5 on E edge of Corwen
Rooms: 10 en suite, S £39–£49 D £59 **Parking:** 15 **Notes:** ⊘
on premises ⌗ allowed in bedrooms ⌗

A short walk from the town centre, this impressive Victorian house sits on the wooded slopes of the Berwyn Mountains in the beautiful Vale of Llangollen. It was built in 1888 as the family home of the Sheriff of Denbigh, and has been carefully restored to retain many original features, including fireplaces, stained glass and a tiled floor in the entrance hall; William Morris decor features throughout. The bedrooms here, two of which are located in the renovated coach house, are all complemented by luxurious en suite bathrooms and are thoughtfully furnished, with kingsize beds, TV – some have video and Playstation as well – free broadband internet connection and hospitality tray. Guests are also provided with fluffy towels, bathrobes, hairdryer and a selection of books and games. Ground-floor areas include a comfortable lounge and a traditionally furnished dining room, where hearty breakfasts and imaginative meals made from local produce are served. Informal evening dining draws on the best of British in combination with flavours from farther east, and chef Lorna's puddings are her passion. Children, vegetarians and those on special diets are all catered for. Guests can also relax with a drink on the terrace, or in the Quarry Garden.

Recommended in the area

Snowdonia; Llangollen Railway; Chester Zoo

Tyddyn Llan

★★★★★ ◉◉ RR

Address: LLANDRILLO, Corwen,
 Denbighshire LL21 0ST
Tel: 01490 440264
Fax: 01490 440414
Email: tyddynllan@compuserve.com
Website: www.tyddynllan.co.uk
Map ref: 5, SJ03
Directions: Take B4401 from Corwen to Llandrillo.
Tyddyn Llan on the right leaving the village.

Rooms: 13 en suite, S £75–£115 D £110–£200 **Parking:** 20 **Notes:** ⊗ on premises ⚐ allowed in bedrooms ⚦ **Closed:** 2 wks Jan

Three acres of beautiful grounds, including shrubs, colourful borders and a croquet lawn, surround this elegant Georgian house in the Vale of Edeyrnion, and in this setting owners Bryan and Susan Webb provide their guests with tranquillity and comfort of the highest order. It's a great place for people who enjoy the available country pursuits such as fishing, walking, horse riding, golf and water sports. Naturally in a house of this character, bedrooms come in different shapes and sizes, but all are individually decorated and stylishly furnished with period furniture. Each has a bathroom, television, CD player, direct-dial telephone and bathrobes, and everything is of the highest quality. The heart of the house, though, is the restaurant, and food remains a strong point. Bryan Webb is the chef, and he maintains an uncompromising attitude to obtaining only the finest ingredients, many of which are delivered daily by local suppliers. All the major wine-producing countries are represented on the wine list, which contains more than 250 labels, and there is an excellent selection of brandies, Armagnacs and digestives. All in all, a stay at Tyddyn Llan represents a taste of good living.

Recommended in the area

Portmeirion; Snowdon Mountain Railway; castles at Caernarfon, Beaumaris and Harlech

River Dee, Llangollen

Pentre Mawr Country House

★★★★★ 🛏 GA

Address: LLANDYRNOG, Denbighshire LL16 4LA
Tel: 01824 790732
Email: info@pentremawrcountryhouse.co.uk
Website: www.pentremawrcountryhouse.co.uk
Map ref: 5, SJ16
Directions: A541 from Denbigh and follow signs
Rooms: 5 en suite, S £70–£90 D £90–£110
Parking: 8 **Notes:** ⊗ 🚫 🐾 under 13yrs
Closed: Nov–Feb

Tucked away in an unspoilt corner of North Wales this former farmhouse, has been in the family for 400 years. The result is classic country house style – sumptuous furnishings, four-poster beds and traditional bathrooms – and a relaxed, welcoming atmosphere. Bedrooms are stylish and comfortable and all have lovely views of the Clwydian hills, the park, or the pool terrace. Unwind in the large drawing room or the study; in good weather breakfast may be served on the terrace beside the saltwater swimming pool.

Recommended in the area

Chester; Snowdonia; Horseshoe Pass, Llangollen

Barratt's at Ty'n Rhyl

★★★★ ◎◎ RR

Address: Ty'n Rhyl, 167 Vale Road, RHYL,
 Denbighshire LL18 2PH
Tel: 01745 344138
Fax: 01745 344138
Email: ebarratt5@aol.com
Website: www.barrattsoftynrhyl.co.uk
Map ref: 5, SJ08
Directions: A55 onto A525 to Rhyl, pass Sainsburys
& B&Q, garden centre on left, Barratts 400yds on r

Rooms: 3 en suite, S £60 D £80 **Parking:** 20 **Notes:** ⊘ on premises ⊗ on premises ⫯⫯

Ty'n Rhyl is a fascinating and rewarding place to stay, with many unique features and, best of all, food cooked by an award-winning chef. The fine old stone house was built in the second half of the 17th century, and is set in an acre of grounds with mature trees and manicured lawns, all enclosed within weathered old walls. Inside it is an elegant retreat, with wood panelling and relaxing lounges with comfortable plump sofas – look especially for the carved fireplace that is, in fact, a remodelling of a bedstead belonging to Catherine of Aragon, first of the many wives of Henry VIII. Once the home of the bard Angharad Llwyd, the house is now owned by chef David Barratt and his wife Elvira. Dining at Barratt's is a highlight of any visit here, and David's creative cooking, based on local produce of the highest quality, has earned many accolades. Breakfasts are no less delicious, and are served in the lovely conservatory overlooking the garden. Special diets can be catered for and, unusually for bed-and-breakfast guests, mealtimes are quite flexible. The spacious bedrooms are well furnished with period pieces and equipped with hospitality trays, clock radio, hair dryer, toiletries and many other thoughtful extras.

Recommended in the area

Rhyl SeaQuarium; Rhuddlan Castle; Offa's Dyke

Firgrove Country House B&B

★★★★ 🛏 🍴 BB

Address: Firgrove, Llanfwrog,
RUTHIN, Denbighshire LL15 2LL
Tel: 01824 702677
Fax: 01824 702677
Email: meadway@firgrovecountryhouse.co.uk
Website: www.firgrovecountryhouse.co.uk
Map ref: 5, SJ15
Directions: 0.5m SW of Ruthin. A494 onto B5105, 0.25m past Llanfwrog church on right
Rooms: 3 (2 en suite), S £50–£80 D £70–£100
Parking: 4 **Notes:** ⊘ on premises ⊗ on premises 🐾
Closed: Dec–Jan

Firgrove was once an old stone house and part of Lord Bagot's estate. In 1800 it was dramatically altered by the addition of a Georgian brick façade and Lord Bagot used it as a separate guest house in addition to his stately pile. Anna and Philip Meadway are proudly continuing the tradition. The Grade II listed building with its inspiring views across the Vale of Clwyd, has been brought up to date with well-equipped bedrooms and modern comforts. The well-proportioned bedrooms retain many original period features and have smart bathrooms designed and fitted for pure pampering. One of the bedrooms has an attractive four-poster bed, while another is actually a self-contained ground-floor suite with an open fire, small kitchen and a private sitting room. Home-made and locally sourced produce features in the splendid breakfasts served in the elegant dining room where, by prior arrangement, evening meals can also be enjoyed. The mature and immaculate garden is an ongoing labour of love – planted with beautiful trees and shrubs it provides a delightful setting for the house.

Recommended in the area

Offa's Dyke Path; Bodnant Garden (NT);Chester

The Wynnstay Arms

★★★★ ◉◉ RR

Address: Well Street, RUTHIN, Denbighshire LL15 1AN
Tel: 01824 703147
Email: reservations@wynnstayarms.com
Website: www.wynnstayarms.com
Map ref: 5, SJ15
Directions: In town centre
Rooms: 7 en suite, S £45–£55 D £65–£90
Parking: 14 **Notes:** ⊗ 🐾 allowed in bedrooms
(£5 per night) ♦♦

This former coaching inn, with a history dating back to 1549, has been beautifully refurbished by three experienced hoteliers and restaurateurs to provide top-quality accommodation, a smart cafe-bar and an award-winning restaurant. The en suite bedrooms, including a family room, have all been stylishly decorated. Downstairs, Fusions restaurant is earning a high reputation for its modern cuisine, prepared by Jason, the head chef/owner, using fine local produce, including Welsh black beef, locally produced cheese and local trout. Bar W serves great bar food,

Recommended in the area

Chester; Snowdonia; Caernarfon Castle

Bach-Y-Graig

★★★★ FH

Address: Tremeirchion, ST ASAPH,
Denbighshire LL17 0UH
Tel: 01745 730627
Fax: 01745 730627
Email: anwen@bachygraig.co.uk
Website: www.bachygraig.co.uk
Map ref: 5, SJ07
Directions: 3m SE of St Asaph. Off A525 at Trefnant onto A541 to x-rds with white railings, left down hill, over bridge & right
Rooms: 3 en suite, S £35–£48 D £64–£72 **Parking:** 3 **Notes:** ⊗ on premises ⊗ on premises ♦♦

The wealth of oak beams and panelling, and Grade II listing, testify to the historic character of this farmhouse set in 200 acres with private fishing rights on the River Clwyd. Bedrooms are furnished with fine period pieces and quality soft fabrics – some rooms have antique brass beds. The ground floor has a quiet lounge and a sitting-dining room where a scrumptious breakfast is served.

Recommended in the area

Bodnant Garden (NT); The Old Gaol, Ruthin; Tweedmill Factory Outlets, St Asaph

Tan-Yr-Onnen Guest House

★★★★★ GH

Address: Waen, ST ASAPH,
Denbighshire LL17 0DU

Tel: 01745 583821

Fax: 01745 583821

Email: tanyronnenvisit@aol.com

Website: www.northwalesbreaks.co.uk

Map ref: 5, SJ07

Directions: W on A55 junct 28, turn left in 300yds

Rooms: 6 en suite, S £50–£80 D £70–£100

Parking: 8 **Notes:** ⊘ on premises 🐾 allowed on premises ⅰ♦

Set in the heart of Wales, in the verdant Vale of Clwyd, Patrick and Sara Murphy's guest house, Tan-Yr-Onnen, is perfectly located for exploring beautiful North Wales and nearby Chester. Quality is the key word here, with very high standards throughout. The house has been extensively refurbished and the bedrooms newly constructed; all are modern and well equipped. Ground-floor rooms feature kingsize beds and some have French doors opening out onto private patios, while those on the first floor offer suite accommodation. All provide home comforts such as bathrobes, fluffy towels, comfy beds, freeview TV/DVD player, free wireless internet connection and tea and coffee-making facilities – little touches to make your stay feel extra special. The hearty breakfast table will set you up for a day's exploration, and features cereals, fruit juices, home-baked bread and locally sourced produce cooked to order and served in the dining room. Adjacent to this is a spacious lounge with a log fire lit on cold winter evenings. A relaxing new conservatory has also been added, and from here you can enjoy views of the six acres of beautiful grounds and gardens at the foot of the Clwydian range. Private parking is available.

Recommended in the area

St Asaph; Bodelwyddan Castle; Offa's Dyke Path

The promenade, Pwllheli

Old Mill Guest Accommodation

★★★★ GA

Address: Melin-Y-Wern, Denbigh Road,
NANNERCH, Mold, Flintshire CH7 5RH
Tel: 01352 741542
Email: mail@old-mill.co.uk
Website: www.old-mill.co.uk
Map ref: 5, SJ16
Directions: A541 NW from Mold, 7m enter Melin-Y-
Wern, Old Mill on right
Rooms: 6 en suite, S £45–£56 D £60–£76 **Parking:**
12 **Notes:** ⊘ on premises ⊗ on premises ♦♦ **Closed:** 1–30 Nov

This converted stable block was once part of a Victorian watermill complex in the Melin-y-Wern
conservation area. The site also includes a restaurant and a wine bar. Landscaped gardens surround
the Old Mill, and two of the well-equipped bedrooms, all of which are en suite, are located on the
ground floor. The spacious, conservatory-style dining room provides a first-class breakfast, with full
English and lighter options.

Recommended in the area

Chester; Clwydian Hills Area of Outstanding Natural Beauty; Snowdonia

Llwyndu Farmhouse

★★★★ ⇔ GA

Address: Llanaber, BARMOUTH,
Gwynedd LL42 1RR
Tel: 01341 280144
Email: Intouch@llwyndu-farmhouse.co.uk
Website: www.llwyndu-farmhouse.co.uk
Map ref: 5, SH16
Directions: A496 towards Harlech where street lights
end, on outskirts of Barmouth, take next right
Rooms: 7 en suite, S £88 D £88–£94 **Parking:** 10
Notes: ⊘ on premises ⌗ allowed on premises ⌗ **Closed:** 25–26 Dec

The converted farmhouse, just north of the seaside town of Barmouth, has been known for its 'hospitality, song and good ale' since the 16th century. Among the original features are a circular stone staircase, inglenook fireplaces, exposed beams and mullioned windows. Owners Peter and Paula Thompson provide bedrooms which are modern and well equipped, some with four-poster beds. There are more rooms in the converted granary next to the house, but all rooms are en suite and have hospitality trays and sofas. There is a cosy lounge to relax in or to chat to fellow travellers and plan your days. Dinner, a treat of imaginative food, local produce and fine wines, is served in the licensed dining room. Lit with candles and old lamps to create an intimate atmosphere and with a little music thrown in, it is a great experience. Breakfast specialities are kippers or naturally smoked haddock, Glamorgan vegetarian cutlets or local herb sausages, and smoked bacon and laver bread. This is a wonderful area for walking, either in the Rhinog Mountains or on the nearby Panorama Walk with stunning views across Cardigan Bay to the Llyn Peninsula. Barmouth itself is situated on a beautiful estuary. Boat trips leave from the harbour and you can always find a quiet place to stroll on the beach.
Recommended in the area
Cader Idris; Portmeirion; Centre for Alternative Technology

Pengwern Farm

★★★★ FH

Address: Saron, CAERNARFON, Gwynedd LL54 5UH
Tel: 01286 831500
Fax: 01286 830741
Email: janepengwern@aol.com
Website: www.pengwern.net
Map ref: 5, SH46
Directions: A487 S from Caernarfon, pass supermarket on right, right after bridge, 2m to Saron, over x-rds, 1st driveway on right
Rooms: 3 en suite, S £48 D £60–£80 **Parking:** 3 **Notes:** ⊘ on premises ♦♦
Closed: Nov–Mar

Pengwern is a delightful farmhouse surrounded by 130 acres of beef and sheep farmland running down to Foryd Bay, noted for its bird life. There are fine views from many bedrooms over to Anglesey, and the top of Snowdon can be seen on clear days. Bedrooms are generally spacious, and all are well equipped with modern facilities. A comfortable lounge is provided and good home cooking is served.

Recommended in the area

Plas Newydd, Anglesey (NT); Caernarfon Castle; Hydro-electric Mountain

Dolgun Uchaf Guesthouse

★★★★ GH

Address: Dolgun Uchaf, DOLGELLAU, Gwynedd LL40 2AB
Tel: 01341 422269
Email: dolgunuchaf@aol.com
Website: www.guesthousessnowdonia.com
Map ref: 2, SH71
Directions: Off A470 at Little Chef just S of Dolgellau, Dolgun Uchaf 1st property on right
Rooms: 4 en suite **Parking:** 6 **Notes:** ⊘ on premises ✝ allowed in bedrooms ✗under 5yrs

Located in the heart of Snowdonia National Park, Dolgun Uchaf, a 16th-century converted farmhouse, offers contemporary comfort amid beautiful surroundings, making it an ideal place for a relaxing weekend or a base for exploring Snowdonia. Beautifully restored it retains many original features, including exposed beams and open fireplaces. Bedrooms are all en suite and equipped with thoughtful extras. Home-cooked breakfasts and pre-booked evening meals are served in the dining room.

Recommended in the area

Cader Idris Mountain; King Arthur's Labyrinth; Centre for Alternative Technology

Beddgelert

Tyddynmawr Farmhouse

★★★★★ FH

Address: Cader Road, Islawrdref, DOLGELLAU,
Gwynedd LL40 1TL
Tel: 01341 422331
Map ref: 2, SH71
Directions: From town centre left at top of square,
left at garage onto Cader Rd for 3m, 1st farm on left
after Gwernan Lake
Rooms: 3 en suite, S £55 D £66 **Parking:** 8 **Notes:**
⊘ on premises ⊗ on premises ⚲ **Closed:** Jan

Birdwatchers, ramblers, photographers and artists see these spectacular surroundings as a paradise, and the farmhouse accommodation appeals equally to those just happy to sit and look. Olwen Evans prides herself on her home cooking and warm hospitality. Oak beams and log fires lend character to the stone house, and bedrooms are spacious and furnished with Welsh oak furniture; one room has a balcony, and a ground floor room benefits from a patio. The en suites are large and luxurious. This breathtaking mountain setting is about 3 miles from the historic market town of Dolgellau.

Recommended in the area

Walking – Cader Idris, Precipice Walk, Torrent Walk, Maddach Estuary Walk; steam railways

Brigand's Inn

★★★★ INN

Address: MALLWYD, Nr Machynlleth,
Gwynedd SY20 9HJ
Tel: 01650 511999
Fax: 01650 531208
Email: info@brigandsinn.com
Website: www.brigandsinn.com
Map ref: 2, SH81
Directions: In village at junct A458 & A470
Rooms: 10 en suite, S £50 D £85 **Parking:** 150
Notes: ⊘ in bedrooms ⊗ on premises ♦♦

Nestling on the edge of the Snowdonia National Park, in the Dovey Valley, the 15th-century Brigand's Inn offers guests the chance to relax and enjoy good food surrounded by spectacular scenery. The inn was once renowned throughout Wales as the haunt of the Gwylliaid Cochion Mawddwy (Red Bandits), but today it has been renovated to provide high standards of comfort and facilities, and is the perfect place for pursuits such as shooting, fishing or superb walking. It was awarded the AA's Welsh Pub of the year award in 2006/7, and is home to a cosy bar, a snug and a tavern. The quality furnishings and decor highlight the many original features throughout, and the elegant en suite bedrooms include one family room and some with four-posters or half-testers. All rooms are spacious, with beautiful oak furniture, sumptuous beds and thoughtful extras such as internet access, cafetiere of coffee and mineral water. Food is served in the comfortable dining rooms, and the chef produces fine dishes using local and seasonal produce, such as Welsh lamb and locally caught crab, to create contemporary and classic Welsh cuisine. All are accompanied by a selection of fine wines.

Recommended in the area

Snowdonia National Park; Centre for Alternative Technology; King Arthur's Labyrinth and Craft Centre

Penrhadw Farm

★★★★ GH

Address: Pontsticill, MERTHYR TYDFIL, CF48 2TU
Tel: 01685 723481
Fax: 01685 722461
Email: info@penrhadwfarm.co.uk
Website: www.penrhadwfarm.co.uk
Map ref: 2, SO00
Directions: 5m N of Merthyr Tydfil, map on website
Rooms: 5 (5 en suite), S £46–£56 D £65–£90
Parking: 22 **Notes:** ⊘ ⊗ on premises 🛉

This former Victorian farmhouse, located in the heart of the glorious Brecon Beacons National Park and with spectacular mountain views, has been totally refurbished to provide high-quality modern accommodation. The well-equipped, spacious bedrooms include two large suites in cottages adjacent to the main building. All rooms are en suite and come with hospitality tray, TV and trouser press. There is also a comfortable guest lounge with a TV and video recorder. Separate tables are provided in the cosy breakfast room, where hearty Welsh breakfasts are served.

Recommended in the area
The Brecon Mountain Railway; Brecon Beacons National Park; Millennium Stadium, Cardiff

Penylan Farm

★★★★ BB

Address: The Hendre, MONMOUTH,
Monmouthshire NP25 5NL
Tel: 01600 716435
Fax: 01600 719391
Email: treghotel@aol.com
Website: www.penylanfarm.co.uk
Map ref: 2, SO51
Directions: 5m NW of Monmouth. B4233 through
Rockfield towards Hendre. 0.5m before Hendre turn
right towards Newcastle. After 1.5m turn left, farm 0.5 m on right.
Rooms: 5 (3 en suite), S £35–£40 D £52–£60 **Parking:** 5 **Notes:** ⊘ on premises ⊗ on premises
🛉 **Closed:** Xmas & New Year

Penylan is a working farm and Dave and Cathy Bowen welcome you to their idyllic country retreat. The converted granary houses the guest bedrooms, furnished to a very high standard, and a private lounge with a TV. The breakfasts are good and include meat from an award-winning local butcher.

Recommended in the area
Offa's Dyke Path; Wye Valley; Brecon Beacons National Park

The Stonemill & Steppes Farm Cottages

★★★★ ◉◉ GA

Address: ROCKFIELD, Monmouth,
Monmouthshire NP25 5SW
Tel: 01600 775424
Email: michelle@thestonemill.co.uk
Website: www.steppesfarmcottages.co.uk
Map ref: 2, SO41
Directions: A48 to Monmouth, B4233 to Rockfield.
2.6m from Monmouth town centre **Rooms:** 6 en suite **Parking:** 53 **Notes:** ⊘ ⊗ in bedrooms ♨

Located in Rockfield, a small hamlet just west of Monmouth, this operation offers accommodation comprising six very well-appointed cottages with comfortable en suite rooms for self-catering or bed and breakfast. All have been architect-designed and lovingly restored with many of the original features remaining. In a separate, converted 16th-century barn stands the Stonemill Restaurant with oak beams, vaulted ceilings and an old cider press. Breakfast is served in the cottages on request.
Recommended in the area
Forest of Dean; Wye Valley; The Kymin

The Newbridge

★★★★ ◉ RR

Address: Tredunnock, USK,
Monmouthshire NP15 1LY
Tel: 01633 451000
Fax: 01633 451001
Email: thenewbridge@tinyonline.co.uk
Website: www.thenewbridge.co.uk
Map ref: 2, SO30
Directions: Off A449, NE of Newport
Rooms: 6 en suite, **Parking:** 60 **Notes:** ⊘ in bedrooms ♨ **Closed:** 1wk Jan

Standing beside the river, just 4 miles south of Usk, The Newbridge is in an idyllic location. The spacious restaurant occupies the ground and first-floor levels of the house and the smart, well-equipped bedrooms are in a purpose-built adjacent building. They feature gorgeous oak and teak furniture, hand-made beds, limestone and marble tiles and roll top baths. The chef Iain Sampson brings his flair and consistency to the excellent menus and uses the best of Welsh produce.
Recommended in the area
Usk Rural Life Museum; Roman Caerleon; Black Mountains

The Crown at Whitebrook

★ ★ ★ ★ ★ ◉◉ RR

Address: WHITEBROOK, Monmouthshire NP25 4TX
Tel: 01600 860254
Fax: 01600 860607
Email: info@crownatwhitebrook.co.uk
Website: www.crownatwhitebrook.co.uk
Map ref: 2, SO50
Directions: 4m from Monmouth on B4293, left at sign to Whitebrook, 2m on unmarked road, then Crown on right
Rooms: 8 en suite, S £75–£90 D £115–£140 **Parking:** 20
Notes: ⊘ on premises ⊗ in bedrooms 🧒 under 12yrs
Closed: 24 Dec–12 Jan

In a secluded spot in the wooded valley of the River Wye, yet just 5 miles from the town of Monmouth, this former drover's cottage dates back to the 17th century and boasts 5 acres of tranquil, landscaped gardens in which guests can wander and relax. A restaurant-with-rooms, its refurbished and individually decorated bedrooms boast a contemporary feel and have the latest in smart facilities. The executive rooms boast the added luxury of walk-in power showers, and two rooms have double-ended baths. All have outstanding views across the rolling countryside and offer a whole host of thoughtful extras such as individually controlled heating, flatscreen TV, internet/email and tea and coffee-making facilities. In addition, the 'comfort-cool' system helps keep the rooms cool and comfortable on hot summer days. Downstairs, the lounge combines many original features with a bright, fresh look, but it is the smart, modern restaurant that lies at the heart of the whole operation. For the outstanding cooking is the thing here, with memorable cuisine featuring locally sourced ingredients skilfully prepared by head chef James Sommerin, and all accompanied by a seriously good wine list.

Recommended in the area

Brecon Beacons; Tintern Abbey; Offa's Dyke

Erw-Lon Farm

★★★★ FH

Address: Pontfaen, FISHGUARD,
Pembrokeshire SA65 9TS
Tel: 01348 881297
Map ref: 1, SM93
Directions: 5.5m SE of Fishguard on B4313
Rooms: 3 (2 en suite), S £35 D £60–£65
Parking: 5 **Notes:** ⊗ on premises ⊗ on premises
🐾under 10yrs **Closed:** Dec–Mar

This lovely old house is at the heart of a working sheep and cattle farm, and its landscaped gardens overlook the stunning Gwaun Valley towards Carningli, the Mountain of the Angels. Lilwen McAllister is an exceptional hostess, acknowledged by her selection as AA Landlady of the Year in 2006. There is a very homely feel to the farmhouse and the lounge is a lovely place to relax. The bedrooms are comfortable and well equipped. Mrs McAllister's traditional farmhouse cooking uses fresh local produce and meals are served in generous portions. Erw–Lon Farm is well situated as a base to explore Pembrokeshire and Cardigan Bay.

Recommended in the area

Castell Henllys; Strumble Head; St David's Cathedral; Pembrokeshire Coastal Path

Swn-Y-Nant B&B

★★★★ BB

Address: MOYLEGROVE, Cardigan,
Pembrokeshire SA43 3BW
Tel: 01239 881244
Email: ludbek@yahoo.com
Website: www.moylegrove.co.uk
Map ref: 1, SN14
Directions: From A487 turn left and follow road for
5m to Moylegrove village, bottom right of hill
Rooms: 3 (2 en suite), S D £54–£60 **Parking:** 3
Notes: ⊗ on premises ⊗ in bedrooms 👫 **Closed:** Jan

Swn-Y-Nant is in the coastal village of Moylegrove, midway between Cardigan and Newport, making it an excellent base for touring the beautiful Pembrokeshire countryside. The accommodation is high quality with comfortable and tasteful, contemporary decor. The ground-floor bedrooms, two of which have wet rooms, are well furnished, spacious, and well equipped. The comprehensive breakfast menu features fresh local produce and caters for most tastes and diets. Dinner is available by arrangement.

Recommended in the area

Pembrokeshire Coast National Park; St Dogmael's Abbey; Preseli Hills

The Waterings

★★★★ BB

Address: Anchor Drive, High Street, ST DAVID'S,
Pembrokeshire SA62 6QH
Tel: 01437 720876
Fax: 01437 720876
Email: waterings@supanet.com
Website: www.waterings.co.uk
Map ref: 1, SM72
Directions: On A487 on E edge of St David's
Rooms: 5 en suite, S £45–£80 D £70–£80
Parking: 20 **Notes:** ⊘ in bedrooms ⊗ on premises ⚲ under 5yrs

The Waterings is set in 2 acres of beautiful landscaped grounds in a quiet location close to the Pembrokeshire Coast National Park Visitor Centre and only a short walk from St David's 800-year-old cathedral, which is the setting for an annual music festival at the end of May. The magnificent coastline with its abundance of birdlife is also within easy reach. The en suite bedrooms in this spacious accommodation are all on the ground floor and are set around an attractive courtyard. All the bedrooms are equipped with TV and have tea- and coffee-making facilities. The accommodation includes two family rooms with lounge, two double rooms with lounge and a double room with small sitting area. Breakfast, prepared from a good selection of local produce, is served in a smart dining room in the main house. Outside amenities at The Waterings include a picnic area with tables and benches, a barbecue and a croquet lawn. The nearest sandy beach is just a 15-minute walk away; other activities in the area include walking, boat trips to Ramsey Island, an RSPB reserve a mile offshore, sea fishing, whale and dolphin spotting boat trips, canoeing, surfing, rock climbing and abseiling.

Recommended in the area

Ramsey Island boat trips; Pembrokeshire Coast National Park; Whitesands Beach

Vine Cottage

★★★★ GH

Address: The Ridgeway, SAUNDERSFOOT,
Pembrokeshire SA69 9LA
Tel: 01834 814422
Email: enquiries@vinecottageguesthouse.co.uk
Website: www.vinecottageguesthouse.co.uk
Map ref: 1, SN10
Directions: A477 S onto A478, left onto B4316, after railway bridge right signed Saundersfoot, cottage 100yds beyond 30mph sign
Rooms: 5 en suite, S £35–£63 D £56–£70 Parking: 10 Notes: ⊘ on premises 🐾 allowed on premises 👶under 6yrs

This pleasant former farmhouse, on the outskirts of Saundersfoot, has been lovingly restored to reflect its original character while incorporating modern facilities to ensure a comfortable stay. The well equipped bedrooms include ground-floor and family rooms. Breakfast is served in the dining room, evening meals are by arrangement, and there is a comfortable lounge with a log fire for chilly days.

Recommended in the area

Pembrokeshire Coast National Park and Coastal Path; Pembroke Castle; Stackpole Estate

---

Canal Bank

★★★★★ BB

Address: Ty Gardd, BRECON,
Powys LD3 7HG
Tel: 01874 623464
Email: enquiries@accommodation-breconbeacons.co.uk
Website: www.accommodation-breconbeacons.co.uk
Map ref: 2, SO02
Directions: B4601 signed Brecon, left over bridge before fuel station & continue to end of road
Rooms: 3 en suite, S £45–£50 D £75–£85 Parking: 4 Notes: ⊘ on premises ⊗ in bedrooms 👶

There are colourful narrowboats on the canal right outside the front door and it's just a short walk along the towpath to Brecon's marina and town centre. There are also views of fields, hills and the River Usk. After a day sightseeing, guests can enjoy a spa bath then sink into a big, comfy bed. In the morning, a hearty Welsh breakfast is an excellent start to the day.

Recommended in the area

Carreg Cennan Castle; the Big Pit; Brecon Beacons National Park

The Coach House

★★★★ GA

Address: Orchard Street, BRECON,
Powys LD3 8AN
Tel: 01874 620043, booking line 07967 328437
Fax: 07050 691217
Email: info@coachhousebrecon.co.uk
Website: www.coachhousebrecon.co.uk
Map ref: 2, SO02
Directions: From town centre W over bridge onto B4601, Coach House 200yds on right
Rooms: 7 en suite, S £45–£65 D £65–£95 **Parking:** 8
Notes: ⊘ on premises ⊗ on premises ⚲ under 16yrs

Coach houses were traditionally warm and welcoming places, and while a warm welcome is assured here in Brecon, this particular example is one of a new breed, offering luxurious townhouse accommodation. The private garden of the Coach House is an oasis of colour, and offers a retreat in which to relax, read a book or take a drink. Hosts Marc and Tony are proud of their local knowledge, and offer advice on the best places to visit, walk, cycle or ride. There are also opportunities for sailing or pony-trekking in the area. The strong sense of place evident in the photographs and maps of the Brecon Beacons on the walls, showing some of the most unspoilt countryside in Wales, continues through to the Welsh-speciality breakfasts – try Eggs Brychan, made with scrambled eggs, smoked salmon and laverbread for starters. Evening meals are similarly inventive and are served in the small restaurant. Much thought has gone into the contemporary design of the light, airy bedrooms, all of which are well equipped, and some of which have a DVD player and a film library. There's even a holistic therapist on hand to soothe away the stresses of the day.

Recommended in the area

Brecon Beacons National Park; Dan yr Ogof Caves; Brecon Catherdral

Carreg Cennen Castle, Carmarthenshire

Llanddetty Hall Farm

★★★★ FH

Address: Talybont-on-Usk, BRECON,
Powys LD3 7YR
Tel: 01874 676415
Fax: 01874 676415
Map ref: 2, SO02
Directions: SE of Brecon. Off B4558
Rooms: 4 (3 en suite), S £35 D £54–£60
Parking: 6 **Notes:** ⊗ on premises ⊗ on premises
🚸 under 12yrs **Closed:** 16 Dec–14 Jan

This listed farmhouse is part of a sheep farm in the Brecon Beacons National Park. The Brecon and Monmouth Canal flows through the farm at the rear, while the front of the house overlooks the River Usk. Bedrooms, including one on the ground floor, feature exposed beams and polished floorboards. Three rooms are en suite and one has a private bathroom – all have radio alarms and tea and coffee facilities. There is a lounge with a television, and a dining room where breakfast is served at an oak refectory table. This is a no smoking house.

Recommended in the area

Brecon Beacons National Park; Hay-on-Wye; Aberglasney

The Usk Inn

★★★★ ◉ INN

Address: Station Road, Talybont-On-Usk,
BRECON, Powys LD3 7JE
Tel: 01874 676251
Fax: 01874 676392
Email: stay@uskinn.co.uk
Website: www.uskinn.co.uk
Map ref: 2, SO02
Directions: Off A40 6m E of Brecon
Rooms: 11 en suite **Parking:** 30 **Notes:** ⊘ in
bedrooms ⊗ in bedrooms ⋔ **Closed:** 25–27 Dec

Established in the 1840s as a railway inn, The Usk Inn is now well suited to those who enjoy outdoor pursuits. There are some wonderful walks nearby in the Brecon Beacons or along the Brecon to Monmouthshire Canal, as well as cycling, horse riding, fishing and golf. There are also cruises on the canal, and the many attractions of south and mid-Wales are within easy reach. The inn has also become very popular with classic car enthusiasts taking part in Brecon Motor Club events. The warm hospitality and enthusiastic management reflect the fact that the inn is family owned; Andrew and Jillian Felix have brought with them a wealth of experience in the hospitality industry and the quality of the accommodation here earned it the AA Welsh Pub of the Year award for 2004–2005. The building has been renovated to a very high standard and improvements are constantly being made to further enhance the guest experience. The bedrooms, named after birds found along the banks of the River Usk, have an en suite bathroom and are individually decorated and furnished with locally made pine furniture. Public areas, including an open-plan bar and lounge, have a great deal of charm, and in the dining room guests can enjoy the high standard of cooking that has brought the inn renown.

Recommended in the area

Brecon Beacons National Park; Brecon Mountain Railway; Brecon to Monmouthshire Canal

Glangrwyney Court

★★★★★ BB

Address: CRICKHOWELL, Powys NP8 1ES
Tel: 01873 811288
Fax: 01873 810317
Email: info@glancourt.co.uk
Website: www.glancourt.co.uk
Map ref: 2, SO21
Directions: 2m SE of Crickhowell on A40 (near county boundary)
Rooms: 10 (9 en suite), S £50–£85 D £70–£95
Parking: 12 **Notes:** ⊘ on premises ⊗ in bedrooms ⁙

A Grade II listed country house, Glangrwyney Court is situated in 4 acres of beautiful gardens in the Brecon Beacons National Park, midway between Abergavenny and Crickhowell. The Georgian mansion dates back to 1825 and has typically Palladian architecture. The family has taken care to sympathetically refurbish the property resulting in an exquisite country house retreat with a relaxing and intimate atmosphere. The interior is furnished with antiques, porcelain and paintings, and blazing log fires welcome guests in winter weather. Breakfast is served in the elegant dining room and you can relax in the sumptuous lounge. There is a good choice of bedrooms, including single, twin, double and family rooms. All rooms are en suite or have private facilities, are well equipped and have wonderful views over the garden and surrounding countryside. The Master Suite has the additional luxury of an extra deep bath, while the twin room has its own Jacuzzi. On warm summer evenings guests can sit and enjoy a drink on one of the patios in the grounds. Croquet, boules and tennis are available and activities such as pony trekking, golf, fishing and shooting can be arranged. There are many lovely walks in the area, with the Brecon Beacons and Black Mountains within easy reach.

Recommended in the area

Brecon Beacons National Park; Dan-Yr-Ogof Caves; Big Pit National Mining Museum of Wales

Lake Vyrnwy, Powys

Hafod-y-Garreg

★★★★ ⬭ BB

Address: ERWOOD, Powys LD2 3TQ
Tel: 01982 560400
Email: john-annie@hafod-y.wanadoo.co.uk
Website: www.hafodygarreg.co.uk
Map ref: 2, SO04
Directions: 1m S of Erwood. Off A470 at Trericket Mill, sharp right, up track past cream farmhouse towards pine forest, through gate
Rooms: 2 en suite, S D £60 **Parking:** 6 **Notes:** ⊘ in bedrooms ⚲ allowed on premises ⅰⅰ **Closed:** Xmas

This Grade II* listed farmhouse, the oldest surviving house in Wales, dates from 1402 and is believed to have been built as Henry IV's hunting lodge. The house is in a superb location, has tremendous character and, combined with stunning early Welsh oak furniture and gorgeous fabrics, it is an ideal place to get away from it all. The attractive bedrooms have beautiful bed linen and modern facilities, dinner is served in the beamed dining room and breakfast includes home-laid free range eggs.
Recommended in the area
Hay-on-Wye; Brecon Beacons; Royal Welsh Showground

Guidfa House

★★★★★ 🛏 ☕ GA

Address: Crossgates, LLANDRINDOD WELLS,
Powys LD1 6RF
Tel: 01597 851241
Fax: 01597 851875
Email: guidfa@globalnet.co.uk
Website: www.guidfa-house.co.uk
Map ref: 2, SO06
Directions: 3m N of Llandrindod Wells, at junct of A483 & A44
Rooms: 6 en suite, S £55 D £70–£95 **Parking:** 10 **Notes:** ⊘
on premises ⊗ on premises ⛬ under 10yrs

Expect a relaxed and pampered stay at Anne and Tony Millan's
charming Georgian house, set within picturesque gardens and located in the village of Crossgates,
just north of Llandrindod Wells. The bright, spacious bedrooms are all individually furnished, and
include a ground-floor room with easy access for less agile guests. All rooms come well equipped
with comfortable beds, huge fluffy towels, soft bathrobes and good-quality Gilchrist and Soames
toiletries. Recently converted is the luxurious Coach House suite, situated off a small courtyard, which
has a super-king double bed and a large, separate sitting room and spa bath. Guests are welcome to
relax in the house's elegant sitting room, where on colder days a log fire blazes; a selection of books,
leaflets and maps, and free wireless internet connection are all available. Tea or coffee can be taken
here, or a drink served from the bar in the evenings. The meals at Guidfa House are both delicious
and imaginative, prepared by Anne, a Cordon Bleu-trained cook, from fresh, local produce and
accompanied by excellent wines – look out also for her naughty puddings. All in all, this is an excellent
base for touring the Brecon Beacons and the Welsh borderlands.

Recommended in the area

Elan Valley RSPB Red Kite Feeding Station; Royal Welsh Showground; Builth Wells

Carlton Riverside

★ ★ ★ ★ ◉◉◉ RR

Address: Irfon Crescent, LLANWRTYD WELLS, Powys LD5 4SP
Tel: 01591 610248
Email: info@carltonrestaurant.co.uk
Website: www.carltonrestaurant.co.uk
Map ref: 2, SN84
Directions: Right in the town centre next to the bridge
Rooms: 4 en suite, S £40–£50 D £60–£90 **Notes:** ⊘ on premises 🐴 allowed on premises 👫 **Closed:** Dec

This characterful restaurant-with-rooms is set on the banks of the River Irfon in Llanwrtyd Wells, Wales's smallest town, which is on the main Central Wales railway line that links Shrewsbury with South Wales. The surroundings of mountains and valley are outstandingly beautiful. As well as superb accommodation, AA Restaurant of the Year for Wales, Carlton Riverside offers award-winning cuisine, prepared by Mary Ann Gilchrist, and accompanied by a wide and varied wine list of stylish bottles chosen by her husband Alan. Served in the spacious and informal dining room, which blends traditional comfort with modern design and river views, the food here makes the best of local produce, and seasonal menus might include diverse temptations such as seared scallops with cauliflower cream and truffle oil, pink rack of lamb with slow-cooked shoulder, Talley goat's cheese with apple, and warm chocolate brownie with vanilla ice-cream. Relaxing pre- and post-dining drinks can be enjoyed in the bar or comfortable lounges, before retiring to the comfortable, individually decorated en suite bedrooms, including a family suite, all of which successfully combine antiques with designer fittings such as flatscreen TV and DVD/CD player to provide a high level of comfort. All-inclusive Gourmet Breaks are available, offering set menus and specially chosen wines.

Recommended in the area

Town of Llanwrtyd Wells; Cambrian Mountains; Brecon

Moors Farm B&B

★★★★★ BB

Address: Oswestry Road, WELSHPOOL,
Powys SY21 9JR
Tel: 01938 553395
Email: moorsfarm@tiscali.co.uk
Website: www.moors-farm.com
Map ref: 2, SJ20
Directions: 1.5m NE of Welshpool off A483
Rooms: 5 en suite, S £50 D £80
Notes: ⊗ on premises ⊗ in bedrooms ♦♦

Once the principal farmhouse of Powis Castle, Moors Farm remains impressive and is well situated on the main A483, between the River Severn and the Montgomery Canal. The farmhouse is still at the heart of a working farm that raises sheep and cattle. The building is full of character, with lots of exposed old beams and log-burning fires that are as warm as the welcome, and has been extensively renovated to provide accommodation that is both spacious and comfortable. Wholesome breakfasts are served in the elegant dining room around a huge family dining table, where guests all sit together in the old traditional manner. House party dinners are available by prior arrangement. The luxury Gate House barn conversion offers well-equipped spacious self-catering accommodation suitable for large families or a group of friends. Popular activities in the area include walking, cycling, golf, fishing, horse riding, quad trekking, canoeing and canal boating. It is just a mile along the canal tow path into the heart of the bustling market town of Welshpool where you'll find cafés, restaurants and traditional pubs alongside shops selling quality local produce. The Moors Farm especially welcomes group and family bookings.

Recommended in the area

Powis Castle and Gardens (NT);Welshpool and Llanfair Light Railway; Offa's Dyke Path; Glyndwr's Way; Glansevern Hall Gardens

Little Langland

★★★★★ GA

Address: 2 Rotherslade Road, Langland,
MUMBLES, Swansea SA3 4QN
Tel: 01792 369696
Fax: 01792 366995
Email: enquiries@littlelangland.co.uk
Website: www.littlelangland.co.uk
Map ref: 2, SS68
Directions: Off A4067 in Mumbles onto Newton
Road, 4th left onto Langland Rd, 2nd left onto
Rotherslade Road
Rooms: 6 en suite, S £65 D £100 **Parking:** 6 **Notes:** ⊘ on premises ⊗ on premises ⚼ under 8yrs

Little Langland has recently undergone a total refurbishment, although the lovely Victorian façade remains intact, and the proprietors Christine and Roger Johnson are justly proud of their comfortable new interior. This family-run establishment is only five miles from Swansea city centre and is within easy access of the stunning Gower Peninsula with its many coves and bays and the first area in Britain to be designated an Area of Outstanding Natural Beauty. The en suite bedrooms here are stylish, comfortable and well furnished, and all include thoughtful extras such as free broadband internet connection, as well as flatscreen LCD TV, hairdryer and tea and coffee-making facilities. Guests can also make use of the brand new café bar, which is an ideal place for a relaxing drink with friends. It offers a bar menu of freshly prepared snacks, made using locally sourced ingredients wherever possible, along with a good variety of coffees, beers and wines. Breakfast is served in the comfortable dining area. All in all, Little Langland makes a great base for visiting South Wales, whether planning a relaxing or a more energetic trip.

Recommended in the area

Rotherslade Bay; Oystermouth village; Mumbles Head

Rhossili Down, Swansea

Crescent Guest House

★★★★ GH

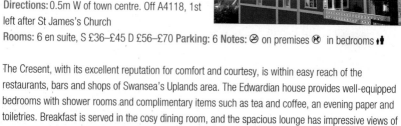

Address: 132 Eaton Crescent, Uplands,
SWANSEA SA1 4QR
Tel: 01792 466814
Fax: 01792 466814
Email: crescentguesthouse@hotmail.co.uk
Website: www.crescentguesthouse.co.uk
Map ref: 2, SS69
Directions: 0.5m W of town centre. Off A4118, 1st
left after St James's Church

Rooms: 6 en suite, S £36–£45 D £56–£70 **Parking:** 6 **Notes:** ⊘ on premises ⊗ in bedrooms ⋔

The Cresent, with its excellent reputation for comfort and courtesy, is within easy reach of the restaurants, bars and shops of Swansea's Uplands area. The Edwardian house provides well-equipped bedrooms with shower rooms and complimentary items such as tea and coffee, an evening paper and toiletries. Breakfast is served in the cosy dining room, and the spacious lounge has impressive views of Swansea Bay. There is a secure car park and easy street parking. Children welcome.

Recommended in the area

Swansea; Gower Peninsula; Mumbles

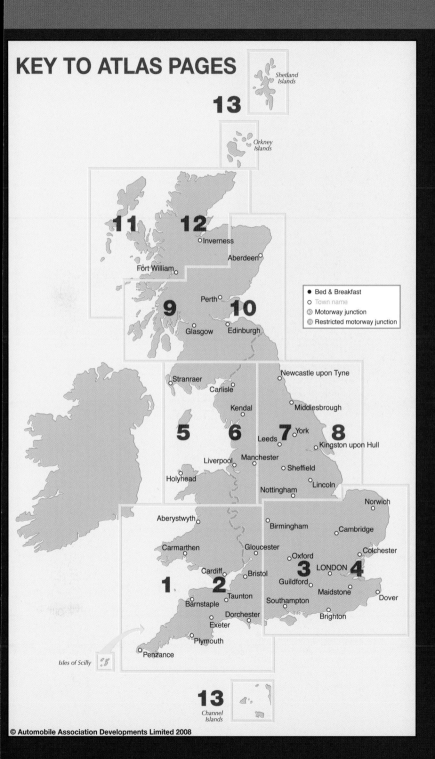

KEY TO ATLAS PAGES

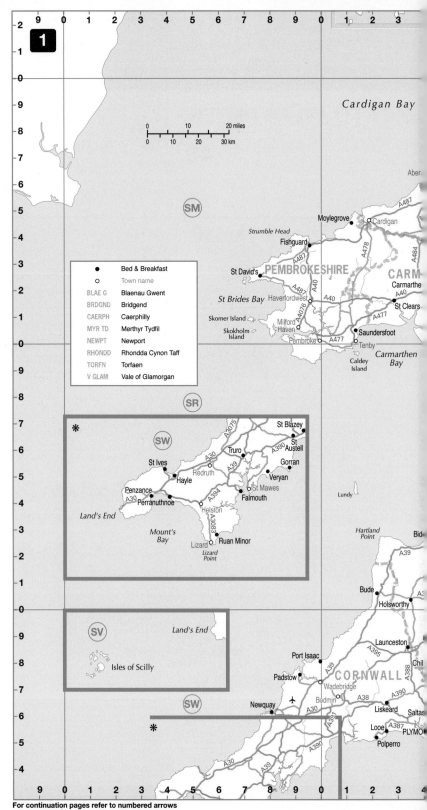

Cardigan Bay

●		Bed & Breakfast
○		Town name
BLAE G		Blaenau Gwent
BRDGND		Bridgend
CAERPH		Caerphilly
MYR TD		Merthyr Tydfil
NEWPT		Newport
RHONDD		Rhondda Cynon Taff
TORFN		Torfaen
V GLAM		Vale of Glamorgan

SM

Moylegrove
Cardigan

Strumble Head
Fishguard

St David's   PEMBROKESHIRE   CARM-

Carmarthe

St Brides Bay   Haverfordwest   A40   St Clears

Skomer Island

Skokholm
Island

Milford
Haven   Saundersfoot

Pembroke   Tenby

Caldey
Island   Carmarthen
Bay

SR

✳

SW

A3075   St Blazey

Truro   St
Austell

St Ives   Redruth   Gorran

Hayle   Veryan

Penzance   St Mawes

Perranuthnoe   Falmouth

Land's End   Helston

Mount's
Bay   Lizard   Ruan Minor

Lizard
Point

Lundy

Hartland
Point   Bid

A39

Bude
Holsworthy

SV   Land's End

Isles of Scilly

Port Isaac

Padstow

Launceston

Chil

CORNWALL

SW   Wadebridge

✳   Newquay   Bodmin

A30   Liskeard   Saltas

PLYMO

Looe

Polperro

For continuation pages refer to numbered arrows

458

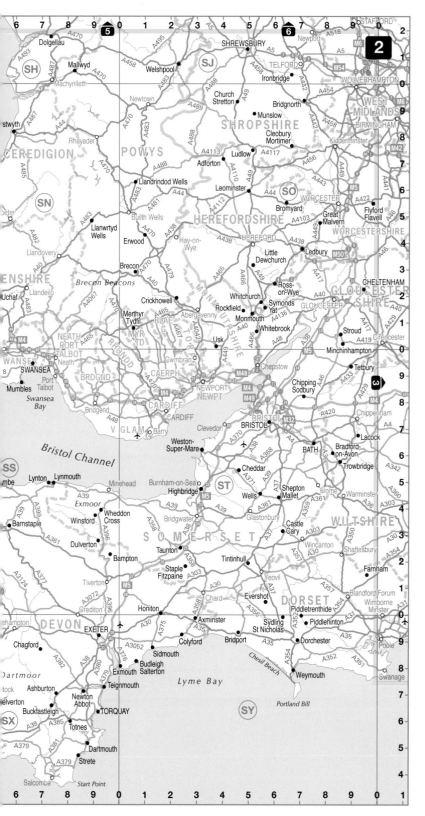

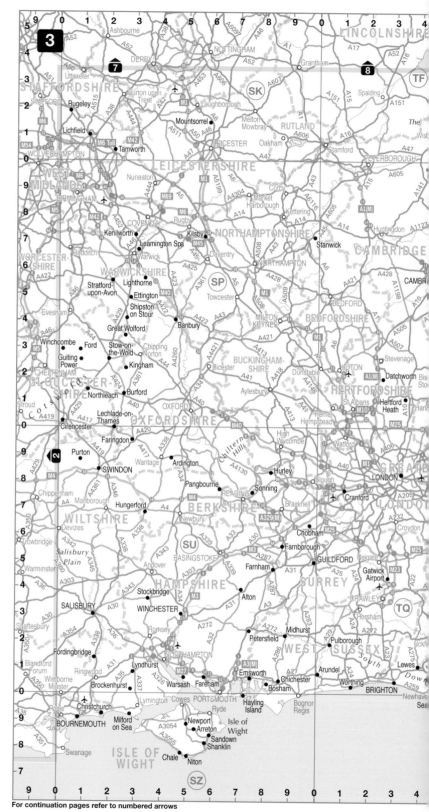

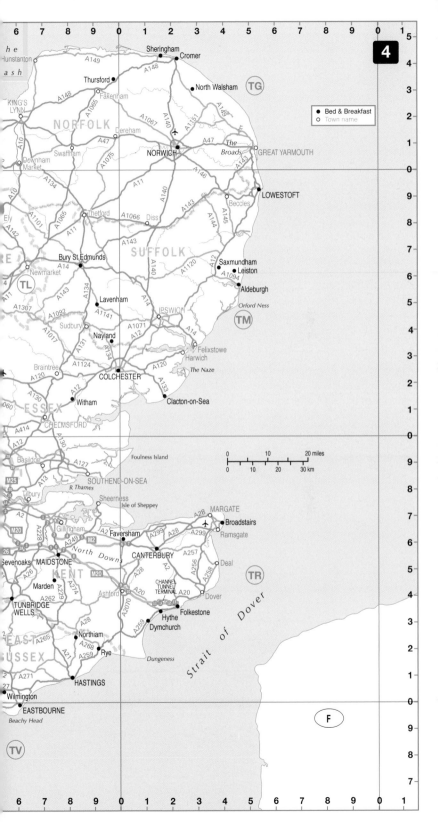

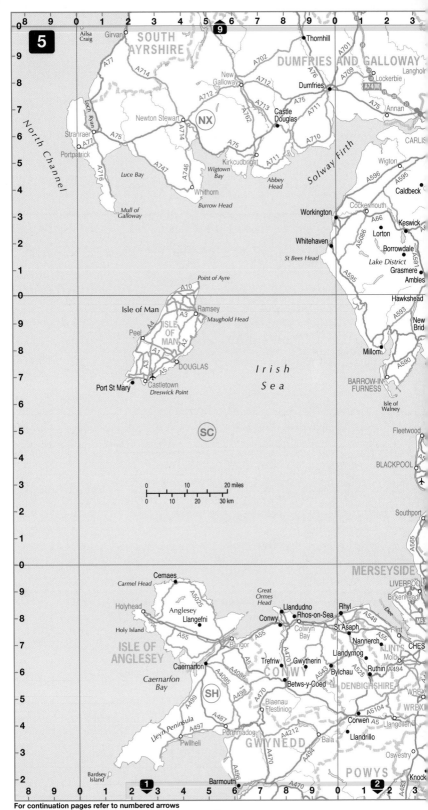

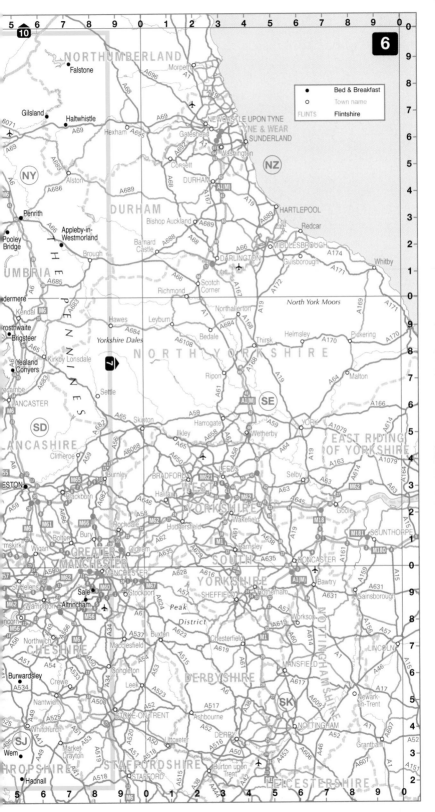

8

● Bed & Breakfast
○ Town name

0   10   20 miles
0 10   20 30 km

ynemouth

TYNE & WEAR
● SUNDERLAND
rlinston

NZ

HARTLEPOOL
A19 A689
● Redcar
MIDDLESBROUGH
A174
A66 ● Guisborough A171 ● Whitby
A19 A172

North York Moors

● Northallerton
A168
● Hawnby
Helmsley ● Kirkbymoorside A170 ○ SCARBOROUGH
Thirsk A170 A169 A171
● Ampleforth ● Pickering ● Flixton
A168 A19 A64 ○ Malton A165
● Westow Flamborough Head
A1(M) Sutton-on- A166 ● Bridlington
naresborough the-Forest A614
A59 A64 ○ Driffield A164 TA
● YORK A1079 A165
○ Wetherby EAST RIDING A165
A58 OF YORKSHIRE
SE A64 A19 A162 A163 A1079 ● Beverley
● Selby A614 A164 ○ KINGSTON UPON HULL
A162 A63 A63 A62 A63 R Humber
M62 A645 A1033
M62 ○ Goole A1077 A160 ● Immingham
kefield A638 A15 A180 ○ GRIMSBY Spurn Head
A19 M18 SCUNTHORPE A18 ● Cleethorpes
M181 A161 M180 A46
Barnsley A635 ● DONCASTER ● Epworth A159
A1(M) ● Bawtry ○ Gainsborough A15 Market A16 The A16 A1031
Rotherham A631 ○ Fillingham Rasen A631 Louth Worlds ● Mablethorpe
SHEFFIELD A57 ● Marton A46 A157 A153 A16 A52
A619 Worksop A156 A158 Horncastle A158
esterfield A57 A1 ● LINCOLN ○ Horncastle ○ Skegness
SK M1 MANSFIELD A616 A15 LINCOLNSHIRE A52 TF
A617 Newark- A46 A607 A153 A52 4
A60 A6097 on-Trent A17 ○ Sleaford Boston The
NOTTINGHAM Hough-on- ● Normanton A17 A52 A16 Wash ○ Hunstanton A149
RBY ● Risley the-Hill A607 NORFOLK
A453 A52 ○ Grantham A151 A17 KING'S A148
LEICESTERSHIRE A606 A607 A151 ○ Spalding A47 LYNN A148
A1

465

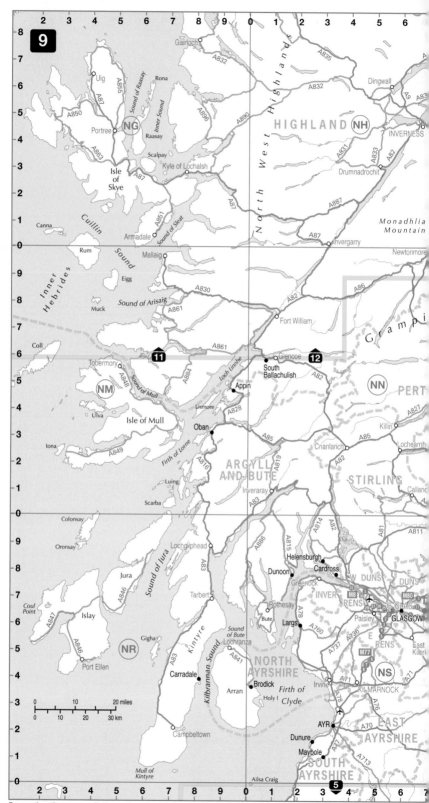

9

For continuation pages refer to numbered arrows

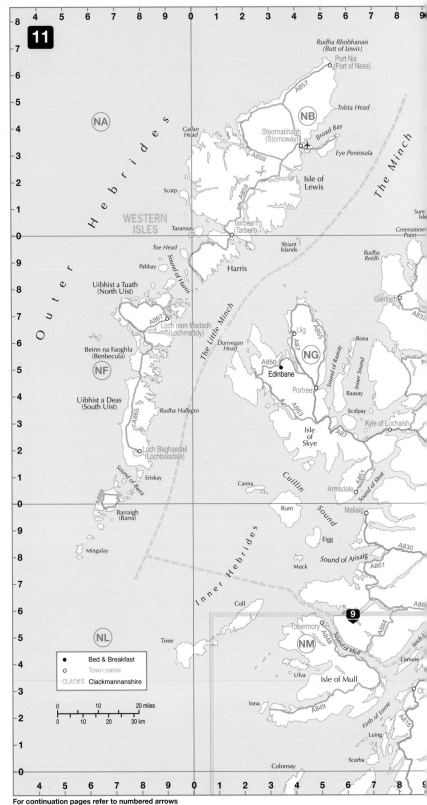

Rudha Rhobhanais
(Butt of Lewis)

Port Nis
(Port of Ness)

A857

Tolsta Head

NB

Steornabhagh
(Stornoway)

Broad Bay

Eye Peninsula

NA

Gallan
Head

A858

Isle of
Lewis

The Minch

Scarp

A859

**WESTERN
ISLES**

Taransay

Tairbeart
(Tarbert)

Sum
Isle

Greenstone
Point

Toe Head

Shiant
Islands

Pabbay

Sound of Harris

Harris

Rudha
Reidh

Uibhist a Tuath
(North Uist)

Gairloch

A832

A861

Loch nam Madadh
(Lochmaddy)

Uig

Rona

The Little Minch

Dunvegan
Head

A855

Beinn na Faoghla
(Benbecula)

A87

NG

Sound of Raasay

Inner Sound

NF

A850

Edinbane

Raasay

Uibhist a Deas
(South Uist)

Portree

Rudha Hallagro

Scalpay

A865

A863

Kyle of Lochalsh

Loch Baghasdail
(Lochboisdale)

Isle
of
Skye

A87

Eriskay

Canna

Cuillin

A851

Armadale

Sound of Sleat

Sound of Barra

A888

Barraigh
(Barra)

Rum

Sound

Mallaig

Mingulay

Eigg

A830

Muck

Sound of Arisaig

A861

Inner Hebrides

A86

Coll

9

A86

NL

Tobermory

A848

Sound of Mull

Tiree

NM

Lismore

	Bed & Breakfast
○	Town name
CLACKS	Clackmannanshire

Ulva

Isle of Mull

Iona

A849

Ob

0   10   20 miles
0   10   20   30 km

Firth of Lorne

A816

Luing

Scarba

Colonsay

For continuation pages refer to numbered arrows

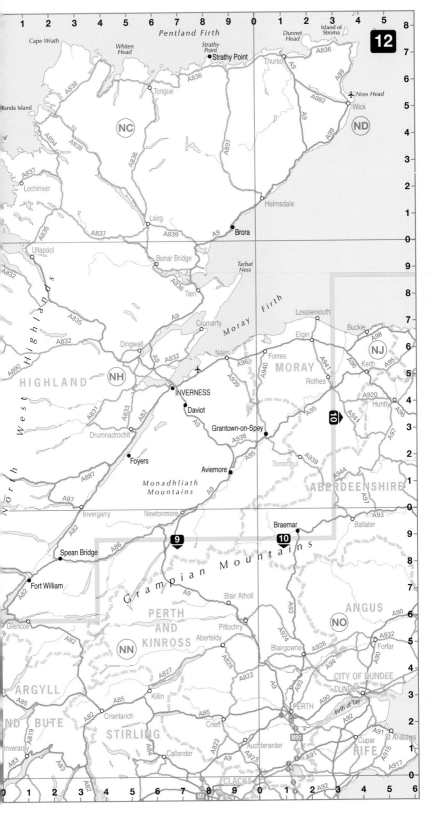

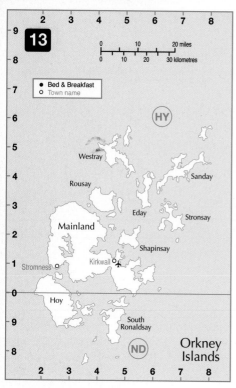

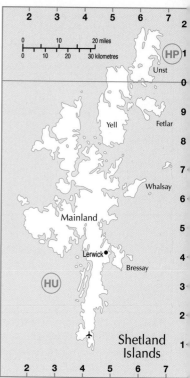

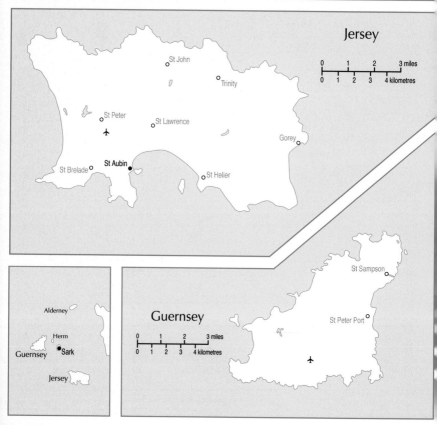

County Map

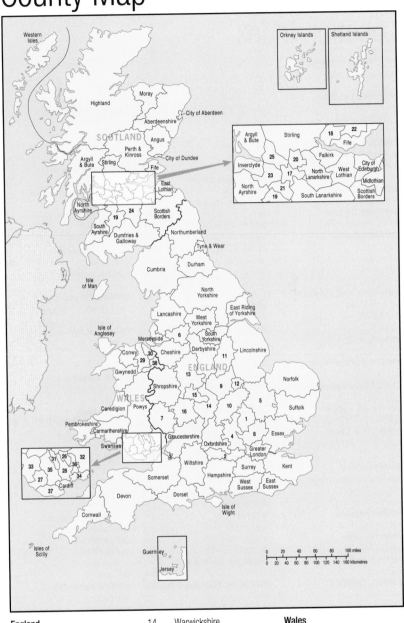

England
1. Bedfordshire
2. Berkshire
3. Bristol
4. Buckinghamshire
5. Cambridgeshire
6. Greater Manchester
7. Herefordshire
8. Hertfordshire
9. Leicestershire
10. Northamptonshire
11. Nottinghamshire
12. Rutland
13. Staffordshire
14. Warwickshire
15. West Midlands
16. Worcestershire

Scotland
17. City of Glasgow
18. Clackmannanshire
19. East Ayrshire
20. East Dunbartonshire
21. East Renfrewshire
22. Perth & Kinross
23. Renfrewshire
24. South Lanarkshire
25. West Dunbartonshire

Wales
26. Blaenau Gwent
27. Bridgend
28. Caerphilly
29. Denbighshire
30. Flintshire
31. Merthyr Tydfil
32. Monmouthshire
33. Neath Port Talbot
34. Newport
35. Rhondda Cynon Taff
36. Torfaen
37. Vale of Glamorgan
38. Wrexham

Location Index

Location Index

Location Index

Location Index

Location Index

B&B Index

B&B Index

B&B Index

479

B&B Index

The Automobile Association would like to thank the following photographers, companies and picture libraries for their assistance in the preparation of this book.

Abbreviations for the picture credits are as follows: (t) top; (b) bottom; (l) left; (r) right; (AA) AA World Travel Library.

4 AA/N Hicks; 5 AA/A Burton; 7 Stockbyte; 8 Photodisc; 10 Stockbyte; 11 Photodisc; 12 Stockbyte; 13 AA/T Woodcock; 14 AA/ J Wood; 16 AA/W Voysey; 20 AA/T Souter; 21 AA/D Ireland; 23 AA/C Coe; 24 AA/M Birkitt; 25 AA/J Mottershaw; 28 AA/L Whitwam; 29 AA/J Wood; 36 AA/N Ray; 41 AA/J Wood; 48 AA/J Wood; 51 AA/R Moss; 55 AA/J Wood; 57 AA/J Wood; 60 AA/J Wood; 61 AA/P Sharpe; 65 AA/P Sharpe; 68 AA/S L Day; 77 AA/E A Bowness; 79 AA/E A Bowness; 82 AA/A Mockford & N Bonetti; 86 AA/T Mackie; 87 AA/A Tryner; 88 AA/J Beazley; 90 AA/P Baker; 97 AA/A J Hopkins; 98 AA/N Hicks; 101 AA/N Hicks; 102 AA/A Lawson; 105 AA/P Baker; 109 AA/N Hicks; 122 AA/P Baker; 124 AA/N Hicks; 126 AA/P Baker; 127 AA/M Jourdan; 129 AA/R Fletcher; 137 AA/M Birkitt; 138 AA/R Coulam; 140 AA/M Birkitt; 142 AA/R Surman; 143 AA/S L Day; 144 AA/S L Day; 153 AA/D Hall; 155 AA/M Trelawny; 157 AA/S L Day; 159 AA/P Baker; 168 AA/W Voysey; 170 AA/H Williams; 177 AA/A J Hopkins; 179 AA/I Burgum; 180 AA/M Birkitt; 182 AA/S McBride; 184 AA/S & O Mathews; 187 AA/D Forss; 190 AA/D Forss; 191 AA/D Forss; 193 AA/P Baker; 199 AA/S L Day; 201 AA/P Baker; 202 AA/R Newton; 203 AA/T Mackie; 204 AA/C Molyneux; 211 AA/M Moody; 215 AA; 216 AA/R Strange; 217 AA/S & O Mathews; 224 AA/M Birkitt; 226 AA/R Coulam; 231 AA/J Beazley; 233 AA/R Coulam; 235 AA/R Coulam; 236 AA/C Jones; 238 AA/C Jones; 242 AA/S L Day; 243 AA/A Tryner; 249 AA/C Jones; 254 AA/J A Tims; 256 AA/J A Tims; 259 AA/C Jones; 263 AA/W Voysey; 268 AA/S & O Mathews; 274 AA/J Tims; 276 AA/W Voysey; 278 AA/J Welsh; 280 AA/M Birkitt; 283 AA/P Baker; 284 AA/T Mackie; 286 AA/A Baker; 291 AA/R Mort; 293 AA/T Souter; 294 AA/C Coe; 302 AA/J Miller; 307 AA/T Souter; 315 AA/V Greaves; 323 AA/C Jones; 326 AA/M Birkitt; 330 AA/E Meacher; 331 AA/M Moody; 332 AA/M Short; 334 AA/P Wilson; 336 AA/G Rowatt; 337 AA/J Morrison; 342 AA/D Tarn; 345 AA/J Morrison; 352 AA/S Gregory; 355 AA/P Wilson; 356 AA/ A J Hopkins; 358 AA/W Voysey; 360 AA; 361 AA/S Bates; 362 AA/A J Hopkins; 370 AA/M Alexander; 378 AA/K Paterson; 381 AA/J Smith; 388 AA/J Carnie; 392 AA/E Ellington; 396 AA/M Taylor; 402 AA/S L Day; 405 AA/E Ellington; 409 AA/S L Day; 410 AA/G Matthews; 414 AA; 425 AA/N Jenkins; 431 AA/N Jenkins; 436 AA/I Burgum; 439 AA/D Croucher; 448 AA/C Molyneux; 451 AA/R Newton; 456 AA/I Burgum.

Every effort has been made to trace the copyright holders, and we apologise in advance for any accidental errors. We would be happy to apply the corrections in the following edition of this publication.